AGE, PERIOD AND COHORT EFFECTS

Age, Period and Cohort Effects: Statistical Analysis and the Identification Problem gives a number of perspectives from top methodologists and applied researchers on the best ways to attempt to answer Age–Period–Cohort related questions about society.

Age–Period–Cohort (APC) analysis is a fundamental topic for any quantitative social scientist studying individuals over time. At the same time, it is also one of the most misunderstood and underestimated topics in quantitative methods. As such, this book is key reference material for researchers wanting to know how to deal with APC issues appropriately in their statistical modelling. It deals with the identification problem caused by the co-linearity of the three variables, considers why some currently used methods are problematic and suggests ideas for what applied researchers interested in APC analysis should do.

Whilst the perspectives are varied, the book provides a unified view of the subject in a reader-friendly way that will be accessible to social scientists with a moderate level of quantitative understanding, across the social and health sciences.

Andrew Bell is a senior lecturer in Quantitative Social Sciences at the Sheffield Methods Institute, University of Sheffield, UK.

AGE, PERIOD AND COHORT EFFECTS

Statistical Analysis and the Identification Problem

Edited by Andrew Bell

Routledge
Taylor & Francis Group

LONDON AND NEW YORK

First published 2021
by Routledge
2 Park Square, Milton Park, Abingdon, Oxon OX14 4RN

and by Routledge
52 Vanderbilt Avenue, New York, NY 10017

Routledge is an imprint of the Taylor & Francis Group, an informa business

British Library Cataloguing-in-Publication Data
A catalogue record for this book is available from the British Library

Library of Congress Cataloging-in-Publication Data
Names: Bell, Andrew, editor.
Title: Age, period and cohort effects : statistical analysis and the identification problem / [edited by] Andrew Bell.
Description: New York : Routledge, 2020. |
Includes bibliographical references and index.
Identifiers: LCCN 2020024454 | ISBN 9780367174422 (hardback) |
ISBN 9780367174439 (paperback) | ISBN 9780429056819 (ebook)
Subjects: LCSH: Cohort analysis. | Age groups–Statistical methods. |
Social sciences–Statistical methods.
Classification: LCC HB849.47 .A35 2020 | DDC 305.2072/7–dc23
LC record available at https://lccn.loc.gov/2020024454

ISBN: 978-0-367-17442-2 (hbk)
ISBN: 978-0-367-17443-9 (pbk)
ISBN: 978-0-429-05681-9 (ebk)

Typeset in Bembo
by Newgen Publishing UK

Visit the eResource: www.routledge.com/9780367174439

MIX
Paper from
responsible sources
FSC
www.fsc.org   FSC™ C013985

Printed in the United Kingdom
by Henry Ling Limited

Dedication by Peer Scheepers

Manfred te Grotenhuis passed away too soon to contribute to the text in this book; however, he provided us with many of the genuine methodological ideas for this text, in particular for Chapter 2. Analyses of Age, Period and Cohort were a common thread throughout his academic life, from his early (Dutch) publications in the *Sociologische Gids* (1995, issue 42, pp. 163–169) and *Mens en Maatschappij* (1997, issue 72, pp. 210–226) via the *Journal for the Scientific Study of Religion* (2001, issue 40, pp. 591–606) and the *American Journal of Sociology* (2005, issue 111, pp. 797–823) to *Demography* (2015, issue 52, pp. 315–327). Moreover, he focused on many fundamental methodological issues to solve, innovatively and profoundly, substantial sociological research questions.

Next to being a very dedicated and highly esteemed teacher, he was a very productive researcher and published in high-ranking journals such as the *International Journal of Epidemiology* and *Demography*. One of his last publications in the *International Journal of Public Health* on reliability coefficients belongs, according to ResearchGate, to the top-ten most consulted articles of all staff members at Radboud University, where he worked with so much intrinsic pleasure, in an atmosphere of methodological rigour aligned with substantial interests. These interests were predominantly in the field of the sociology of religion to which he contributed via numerous outstanding publications in the *Journal for the Scientific Study of Religion*, the *Review of Religious Research*, the *American Sociological Review* and the *European Sociological Review*.

He will be missed as a researcher, as a teacher, as a colleague and as a friend.

CONTENTS

CONTRIBUTORS

Andrew Bell is Senior Lecturer (Associate Professor) in Quantitative Social Sciences at the Sheffield Methods Institute, University of Sheffield, UK.

Louis Chauvel is Professor of Sociology at the University of Luxembourg. He is former General Secretary of the European Sociological Association.

Adel Daoud is Bell Fellow at the Center for Population and Development Studies, Harvard University, USA.

Ethan Fosse is Assistant Professor at the University of Toronto, Canada.

Manfred te Grotenhuis was Associate Professor of Quantitative Data Analysis at Radboud University Nijmegen, Netherlands.

Theodore R. Holford is Susan Dwight Bliss Professor of Epidemiology and Public Health, Yale University.

Kelvyn Jones is Professor Emeritus of Quantitative Human Geography at the University of Bristol, UK. He is a fellow of the British Academy and former director of the Centre for Multilevel Modelling.

Anja K. Leist is Associate Professor at the University of Luxembourg.

Jon Minton is a public health intelligence researcher for NHS Scotland.

Robert M. O'Brien is Professor Emeritus in Sociology at the University of Oregon, USA.

Peer Scheepers is Professor of Sociology at Radboud University, Netherlands.

Herbert L. Smith is Professor of Sociology and Director of the Population Studies Center, University of Pennsylvania, USA.

Paula Thijs is a postdoctoral researcher in the Department of Sociology, University of Amsterdam, Netherlands.

Christopher Winship is Diker-Tishman Professor of Sociology, Harvard University, USA, and editor of the journal *Sociological Methods and Research*.

1

INTRODUCING AGE, PERIOD AND COHORT EFFECTS

Andrew Bell

Age, period and cohort (APC) effects are three ways in which societies can change over time, and as such they are of great interest to social scientists across a range of disciplines. However, despite these concepts being fundamental to much social science research, they are poorly understood – in terms of how they can be uncovered, what they really mean and even fundamentally what they are.

This book brings together a collection of perspectives on how applied social scientists should approach age, period and cohort effects. In some cases, this involves complex statistical models; in others, carefully thought through but simple models; in others, data visualization. Why the need for such a plethora of approaches for the apparently simple question of how things change over time? As we will see, the answer is that understanding age, period and cohort effects is not as simple as it may seem at first glance and, as such, attempting to empirically uncover those effects requires making decisions relating to what specifically we want to find out, what assumptions we are able to make and the nature of the data available to us.

In this chapter, I aim to introduce APC effects, both in terms of how they should be understood and the difficulties that modelling them pose. I will do so in relatively simple terms (also see Bell, 2020; Fosse & Winship, 2019 for other accessible introductions to/reviews of the subject). Hopefully, by the end of this introduction, the methodological issues that the subsequent chapters are grappling with will become clear.

What are age, period and cohort effects[1]

A: I can't seem to shake off this tired feeling. Guess I'm just getting old. [Age effect]

B: Do you think it's stress? Business is down this year, and you've let your fatigue build up. [Period effect]

A: Maybe. What about you?

B: Actually, I'm exhausted too! My body feels really heavy.

A: You're kidding. You're still young. I could work all day long when I was your age.

B: Oh, really?

A: Yeah, young people these days are quick to whine. We were not like that. [Cohort effect]

(Suzuki, 2012, 452)

Age effects are perhaps the easiest of the APC trio to understand – as we get older, we become, say, more conservative, or more likely to die, or more religious. There might also be effects that are specific to a particular age – perhaps we become more likely to drink to excess on our 18th/21st birthday, or more likely to buy a sports car around the age of 45.

Period effects are the effect of a particular year – that is the effect of existing in a particular historical moment. The mortality rate of young men is much greater, for instance, during times of war or disease epidemics; mortality rates might also be higher during a recession, as might the likelihood of an individual holding a particular political viewpoint. These are generally associated with discrete events, although we could also imagine long-run, continuous-period effects: for instance, improvements in healthcare or in air quality over time might result in gradual reductions in mortality for all people.

Finally, cohort effects are the effect of being in a particular birth cohort, or generation. Often this is conceived of as the effect of our 'formative years' – that is, much of what we think, how healthy we are, and who we are, is defined by the first few years of our lives, and the effect of these early years stays with us throughout the rest of our lives. Again, these could be continuous trends, whereby successive birth cohorts experience better healthcare in their early years, which sets them up to be healthier throughout the rest of their lives. But it could also be a result of discrete events – for instance, wars, pandemics or recessions could, if lived through in our formative years, affect individuals for the rest of their lives. There is strong evidence of such effects on mortality for people born during or just before the Siege of Leningrad or the Spanish Flu pandemic. Those people had higher mortality rates many years after those events took place, because they occurred in their formative years.

In each of these cases, we have seen that APC effects can have both discrete and continuous components; indeed we may have both discrete and continuous effects of one or all of APC. The continuous components explain how things change gradually with one of APC. The discrete components express the effect of being at a particular value of one of APC (on top of any gradual change). This distinction is particularly important throughout this book.

Some readers might already be thinking about some of the conceptual difficulties with understanding and distinguishing between these three. First, all three of APC operate through other variables – that is, it isn't a particular year that has an effect, but the war, or recession, or healthcare policies that are occurring at that time. As such, understanding APC is often only the first step in understanding what is happening. Related to this, many of those other variables could operate through more than one of APC – for instance, a war could have both a period and a cohort effect, as could changes in healthcare policies. It is also possible to imagine inter-action effects between each of APC – for instance, a war might have a period effect for only people of a certain age (and gender). Given this, we can see that a simple question ("how do things change over time?") is often not simple at all.

Different types of data and identifying APC

There has been a vast increase in the amount of longitudinal data available to researchers, which has made the prospect of empirically uncovering APC effects all the more credible. However, even with cross-sectional data (that is measured at the same time and not longitudinally), it is possible to think through some questions regarding APC. With such data, there is no variation in period, and age and cohort are exactly collinear, so that we cannot know if any differences are the result of cohort differences (when people were born), or age differences (how old people are), although we will often have a good idea based on theory or intuition. Similarly, single cohort studies, that follow a single birth cohort through their lives, have no variation in cohort, and period and age are exactly collinear (although again, we might be more likely to interpret any patterns in a particular way).

However, when analysing APC, we might group multiple cross-sectional studies, or multiple cohorts, together. Alternatively, we might have panel data, which follow the same individuals through time, but measure individuals of all ages on all occasions. In these instances, we have variation in all of APC – however, as we will see in the next section, there remains a difficulty in identifying these effects.

In all these cases, we can see why one of APC might be forgotten about. With cross-sectional data, we might forget about period and cohort, and just consider age. With panel data, we might see a square age-by-year table and think we only need to think about age and year, even though cohort varies in the data as well. Such errors can be problematic, however, and produce a less nuanced, misleading and often incorrect impression of the effects that APC have. However, attempting to consider all three of APC is also problematic, as we will see now.

The identification problem

Age, period and cohort are intrinsically linked, such that the age of any individual is equal to the year of measurement (period), minus their birth year (cohort).

$$Age = Period - Cohort \tag{1.1}$$

This is a problem if we want to find the continuous effect of all three of these because, just like two of APC with a single cross section or cohort study, the three variables are exactly collinear. That is not to say that all three couldn't have an effect – indeed in the previous sections we have seen plausible examples of all three of these variables. But it does mean that working out which *linear* effects are producing the data is often impossible from the data alone.

For instance, consider the following example of a data-generating process that might exist, to explain the changes in people's political opinions:

$$Rightwingness = \beta_0 + 1 \star Age + 1 \star Period + 1 \star Cohort + residual \tag{1.2}$$

Here we have a situation where, on average, an individual becomes more right wing as they age; as time goes on (period), people generally become more right wing; and each successive generation (cohort) is more right wing than the last.

Now imagine a different data-generating process

$$Rightwingness = \beta_0 + 2 \star Period + residual \tag{1.3}$$

Here, there is no effect of age or cohort, but a stronger effect of period. However, because Age = Period – Cohort, these two data-generating processes would produce exactly the same outcome variable – exactly the same levels of rightwingness. This is a problem if, as a researcher, we are presented with this data, since we cannot know which is true. If we fit a standard regression model, such as

$$Rightwingness = \beta_0 + \beta_A Age + \beta_P Period + \beta_C Cohort + residual \tag{1.4}$$

the model would not be able to run, due to the exact collinearity between the three variables in the model.

Instead, we would need to make some kind of assumption, which would push our model to find one equation or the other. The problem is that the difference between these two equations is not a question of a small amount of bias. The difference in how we would interpret these two equations is huge.

Note that, alternatively, we might want to fit the model using dummy variable coding, with a variable for each of the values of age, period or cohort (less a reference category for each). Whilst it is only linear effects that are affected by the identification problem described above, and such an approach would allow non-linear, discrete effects to be modelled, using dummy variables does not solve the problem. Regardless of how we model our data, any linear components of APC effects in the data-generating process will remain in the data. The choice of model would not change the fact that the linear component of those effects would be unable to be told apart, and the model would experience the same problems of exact collinearity between the dummy variables. This is the case even if the data-generating process isn't exactly linear. Different chapters in this book refer to models that use both linear and dummy effects of APC, but in each case, the underlying effects in the data will often be a mixture of linear, continuous effects and non-linear effects. Whilst the latter can be identified, the former cannot, unless we are willing to make some quite strong assumptions about APC.

That is the key point: we cannot identify linear trends in APC without making some quite strong assumptions about at least one of APC, and whilst we can identify non-linear patterns around those trends, they may be difficult to understand without the linear trends around which they vary. The assumptions and approaches that we choose to help us to understand these patterns will have a big effect on the results that we find. The next section outlines some of those approaches, including those demonstrated in the rest of this book.

What we should and shouldn't do: the chapters that follow

It should be clear from the preceding section that the identification problem is not a problem that can be easily solved with particular statistical methods, because it is an issue with dependency in the data, rather than an issue with a particular model. However, over the last 50 years, there has been a large number of solutions proposed to the identification problem, many of which have since been shown to rely on rather large assumptions that may not have been clear at first glance. One such solution is simply to group data – for instance, by grouping two consecutive years and coding them as if they are the same year. One could think of this as the introduction of a relatively small amount of measurement error. However, it turns out that this can have a big effect on the results that are subsequently found, and different grouping choices can produce very different results. Chapter 2 considers this further, showing that those choices of grouping need to be defined based on very strong theory. If we have good, strong theory, such methods can be used effectively, but without that theory, the results are likely to be highly problematic.

Other statistical solutions may appear more sophisticated; however, often those solutions are actually making equally problematic assumptions, and simply hiding those assumptions behind difficult-to-understand statistical notation. Examples of these include the Intrinsic Estimator (Luo, 2013; Luo, Hodges, Winship, & Powers, 2016; Te Grotenhuis, Pelzer, Luo, & Schmidt-Catran, 2016; Yang, Schulhofer-Wohl, Fu, & Land, 2008) or Partial Least Squares (O'Brien, 2015; Tu, Smith, & Gilthorpe, 2011), as well as the Hierarchical APC (HAPC) model, which is the focus of Chapter 3. In that chapter, I (with Kelvyn Jones) consider more broadly how APC can be modelled using multilevel models, showing how and why the HAPC model makes unintended assumptions that might not be clear to those using it. We also show the ways that such models can be used, but with strong assumptions clearly and explicitly stated. In one example in that chapter, the assumption of no continuous period trends is used, and that assumption is justified based on theory.

It is often stated, not just in APC analysis but in statistical analysis more broadly, that data visualization is important to fully understand our data, and it might seem like plotting our data might be a good way of getting around the identification problem. However, as we might expect, with APC measuring three dimensions in time, expressing them in two dimensions is often difficult. Not only that, but our plotting decisions could affect the message conveyed by the visualizations that might not be justified by the data, just like our statistical modelling decisions. For instance, we could plot an outcome of interest against age, with the data grouped by cohorts. However, this graph would look very different, and convey a very different message, to a graph plotting the same outcome and data against age and period. In this sense, data visualization is as much subject to the identification problem as statistical analysis (Holford, 1991).

Another data visualization that is often used when considering APC data is the Lexis plot, and this is the subject of Chapter 4. Jon Minton argues that Lexis plots allow us to see data in a much more nuanced way than *a priori* statistical models, because it allows us to see complex patterns in and interactions between APC – key features in the data that can be identified and then theorized about. This is not to say that it is a solution to the identification problem – indeed if different combinations of APC linear effects can produce identical data, there can be no way of telling those data apart. However, it can be a useful way of identifying non-linear APC effects and interactions between APC that would perhaps be too complex to be found in many standard models. Chapter 5 takes a similar approach, in which Louis Chauvel and colleagues use models to find overall patterns in APC trends and fluctuations around those trends, and then use Lexis plots to find additional interactions. This is exemplified using mortality data from a number of European countries, revealing spikes in mortality related to the HIV/AIDS epidemic.

Chapter 6 considers the ways that we make our assumptions, and makes two key contributions in how we might choose to model APC effects. First, Ethan Fosse and colleagues suggest using bounding assumptions in order to narrow down the different linear APC combinations that are possible given the data. Second, they suggest considering the mechanisms by which APC operate – that is, the variables by which APC have the effect on an outcome. Mechanisms are a useful way of thinking through APC effects, not least because they actually explain any APC trends that we might find. However, they are also not a solution to the identification problem, relying on assumptions to ensure that any unexplained APC trends are correctly apportioned. It might be, though, that in some cases those assumptions are less strong (or in other words, more plausible) than the assumptions about APC we might otherwise have to make.

In Chapter 7, Theodore Holford takes that second point further – using the example of smoking as the key cause of lung cancer variation that has age, period and cohort elements. Assuming, based on theory, that the effect of smoking occurs mainly through cohort processes, the author compares the population rates of lung cancer with what would be expected given APC changes in smoking.

Chapter 8 considers Bayesian models for APC analysis. Bayesian analysis is often seen as advantageous for many reasons; however, as with any other APC model, Fosse shows that it is not a solution to the identification problem. Rather, it presents a useful way of expressing the assumptions that we want to make regarding APC, using particular informative priors.

The last two chapters of the book take an overarching approach to the question of what it means to identify APC effects. In Chapter 9, Herb Smith makes the argument that, often, for a range of reasons, it makes most sense to assume flat period trends, since period effects are more likely to be in the form of discrete 'shocks' with limited long-run consequences. This relates to a number of other chapters in the book, where similar assumptions are made.

Finally, in Chapter 10, Bob O'Brien attempts to bring all the previous chapters together, around the idea of the 'line of solutions'. This is a line which represents all of the possible combinations of linear age, period and cohort effects that could be true given the data (see also Chapter 6 for further discussion and visualization of this). He shows that, for the chapters in this book that utilize (generalized) linear regression, the line of solutions is exact in describing all of the best fitting solutions and estimable functions based on these solutions. For the other approaches described in this book, the line of solutions typically informs researchers about why a particular solution is obtained and/or can help the researcher evaluate the strengths and weaknesses of solutions using a particular approach. Fundamentally, all APC methodology (such as 'estimable functions') are doing one of three things: (1) expressing the line of solutions; (2) choosing a point along the line of solutions based on some kind of assumption(s); or (3) expressing deviations, from the linear APC effects that make up the line of solutions, that are not affected by the identification problem. In this sense, the line of solutions is central to the analysis and understanding of APC effects.

Where this book came from

This book arose from a conference in Sheffield, UK, held on 24 January 2017, kindly funded by the British Academy, which aimed to help those who attended to understand different perspectives on what age, period and cohort effects are, how they can be modelled, and what assumptions we, as researchers, need to make in order to do so. The conference included presentations that were the basis for a number of the chapters presented here, whilst other chapters were created later. All have since undergone peer review. What is perhaps most surprising about the chapters is their level of agreement in a subject area that has often been the subject of vigorous debate. Despite the chapters here being written by 14 authors across many disciplines, countries, departments and perspectives, all come to similar conclusions: that there can be no statistical solution to the APC identification problem; that the identification problem is a conceptual, rather than a statistical, problem; that strong, theoretically informed and clearly stated assumptions must be made to identify linear and near-linear APC effects; that non-linear APC effects can be estimated but must be carefully interpreted in the absence of linear effects; that claims to have solved the identification problem mechanically should be viewed with scepticism; and so on.

I want to thank all the contributing authors for their chapters, for agreeing to peer review other chapters, but also for their continued discussions, support and suggestions that have made editing this book feel more like a collaborative exercise than a solo effort. The discussions with authors, and reading their chapters, have helped me consolidate my own understanding of APC and the methods we use to disentangle them, and it has made me feel confident about the collection of works presented in this volume. I hope you find them as useful as I have.

Online supplementary material relating to this book can be found at www.routledge.com/9780367174439.

Note

1 The next three sections are adapted from Bell (2020).

References

Bell, A. (2020). Age–Period–Cohort Analysis: A Review of What We Should and Shouldn't Do. *Annals of Human Biology*, 47(2), 208–217.

Fosse, E., & Winship, C. (2019). Analyzing Age–Period–Cohort Data: A Review and Critique. *Annual Review of Sociology*, 45(1), 467–492.

Holford, T. R. (1991). Understanding the Effects of Age, Period, and Cohort on Incidence and Mortality Rates. *Annual Review of Public Health*, 12(1), 425–457.

Luo, L. (2013). Assessing Validity and Application Scope of the Intrinsic Estimator Approach to the Age–Period–Cohort Problem. *Demography*, 50(6), 1945–1967.

Luo, L., Hodges, J., Winship, C., & Powers, D. (2016). The Sensitivity of the Intrinsic Estimator to Coding Schemes: Comment on Yang, Schulhofer-Wohl, Fu, and Land. *American Journal of Sociology*, 122(3), 930–961.

O'Brien, R. M. (2015). Age-Period-Cohort Models and the Perpendicular Solution. *Epidemiologic Methods*, 4(1), 87–99.

Suzuki, E. (2012). Time Changes, So Do People. *Social Science & Medicine*, 75(3), 452–456.

Te Grotenhuis, M., Pelzer, B., Luo, L., & Schmidt-Catran, A. W. (2016). The Intrinsic Estimator, Alternative Estimates, and Predictions of Mortality Trends: A Comment on Masters, Hummer, Powers, Beck, Lin, and Finch. *Demography*, 53(4), 1245–1252.

Tu, Y. K., Smith, G. D., & Gilthorpe, M. S. (2011). A New Approach to Age–Period–Cohort Analysis Using Partial Least Squares Regression: The Trend in Blood Pressure in the Glasgow Alumni Cohort. *Plos One*, 6(4), e19401. https://doi.org/10.1371/journal.pone.0019401

Yang, Y., Schulhofer-Wohl, S., Fu, W. J. J., & Land, K. C. (2008). The Intrinsic Estimator for Age–Period–Cohort Analysis: What It Is and How to Use It. *American Journal of Sociology*, 113(6), 1697–1736.

2

THE PROS AND CONS
OF CONSTRAINING VARIABLES

Paula Thijs, Manfred te Grotenhuis[1] and Peer Scheepers

Introduction

In the early days of age, period and cohort (APC) analysis, the identification of the separate effects of age, time period and birth cohort was typically 'solved' by placing a non-linear restriction (a constraint) on one (or more) of the APC effects. The approach became known through the pioneering article by Mason and colleagues (Mason et al. 1973), who argued that it is possible to simultaneously estimate APC effects if one assumes that several age groups, birth cohorts or time periods have identical effects on the dependent variable. For example, we take the case of researchers who want to address the research question of to what extent differences in body length are due to period effects (to which every member of a society is exposed, resulting in over-time differences), cohort effects (to which only members of that typical cohort are exposed, resulting in differences between cohorts) or age effects (differences between people of different age categories). There is abundant medical or biological evidence that the age effect is generally positively linear up to a certain age, when it becomes sometimes slightly curvilinear. To model the rapid increase in body length as young people grow older, one may use a logarithmic transformation of the age variable and further set all age effects on body length after 25 years to be equal (i.e., to zero). This decision or choice to treat the age variable in such a way decreases somewhat the perfect collinearity between the age and cohort variables and therefore 'solves' the identification problem, at least to some extent. Constraining the age variable in this way may result in potentially unbiased effects of age, period and cohort on body length.[2]

In the study of demographic and social changes, however, it is generally unknown what the exact effects are of age, time period and birth cohort on a phenomenon (since that is typically why research is done in the first place). The difficulty of this Constrained Variables Method (CVM) lies in the choice of which effects can be constrained to be equal. Therefore, the most important objection to this method is the (potential) arbitrariness of the chosen constraint(s). The APC estimates from the constrained model are only unbiased if the constraints are valid. This, however, cannot be verified or tested by the APC model itself, as it depends on this very constraint. As a result, the method lost its appeal and was surpassed by other methods. Yet, these methods have been criticized as just being a special case of the CVM, with similar untested assumptions. So, researchers were right back at where they had started.

In this chapter we argue that the original CVM is by no means useless when information from other sources is available to ground and statistically justify the constraint(s). For instance, in the age–body length example, there is plenty of medical research into which biological processes govern the growth of the human body, and which eventually cease to work. This information can be used to modify the age variable and pave the way for the estimation of possible period and cohort effects. We will first explain what the CVM basically is and we provide an overview of the main criticisms and pitfalls. Next, we describe some counter-examples and provide some recommendations. We conclude that the CVM may lead to plausible estimates of age, period and cohort effects if the constraints have a strong theoretical and, moreover, empirical foundation. Hence, we feel that scholars gave up on CVM too quickly and thereby missed out on an opportunity to show age, period and cohort effects.

Typical features of the Constrained Variables Method

The most common method to identify the separate contribution of age, period and cohort effects in the study of social change is to set a constraint to one (or more) of these variables. There are several versions of this approach.

Omitted variable approach

One of the first approaches, that is still widely used, is to simply omit one of the variables of age, period and cohort entirely (Baltes 1968). This method comes down to constraining the linear and non-linear effects of the omitted variable to zero, based on theoretical justifications that such effects may be (statistically) negligible. For example, analysing, over time, changes in gender role attitudes in the U.S., Brooks and Bolzendahl (2004) assume that the effect of ageing is negligible, once birth cohort and major life events are accounted for. They derived this assumption from the Ageing/Stability Thesis or the Increasing Persistence Model (Glenn 1980) which predicts that, once formed during childhood or adolescence, attitudes in adulthood are relatively stable across the life course and only change in response to major transitions in the life cycle, such as marriage or labour force entry. By excluding the age variable on these grounds, the perfect collinearity between age and cohort is explained away theoretically. As a consequence, it is possible to simultaneously estimate the effects of time period and birth cohort on the dependent variable.

In the social sciences, however, it is very unlikely that either age, time period or birth cohort has absolutely no effect on the social phenomenon under study. Hence, this approach of omitting (or ignoring) one of the APC variables entirely has been widely criticized. If the assumption that one of the variables has no effect on the dependent variable is not valid, then the estimates of the other variables in the analysis may be spurious (Fosse and Winship 2019; Mason et al. 1973; Rodgers 1990). A three-way analysis including age, period and cohort effects has, therefore, been preferred over a two-way analysis (Mason et al. 1973).

Equality constraints

Mason and colleagues (1973) laid the foundation for an approach to identify the effects of age, period and cohort in a three-way analysis. The solution they proposed in their seminal article is 'to assume that several age groups, birth cohorts or time periods have identical effects on the dependent variable' (Mason et al. 1973, 247), decreasing the perfect collinearity between these crucial variables and solving the identification problem, which makes it feasible to simultaneously estimate age, period and cohort effects. This method of imposing a so-called 'equality constraint' to one of the APC variables is known as the Constrained Estimators Method or Constrained Variables Method[3] and was frequently used in age–period–cohort studies during the 1970s and 1980s (see e.g. Fienberg and Mason [1979]; Mason and Smith [1985]). This method is typically applied to generalized linear models and therefore also labelled Constrained Generalized Linear Models estimator (CGLIM) (Yang, Fu, and Land 2004).

The basic idea behind the CVM is to treat each of the effects of age, period and cohort as a set of dummy variables and to constrain the effects for two (typically adjacent) categories of either of the APC variables to be equal to each other (Glenn 2005; Mason et al. 1973).[4] When entering dummy variables in a regression analysis, it is required that one of them from each set of variables representing age, period and cohort is omitted (serving as the reference category to which all other estimates of dummies are compared). In the CVM, only one additional dummy variable from one of the sets is dropped. This procedure results in a just-identified model, which allows the estimation of the effects of age, period and birth cohort on the dependent variable with minimal assumptions.

Multiple constraints

This procedure, however, does not rule out multicollinearity between all dummies included, possibly biasing their estimation. Therefore, in addition to one identifying constraint, one can apply multiple constraints, such as constraining the effects for categories (dummies) of two rather than one of the APC variables to be equal, or grouping more than two categories (dummies) of one of the APC variables together, which implies that the effects of several adjacent birth cohorts, periods or age categories are constrained to be equivalent. For example, in studies that are interested in research questions on cohort effects, people from adjacent birth cohorts are often grouped together and labelled according to their formative experiences resulting from a shared location in history (Mannheim 1952). Examples are to group together birth cohorts such as 'Children of the Great Depression' to indicate people who came of age during the Great Depression in the 1930s; or group together birth cohorts of the 'Baby Boom generation' for those who were born after the Second World War. The theoretical justification is that people belonging to these cohorts have been exposed to similar societal events and hence have shared experiences which are different from cohorts before or after them (Mannheim 1952). Such the-oretical justifications translate into statistical decisions to assume that there are no differences within such a cohort, which cannot, however, be justified with statistical procedures. In a similar fashion, it is possible to create age groups. In a study of white males' educational attainment in the U.S., Fienberg and Mason (1979) group the age variable in five-year categories (e.g. 20 to 24, 25 to 29, 30 to 34) and subsequently constrain the effects of all age groups between 30 and 59 to be equal. To justify this restriction, they argue to have a priori grounds to expect most of the age effects to occur at the tails of the age distribution, because the left tail includes individuals who have not yet completed their education, whereas at the right tail the effect of age likely increases because the highest educated individuals are less likely to die. Again, such theoretical justifications translated into statistical decisions are difficult to test.

Applications of multiple identifying constraints reduce collinearity and result in a so-called over-identified model (or, as Mason et al. [1973, 252] put it, 'more-than-minimally restricted models'), which is preferred over just-identified models because the latter can be 'tested against the data' (Fosse and Winship 2019, 469). That is, over-identified models can be compared with reduced models that include just one restriction or omit one of the APC variables altogether, which may provide clues about which components of the model fit the data better.

The CVM has generated a lively scholarly debate about the pros and cons of the approach, most notably in the *American Sociological Review*: between Glenn (1976) and Mason, Mason, and Winsborough (1976), and between Rodgers (1982a, 1982b) and Smith, Mason, and Fienberg (1982). Much of the criticism essentially comes down to the question of how to determine which categories of age, period and cohort can be constrained as being equal. Or phrased differently: whether such an identifying restriction, based on theoretical grounds, can ever be justified statistically. To impose such a constraint on one of the APC effects, the researcher needs to make some kind of theoretical assumption about the nature of these effects, which may have consequences for the estimation of all parameters. This is a serious drawback of the CVM, for which earlier approaches of APC analysis have also been criticized.

Pitfalls of the Constrained Variables Method

It is impossible to statistically verify the constraint(s)

The main problem of the CVM as pointed out by its critics is the choice of which two categories (and hence coefficients) of the age, period or cohort variable are assumed to be equal. Selection of such constraints on the basis of the data is hardly possible. Researchers usually have no a priori knowledge about the relationship between age, period and cohort effects and their relationship to the dependent variable, since obtaining such knowledge is exactly why the analysis is performed (Luo and Hodges 2016). Thus, when the true effects of age, period and cohort are unknown, the constraints cannot be verified by the estimates from the APC model itself, as the estimates depend on this very constraint.

Estimates are only valid if the constraint is correct

Moreover, choosing the wrong restriction can have detrimental consequences for the estimates obtained in an APC analysis. Several researchers have demonstrated that the estimated effects of the age, period and cohort variables can differ hugely depending on which restriction is used (e.g. Glenn 1976, 2003, 2005; Rodgers 1982a). For example, by using simulations, Glenn (2003, 2005) showed that even constraints that only slightly deviate from reality can lead to grossly inaccurate estimates of APC effects. He argued that this is a very serious problem of the CVM (which he labelled the Dummy Variable Method), because in real-world research it is very unlikely that one is able to make a simplifying assumption that is precisely correct. Yang, Fu, and Land (2004) also demonstrated that models in which they applied different constraints on subsets of adjacent categories of the age, period or cohort variables produced widely different estimates of APC effects, while each of these models fitted the data equally well. Hence, they concluded that the estimates from CVM models in which different constraints are applied are very sensitive to the choice of the equality constraints. This is problematic because substantially different conclusions could be drawn from different models with different constraints. Further complicating the selection of the constraints is that models including different constraints will produce the same levels of goodness-of-fit to the data (Smith 2004; Yang et al. 2004), so inspecting the model fit as a criterion is not very helpful.

Interactions between age, period and cohort

Another criticism of the CVM, expressed by Glenn (1976, 2003, 2005), is that the effects of one of the APC variables may not be the same for each category of the other two variables. For example, the effect of period may not be the same for all age groups or birth cohorts. Following from theories of socialization, younger people are supposed to react more strongly to changes in their surroundings than older people. In other words, there may be interactions between the effects of age, period and cohort. Glenn refers to this as non-additivity of effects, that is, that the combined effects of age, period and cohort are not equal to the sum of their separate effects. Besides an assumption of the equality of two or more categories of one of the age, period or cohort effects, models to separate the effects of age, period and cohort thus also depend on an assumption that the effects are additive, which is rarely realistic in 'real-world' social processes (Glenn 1976, 902).

To summarize, the application of CVM is restricted due to the following pitfalls:

- It is impossible to determine which constraint(s) are valid on the basis of the relationship between age, period and cohort effects on the dependent variable, since it is exactly this relationship that researchers are aiming to analyse.
- The estimates from a constrained model reflect the true effects of age, time period and birth cohort only if the chosen constraints reflect the true structure of the data. In other words: one can only find the true effects of age, period and cohort in CVM models if the applied constraint is true.
- Models with different equality constraints can produce different results, while goodness-of-fit levels are similar. Arbitrarily chosen constraints may therefore lead to biased estimates of age, period and cohort effects.
- The effects of age, period and cohort may interact with one another. Models to separate APC effects therefore also rely on an additional assumption that the effects are additive (the separate effects of age, period and cohort do not depend on one another). This is rarely the case in the 'real world'.

These pitfalls have led several researchers to abandon the CVM and adopt other methods, such as the Proxy Variable Method or Mechanism-based Approach, in which one (or more) of the age, period and cohort variables are replaced by more accurate indicators of the biological, psychological or social phenomena that are presumed to underlie the effects of age, period and cohort on the dependent variable (Rodgers 1990; Winship and Harding 2008). More recently, researchers have turned towards purely statistical methods to estimate APC models, such as the Intrinsic Estimator approach (IE), which circumvents the identification problem by using a mechanical constraint (e.g. Yang et al. 2004, 2008) or Hierarchical APC models (HAPC) (Yang and Land 2006), in which age is modelled at the individual level, and period and cohort at a higher level.

Each of these methods, however, has also been criticized for relying on assumptions that are hardly possible to verify (see e.g. Bell and Jones 2014, 2015, 2018 on HAPC models; and Luo 2013; Pelzer et al. 2015; Te Grotenhuis et al. 2016 on IE; see also Chapter 3), which is exactly what the CVM has been criticized for. In fact, mechanical approaches such as the IE are sometimes considered to be even worse, because they rely on assumptions that are often arbitrary, implicit and hidden (Bell and Jones 2018; Winship and Harding 2008), and therefore untested or untestable (Fosse and Winship 2019). As a response to the criticisms that the linear cohort effects cannot be reliably estimated with methods like the IE or the HAPC, some recently developed methods, such as the Zero Linear Trend Estimator (O'Brien 2011) or the APC Detrended (APCD) model (Chauvel and Schröder 2014), focus on the deviations from the linear trends which can be identified. Such methods add a more elaborate set of constraints, for example to detect particularly (un)lucky or (dis)advantaged birth cohorts and the durability of these deviations from the overall linear trend (Chauvel, Leist, and Ponomarenko 2016). But linear effects cannot be assumed on the basis of non-linear effects, so these approaches do not solve the identification problem (Bell and Jones 2018).

Can CVM be successfully applied, and when?

So where does this leave the researcher who tries to trace the extent to which longitudinal changes in any societal phenomenon are due to age, period and/or cohort effects? Should CVM be rejected altogether or are there any cases in which it can be applied successfully?

What is agreed upon by both critics and defenders of the method, is that CVM is no solution to the identification problem, just as the statistical approaches that have emerged since the CVM are no solution. So, it is all about the assumptions. In the words of Bell and Jones (2014, 335): 'There is no technical solution to the identification problem, without the imposition of strong (and correct) a priori assumptions'. Yet, from the extensive body of literature that has appeared about the CVM, several recommendations can be distilled to simultaneously estimate the effects of age, period and cohort.

Make the assumptions explicit

First and foremost, it is important to make the assumptions explicit: Which age categories or cohorts or periods are assumed to be similar and hence statistically non-significantly different? In this way, the assumptions can be justified or verified using theoretical arguments or empirical evidence, which is a strength of the CVM in comparison to most mechanical approaches to the identification problem, which have been criticized for relying on constraints which are often arbitrary, implicit and therefore impossible to verify (Bell and Jones 2018; Luo 2013; Luo and Hodges 2016).

Use theoretical and empirical information to ground constraints

Second, one can minimize the arbitrariness of the applied constraints. Most critics of the CVM agree that a priori knowledge is the best way to inform the choice of constraints, just as in the case of the relationship between age and body length. Mason et al. (1973) already warned that without a priori knowledge or strong theoretical preconceptions about which constraints to choose, it is difficult to judge which model is most appropriate. Such knowledge can be derived from 'side information' (Converse 1976, 20 in Rodgers 1982a, 786): theory and/or empirical evidence outside the data. There may be cases in which there is more of a theoretical and empirical basis to apply a restriction on the effects of age, period or cohort (Alwin and McCammon 2003).

Such side information can for example be found in a 'conjunction of social circumstances' (Firebaugh and Chen 1995, 977). To illustrate, Firebaugh and Chen

(1995) use the Nineteenth Amendment, which granted U.S. women the right to vote in 1920, to test whether historical conditions during childhood and adolescence have lasting effects. They observe a striking decline in the gender gap in voting behaviour in the U.S. since the middle of the 21st century, with continuously more women voting over time. This over-time decline of the gender gap may have taken place across the board, with differences in voting between men and women declining for all birth cohorts (period effect), or only among women who came of age before or during the Amendment (cohort effect). The Nineteenth Amendment provides a unique opportunity to estimate such effects, since people of the same age are randomly assigned to this event (on the basis of sex, and the sex of a baby is generally random) during their formative years. Exposure to the Nineteenth Amendment can therefore be seen as the treatment in a kind of 'natural experiment'. This allows for the development of strong theoretical arguments about the nature of the APC variables and may provide some clues for the interpretation of estimates obtained from a constrained linear regression analysis: if there is no gender gap in the cohorts socialized after the enactment of the Amendment, then this lends support for the existence of a cohort effect.

Firebaugh and Chen (1995) apply a restriction on the APC variables by grouping birth cohorts together on the basis of their socialization before, during or after women's disenfranchisement. They justify this restriction by arguing that disenfranchisement should have the greatest lasting effects on women who never before had the right to vote, followed by women who came of age during the disenfranchisement, with the smallest effect for women who were children during the disenfranchisement era, and no effect for women born after the Nineteenth Amendment. Indeed, this pattern is actually found in their analyses, from which they concluded that historical conditions to which people are exposed during their formative years have enduring effects. Moreover, the authors tested the robustness of their findings by changing the cohort categories, which did not alter their conclusions.

Information to validate a constraint can also be found in the nature of the dependent variable that is studied. For example, it is more plausible that trust in the government is affected by what the government does at a particular point in time (a period effect) than by people's age or the cohort they belong to (Alwin 2002). In a study in which we analysed changes in support for gender egalitarianism in the Netherlands (Thijs, Te Grotenhuis, and Scheepers 2017), we used the nature of the relationship between age and the dependent variable to ground a restriction on the age variable. We observed, based on representative samples of the Dutch population, that support for the statement that a woman is better suited to raise little children than a man declined substantially between 1979 and 2012. Such a liberalizing trend had been found in a range of countries. We wondered whether this trend could be explained by exposure to historical events to which all people in Dutch society had been exposed (e.g. period effects of secularization or educational expansion); or by events to which certain cohorts had typically been exposed (e.g. cohort effects of secularization or educational expansion); versus age effects.

To test these expectations, we used repeated cross-sectional data from 16 national samples of the Cultural Changes in the Netherlands (CCN) surveys, covering 1979–2006. To separate the effects of period, cohort and age, we constrained the age effects of people younger than 30 to be equal. Since our dependent variable concerns opinions on (the appropriate roles of women and men in) child rearing, we expected younger people, especially those who do not have children yet, to be rather similar in their attitudes regardless of birth cohort and time period, whereas people older than 30 may diverge more in their attitudes depending on whether they have children themselves and other life course experiences, with a decline in support for gender egalitarianism as people grow older. Indeed, we observed that mean support for gender egalitarianism among men and women was rather stable and at comparable levels (i.e., statistically non-significantly different) until the age of 30, after which it decreased as people grow older. A similar pattern was found in each time period. This was the case in the CNN data, but also in different datasets of a representative sample of the Dutch population, covering 1979–2012. Moreover, we found additional support for this assumption in empirical studies that showed that entry into marriage and birth of the first child decrease support for gender egalitarianism among male and female adolescents (Baxter et al. 2015; Corrigall and Konrad 2007; Fan and Marini 2000; Kaufman, Bernhardt, and Goldscheider 2017). To further ground the constraint, we ran several models in which we varied the cut-off point for the restriction on age, which did not substantially change the estimates of the age, period and cohort variables. Our results suggest that support for gender egalitarianism has mainly changed due to the replacement of older cohorts by younger cohorts who came of age in more progressive times.

Of course, the estimates of age, period and cohort effects that these studies found, based on the CVM using side information, may still be biased if the constraints are not perfectly correct, so the conclusions should be interpreted tentatively. Yet, these examples do demonstrate how theoretical justifications and empirical information can be used to make more plausible assumptions about constraints, which is preferred over arbitrarily chosen constraints which rely on often implicit assumptions that cannot be tested.

Compare results across models with different constraints

Lastly, it is recommended to compare the results from models with different equality constraints, in order to test the robustness of the findings (Mason et al. 1973; O'Brien 2011). Smith, Mason and Fienberg (1982, 788) argue that

> a researcher who believes that more than one set of identifying restrictions might be feasible would be advised to estimate a model with first one set of restrictions only, then another, and so forth. Again, these specifications would be substantively based. To the extent that the contrasts between coefficients are similar across models, one garners confidence in the identifying restrictions.

A rigorous example of such comparison of different identifying constraints can be found in a study about trends in interpersonal trust using the General Social Survey from 1972 through 1998 by Robinson and Jackson (2001). The authors ran a variety of regression analyses, each with a different set of equality constraints, in order to see whether the constraints were empirically justified. Rodgers ([1982b, 794] in a reply to Smith, Mason, and Fienberg [1982]) stresses that such comparison of estimates derived from various identifying constraints does not necessarily tell anything about the validity of these estimates, but if each of the restrictions is justified on theoretical grounds rather than on an inspection of the data,[5] then stability across estimates derived from models with different constraints increases the researcher's confidence in the estimates. Thus, although it is impossible to verify whether the estimates from these models are correct on the basis of the data and consistency across different models cannot prove this either, stability across different models with various theoretically informed constraints at least provides some confidence in the accuracy of the estimates of age, period and cohort effects.

Accept uncertainty and be cautious about conclusions

The question remains as to how to deal with the possibility that the age, period and/or cohort variables interact with one another. Although the estimation of interactions in constrained models is feasible, again, it is hardly possible to verify which interaction(s) should be included, as numerous combinations may exist, which further complicates the interpretation of the estimates of age, period and cohort. So, without strong theoretical and empirical justifications, additional assumptions about the non-additivity of APC effects are needed. Yet, models always involve simplifying assumptions, and researchers in social science should therefore accept that there is no way to separate the effects of age, period and cohort with absolute certainty. This implies that the conclusions that are drawn from APC analysis should always be interpreted in a tentative way.

To summarize, there are several things the researcher can do to apply the CVM:

- Make assumptions explicit, so they can be tested.
- Use as much theoretical and empirical knowledge from outside the data as is available to justify the constraints.
- Run a variety of models using different sets of constraints to check robustness of the findings.
- Accept that a solution of the identification problem does not exist and be tentative in the conclusions made on the basis of the estimates.

Conclusion

The CVM is one of the first and most common approaches to try to 'solve' the identification problem in demographic and social research. The approach became known through the pioneering article of Mason and colleagues (1973), who proposed that there is one kind of model in which the effects of age, period and cohort can be estimated simultaneously, and that is one in which the researcher assumes at least two categories of one (or more) of the age, period and cohort variables to be equal on the basis of strong a priori information.

Since the article of Mason et al., a lively and still ongoing debate has emerged about the appropriateness of the CVM to estimate APC models. Many scholars (including Mason and colleagues) have warned against several pitfalls of the method: it is impossible to determine which constraint(s) is/are valid on the basis of the data; the estimates are only true or non-biased to the extent that the chosen constraint is true or non-biased; and even small changes in the choices of the constraints may lead to very different estimates of age, period and cohort effects. Arbitrarily chosen constraints may therefore lead to biased, even invalid, substantial conclusions. As a result, the method lost appeal and was surpassed by other methods, such as the Proxy Variables Method (Rodgers 1990), the IE approach (Yang et al. 2004, 2008) and HAPC models (Yang and Land 2006).

Yet, none of the available methods offers a solution to the identification problem, and any attempts to separate the effects of age, period and cohort rely on simplifying assumptions. In fact, this is an essential part of social research: 'the purpose of models is to simplify, and [...] models for this reason are necessarily "unrealistic"' (Mason et al. 1976, 904). That one cannot be entirely sure about the accuracy of the constraints and the resulting estimates does not mean, however, that the CVM should be rejected altogether. We concur with the view of Glenn (2003, 474) that

> once the quest to separate the effects with precision and absolute certainty is abandoned, reasonable judgements about the effects can usually be made. One needs only to draw on theory, common sense, and information about the dependent variable being studied from all available sources and then be appropriately tentative in the conclusions made.

If the constraints are made explicit and have a strong theoretical and empirical foundation, then the CVM may yield plausible information about the nature of age, period and cohort effects which can be further tested in future studies. We therefore conclude that scholars gave up on CVM too quickly and thereby missed out on an opportunity to show age, period and cohort effects.

Online supplementary material relating to this book can be found at www. routledge.com/9780367174439.

Notes

1 This chapter was an idea of Manfred te Grotenhuis, who sadly died too soon.
2 In general, it is always necessary to check whether and to what extent multicollinearity may bias the estimated effects.

3 Glenn refers to this approach as the Dummy Variable Method, because age, period and cohort are usually entered as sets of dummy variables in these models (Glenn 2003, 2005).
4 For a technical explanation of the CVM, we refer to Mason et al. (1973).
5 Robinson and Jackson's (2001) article can be criticized in this respect, since the authors rely on a data-based strategy rather than a theoretical one to justify their identifying restrictions. They argue that 'no compelling *a priori* reasons exist for thinking that trust levels remain unchanged from one particular age to the next, one survey year to the next, or one cohort to the next' (Robinson and Jackson 2001, 133). There is considerable debate about whether one can rely on an inspection of the data to justify a constraint (see e.g. Rodgers 1982a, 1982b; Smith et al. 1982). What is agreed upon, however, is that a comparison of models at least renders some robustness to the findings.

References

Alwin, D. F. 2002. "Generations X, Y and Z: Are They Changing America?" *Contexts* 1 (4): 42–51. doi:10.1525/ctx.2002.1.4.42.

Alwin, D. F., and McCammon, R. J. 2003. "Generations, Cohorts, and Social Change." In *Handbook of the Life Course*, edited by J. T. Mortimer and M. J. Shanahan, 23–49. New York: Kluwer Academic/Plenum Publishers.

Baltes, P. B. 1968. "Longitudinal and Cross-sectional Sequences in the Study of Age and Generation Effects." *Human Development* 11 (3): 145–171.

Baxter, J., Buchler, S., Perales, F., and Western, M. 2015. "A Life-Changing Event: First Births and Men's and Women's Attitudes to Mothering and Gender Divisions of Labor." *Social Forces* 93 (3): 989–1014. doi:10.1093/sf/sou103.

Bell, A., and Jones, K. 2014. "Another 'Futile Quest'? A Simulation Study of Yang and Land's Hierarchical Age–Period–Cohort Model." *Demographic Research* 30: 333–360. doi: 10.4054/DemRes.2013.30.11.

Bell, A., and Jones, K. 2015. "Should Age–Period–Cohort Analysts Accept Innovation Without Scrutiny? A Response to Reither, Masters, Yang, Powers, Zheng and Land." *Social Science & Medicine* 128: 331–333. doi:10.1016/j.socscimed.2015.01.040.

Bell, A., and Jones, K. 2018. "The Hierarchical Age–Period–Cohort Model: Why Does It Find the Results that It Finds?" *Quality and Quantity* 52 (2): 783–799. doi:10.1007/s11135-017-0488-5.

Brooks, C., and Bolzendahl, C. 2004. "The Transformation of Us Gender Role Attitudes: Cohort Replacement, Social-Structural Change, and Ideological Learning." *Social Science Research* 33 (1): 106–133. doi:10.1016/S0049-089X(03)00041-3.

Chauvel, L., and Schröder, M. 2014. "Generational Inequalities and Welfare Regimes." *Social Forces* 92 (4): 1259–1283. doi:10.1093/sf/sot156.

Chauvel, L., Leist, A. K., and Ponomarenko, V. 2016. "Testing Persistence of Cohort Effects in the Epidemiology of Suicide: An Age–Period–Cohort Hysteresis Model." *PLoS ONE* 11 (7): e0158538. doi 10.1371/journal.pone.0158538.

Converse, P. E. 1976. *The Dynamics of Party Support: Cohort-analyzing Party Identification.* Beverly Hills, CA: Sage.

Corrigall, E. A., and Konrad, A. M. 2007. "Gender Role Attitudes and Careers: A Longitudinal Study." *Sex Roles* 56 (11–12): 847–855. doi:10.1007/s11199-007-9242-0.

Fan, P.-L., and Marini, M. M. 2000. "Influences on Gender-Role Attitudes During the Transition to Adulthood." *Social Science Research* 29 (2): 258–283. doi:10.1006/ssre.1999.0669.

Fienberg, S. E., and Mason, W. M. 1979. "Identification and Estimation of Age–Period–Cohort Models in the Analysis of Discrete Archival Data." *Sociological Methodology* 10 (1979): 1–67. doi:10.2307/270764.

Firebaugh, G., and Chen, K. 1995. "Vote Turnout of Nineteenth Amendment Women: The Enduring Effect of Disenfranchisement." *American Journal of Sociology* 100 (4): 972–996.

Fosse, E., and Winship, C. 2019. "Analyzing Age–Period–Cohort Data: A Review and Critique." *Annual Review of Sociology* 45: 467–492. doi:10.1146/annurev-soc-073018-022616.

Glenn, N. D. 1976. "Cohort Analysts' Futile Quest: Statistical Attempts to Separate Age, Period and Cohort Effects." *American Sociological Review* 41 (5): 900–904.

Glenn, N. D. 1980. "Values, Attitudes, and Beliefs." In *Constancy and Change in Human Development*, edited by O. G. Brim, Jr. and J. Kagan, 596–640. Cambridge, MA: Harvard University Press.

Glenn, N. D. 2003. "Distinguishing Age, Period, and Cohort effects." In *Handbook of the Life Course*, edited by J. T. Mortimer and M. J. Shanahan, 465–476. New York: Kluwer Academic/Plenum Publishers.

Glenn, N. D. 2005. *Cohort Analysis.* Thousand Oaks, CA: Sage.

Kaufman, G., Bernhardt, E., and Goldscheider, F. 2017. "Enduring Egalitarianism? Family Transitions and Attitudes Toward Gender Equality in Sweden." *Journal of Family Issues* 38 (13): 1878–1898. doi:10.1177/0192513X16632266.

Luo, L. 2013. "Assessing Validity and Application Scope of the Intrinsic Estimator Approach to the Age–Period–Cohort Problem." *Demography* 50 (6): 1945–1967. doi:10.1007/s13524-013-0243-z.

Luo, L., and Hodges, J. S. 2016. "Block Constraints in Age-Period-Cohort Models with Unequal-width Intervals." *Sociological Methods & Research* 45 (4): 700–726. doi:10.1177/0049124115585359.

Mannheim, K. 1952. "The Problem of Generations." In *Essays in the Sociology of Knowledge (Vol. 5)*, edited by P. Kecskemeti, 276–322. Boston: Routledge and Kegan Paul.

Mason, K. O., Mason, W. M., Winsborough, H. H., and Poole, W. K. 1973. "Some Methodological Issues in Cohort Analysis of Archival Data." *American Sociological Review* 38 (2): 242–258.

Mason, W. M., Mason, K. O., and Winsborough, H. H. 1976. "Reply to Glenn." *American Sociological Review* 41 (5): 904–905.

Mason, W. M., and Smith, H. L. 1985. "Age–Period–Cohort Analysis and the Study of Deaths from Pulmonary Tuberculosis." In *Cohort Analysis in Social Research. Beyond the Identification Problem*, edited by W. M. Mason and S. E. Fienberg, 151–127. New York: Springer-Verlag. doi:10.1007/978-1-4613-8536-3_6.

O'Brien, R. M. 2011. "Constrained Estimators and Age–Period–Cohort Models." *Sociological Methods & Research* 40 (3): 419–452. doi:10.1177/0049124111415367.

Pelzer, B., Te Grotenhuis, M., Eisinga, R., and Schmidt-Catran, A. W. 2015. "The Non-uniqueness Property of the Intrinsic Estimator in APC Models." *Demography* 52 (1): 315–327. doi:10.1007/s13524-014-0360-3.

Robinson, R. V., and Jackson, E. F. 2001. "Is Trust in Others Declining in America? An Age–Period–Cohort Analysis." *Social Science Research* 30 (1): 117–145. doi:10.1006/ssre.2000.0692.

Rodgers, W. L. 1982a. "Estimable Functions of Age, Period, and Cohort Effects." *American Sociological Review* 47 (6): 774–787. doi:10.2307/2095213.

Rodgers, W. L. 1982b. "Reply to Comment by Smith, Mason, and Fienberg." *American Sociological Review* 47 (6): 793–796. doi:10.2307/2095215.

Rodgers, W. L. 1990. "Interpreting the Components of Time Trends." *Sociological Methodology* 20 (1990): 421–438. doi:10.2307/271092.

Smith, H. L. 2004. "Response: Cohort Analysis Redux." *Sociological Methodology* 34 (2004): 111–119. doi:10.1111/j.0081-1750.2004.00149.x.

Smith, H. L., Mason, W. M., and Fienberg, S. E. 1982. "Estimable Functions of Age, Period, and Cohort Effects: More Chimeras of the Age-Period-Cohort Accounting Framework: Comment on Rodgers." *American Sociological Review* 47 (6): 787–793.

Te Grotenhuis, M., Pelzer, B., Luo, L., and Schmidt-Catran, A. W. 2016. "The Intrinsic Estimator, Alternative Estimates, and Predictions of Mortality Trends: A Comment on Masters, Hummer, Powers, Beck, Lin, and Finch." *Demography* 53 (4): 1245–1252. doi:10.1007/s13524-016-0476-8.

Thijs, P., Te Grotenhuis, M., and Scheepers, P. 2017. "The Relationship between Societal Change and Rising Support for Gender Egalitarianism among Men and Women: Results from Counterfactual Analyses in the Netherlands, 1979–2012." *Social Science Research* 68: 176–194. doi:10.1016/j.ssresearch.2017.05.004.

Winship, C., and Harding, D. J. 2008. "A Mechanism-Based Approach to the Identification of Age-Period-Cohort Models." *Sociological Methods & Research* 36 (3): 362–401. doi:10.1177/0049124107310635.

Yang, Y., Fu, W. J., and Land, K. C. 2004. "A Methodological Comparison of Age–Period–Cohort Models: The Intrinsic Estimator and Conventional Generalized Linear Models." *Sociological Methodology* 34: 75–110. doi:10.1111/j.0081-1750.2004.00148.x.

Yang, Y., and Land, K. C. 2006. "A Mixed Models Approach to the Age–Period–Cohort Analysis of Repeated Cross-section Surveys, with an Application to Data on Trends in Verbal Test Scores." *Sociological Methodology* 36: 75–97. doi:10.1111/j.1467-9531.2006.00175.x.

Yang, Y., Schulhofer-Wohl, S., Fu, W. J., and Land, K. C. 2008. "The Intrinsic Estimator for Age-Period-Cohort Analysis: What It Is and How to Use It." *American Journal of Sociology* 113 (6): 1697–1736. doi:10.1086/587154.

3

MULTILEVEL MODELS FOR AGE–PERIOD–COHORT ANALYSIS

Andrew Bell and Kelvyn Jones

Introduction

Over the last 30 years, multilevel models (also called mixed models, random effects models and hierarchical linear models, depending on the discipline) have become one of the most-used statistical methods in social science. The models are able to separate variation in a dependent variable into a number of different 'levels' with different units, and have allowed a nuanced understanding of how much different sources of variance matter. They have allowed, for instance, understanding of how much schools (in comparison to individual attributes) matter for educational attainment (O'Connell and McCoach, 2008), how much hospitals matter to patient outcomes (Leyland and Goldstein, 2001) and how much neighbourhoods or countries affect individuals that live within them (Jones, 1991).

The age–period–cohort identification problem can also be thought of as a problem of partitioning variance into different parts – that is, understanding to what extent change in a given outcome's variance is dependent on age, period and cohort (APC). Not only that, but longitudinal data that is often used to attempt APC identification is inherently multilevel (Bell, 2019; Fitzmaurice et al., 2011). Panel data consists of individuals measured on multiple occasions, creating a multilevel structure of occasions nested in individuals. Repeated cross-sectional data consists of individuals nested within surveys. As such, it is perhaps unsurprising that multilevel models have become a key focus of age–period–cohort analysis, both as a framework through which to specify identifying constraints (see Chapter 2) and as a potential solution to the identification problem itself.

This chapter discusses those models and the extent to which they provide a useful framework for the analysis of age–period–cohort effects. We will also show why these models do not work as a solution to the age–period–cohort identification problem and why multilevel age–period–cohort models produce the potentially biased results that they do. If you have read the preceding chapters, it will not surprise you to learn that and other such models these models are not panaceas that solve the identification problem – indeed we show that these models make implicit assumptions that are as strong as any made by other models. The purpose of this chapter is to make the models' implicit assumptions explicit, so that researchers can fully understand the strengths and limitations of multilevel models, and make decisions about when these models will and will not be useful.

The chapter proceeds as follows. First, we give a brief introduction to multilevel models and how they work, before proceeding to thinking about how such models could work in an age–period–cohort framework. We then discuss the different combinations of fixed and random parameters that we can use to estimate as age, period and cohort effects, and discuss what those different parameterizations mean in terms of the explicit assumptions that they make. We then focus in particular on the Hierarchical Age–Period–Cohort model (HAPC) (Yang and Land, 2006), which uses a multilevel model to attempt to disentangle APC and solve the identification problem – we show that it does not work as an all-purpose solution, and explain why it finds the results that it does. Finally, we finish with a discussion of what the models discussed in this chapter can achieve, with examples focussing on mental health and mortality.

What are multilevel models?

Multilevel models are an extension of regression models, used when data spans multiple 'levels' – that is, there are multiple units of analysis at which an outcome variable varies. These models are used extensively across social science. In education research, there is often interest in how attainment is affected by different attributes of pupils, classes and schools. In this instance, multilevel models can be used both to find how pupil, class and school attributes affect attainment, but also to consider how individual classes and schools achieve higher and lower attainment, controlling for their measured attributes.

A multilevel model might be specified as follows:

$$Y_{ij} = \beta_0 + \beta_1 X_{1ij} + \beta_2 X_{2j} + u_j + e_{ij} \tag{3.1}$$

In this two-level model, Y_{ij} measures the attainment of a pupil i in a school j. X_{1ij} is a pupil-level variable (e.g., past performance in an exam). X_{2j} is a school-level variable (e.g., the size of the school). There are then two residual terms: u_j the school-level residual and e_{ij} the pupil-level residual. Both of these are assumed to be normally distributed, with a mean of zero and a variance that is estimated:

$$u_j \sim N\left(0, \sigma_u^2\right), \quad e_{ij} \sim N\left(0, \sigma_e^2\right) \tag{3.2}$$

We can tell, from such a model, the effects of the measured variables (through β_1 and β_2), just as with single-level regression – we call this the 'fixed part' of the model as its effect is unchanging across school and pupil. Additionally, we are estimating the model's 'random part', which includes the effect of unmeasured school effects (through the variance of the school-level residuals u_j) where 'random' simply means 'allowed to vary'. Thus, we could answer questions around how much an attribute of schools (such as X_{2j} above) is related to attainment, as well as how much schools seem to matter generally in comparison to unmeasured student attributes (through the estimates of the school variance σ_u^2 in comparison to the student-level variance σ_e^2). We can also use these models to consider attainment differences between specific schools once the variables in the fixed part of the model have been accounted for (on the basis of different estimated values of u_j).

This is a two-level model (where the two levels are students and schools). However, the models are extendable to include additional levels (e.g., extending the above model to include three levels: pupils, classes and schools). These levels do not need to be exactly nested in one another, such that one could include for example both a school and neighbourhood level in a model, to understand how both a pupil's school and their home neighbourhood are related to their attainment. So, students at a given school might live in multiple neighbourhoods, and students that live in a particular neighbourhood might go to different schools. These models, where the levels are not exactly nested, are called cross-classified models. Clearly, multilevel models are highly flexible at capturing the complex structures present in many social situations.

Such models are frequently used with longitudinal data. When using panel data – data that follows individuals over time – we can use a multilevel structure of occasions (or, repeated measures) nested in individuals (that could be nested in further levels such as schools or neighbourhoods). When using repeated cross-sectional data – repeated surveys of the same population, but different samples each time – again, there is an inherent multilevel structure of individuals nested within surveys/years. Because of this, multilevel models are a standard way of modelling data over time.

Why use multilevel models for age–period–cohort analysis?

Given the use of multilevel models in longitudinal analysis, it makes sense that such models would be used, in some form or another, for analysing APC. Indeed, conceptualizing at least period and cohort as 'levels' in a multilevel model makes a lot of sense. Periods and cohorts can be understood as contexts in which people exist – individuals are situated within the occasion of measurement, and they are situated within the generation (birth cohort) that they were born into. Just as neighbourhoods and schools influence individuals that reside within them, generations and occasions also have a conceptual top-down effect on individuals. And whilst it is less conceptually clear that age can be thought of as a context (rather than an attribute of an individual), there is no technical reason why it should not be treated in that way, given individuals of the same age share common experiences at a given time of their lives.

One could, therefore, at least in theory, estimate a model that treats all of age, period and cohort as levels in a multilevel model, with each discrete value of the three terms treated as additive random effects:

$$Y_{ij} = \beta_0 + u_p + u_c + u_a + e_i$$

$$u_p \sim N\left(0, \sigma_{up}^2\right), \quad u_c \sim N\left(0, \sigma_{uc}^2\right), \quad u_a \sim N\left(0, \sigma_{ua}^2\right), \quad e_{ij} \sim N\left(0, \sigma_e^2\right) \quad (3.3)$$

Here, p, c and a represent discrete period, cohort and age groups respectively, with u_p giving the effect of being in year p, u_c giving the effect of being born in birth cohort c, and u_a giving the effect of being in age group a. This would imply a multilevel structure as shown in Figure 3.1.

There are, however, a number of issues with models such as these. First, as mentioned in previous chapters, the identification problem is likely to be a problem in models like these if there are any linear effects present in the processes that generated the data. Interestingly, because APC are treated as random effects, and so are subject to shrinkage (i.e., being pulled back towards a zero effect, especially strongly when unreliably estimated), these models will be identifiable, even when there is no grouping across APC years. This would not be the case in a fixed-classification model in which dummies are used to represent each and every age group, year and birth year. However, this doesn't mean that the estimates that are produced by the multilevel model will be correct. Second, the assumption that the random effects u_a, u_p and u_c are independent and identically distributed is likely to be incorrect. Consecutive years are likely to be more related to each other than years that are far apart in time; people born in 1950 are likely to be more similar to those born in 1951 than to those born in 1980; and so on.

Given this, it might make more sense to model a mixture of fixed and random classifications, with the fixed part modelling continuous, long-run changes, and the random part of the model providing estimates of discrete changes net of any long-run changes. However, this needs to be done on the basis of theory and an

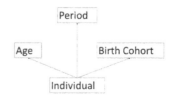

FIGURE 3.1 The multilevel structure specified by Equation 3.3

understanding of the APC processes that are being modelled. For instance, age is a parameter that is likely to have only a continuous effect – that is, it is unlikely there is a specific effect of being, for example, age 24, but rather an underlying smooth effect of getting older across a longer age range. It will usually make more sense, therefore, to model this as a linear (or polynomial) trend in the fixed part of the model, showing a smooth change in an outcome variable through the life course. This is not necessarily the case for periods and cohorts, where a specific event (like a war or an economic recession) might lead to an effect on an outcome related to a very specific year or birth cohort. There might also be a combination of these two sorts of effects – that is, there might be a continuous effect of successive birth cohorts, as well as more discrete effects associated with specific birth cohorts born in very specific moments in history. For example, in general people born longer ago have higher rates of mortality, whilst there are also specific events (being born during the Spanish flu epidemic of 1919, or the Dutch famine of 1944) that also additionally impact on individuals' mortality.

As such, we want to develop a model that can represent both of the above – smooth changes over time, and isolated events with discrete effects. Not only that, but if we model smooth effects in the fixed part of a multilevel model, it will account for much of the dependency across APC units, meaning the random effects assumptions are more likely to be met in modelling discrete effects. For example, we might believe that there is a smooth trend associated with age (with no additional discrete effects associated with particular ages). We might also think that there are only discrete period effects, and both discrete and smooth cohort effects. This would result in a model along the lines of:

$$Y_{ij} = \beta_0 + \beta_1 Age_i + \beta_2 Age_i^2 + \beta_3 Cohort_i + \beta_4 Cohort_i^2 + u_p + u_c + e_i$$

$$u_p \sim N\left(0, \sigma_{up}^2\right), \quad u_c \sim N\left(0, \sigma_{uc}^2\right), \quad e_{ij} \sim N\left(0, \sigma_e^2\right) \tag{3.4}$$

Here, we have included a polynomial effect for age (estimated by β_1 and β_2) and cohort (β_3 and β_4), and discrete random effects for period (u_p) and cohort (u_c). It would also simplify the multilevel structure implied by the model to that in Figure 3.2 where age is no longer a 'structure' but treated as a measured variable.

One of the advantages of multilevel models is that they are highly extendable, and that applies to models like the above as well. We could add additional levels into a model like this – if we have panel data, we would usually include an additional individual-person level (see Figure 3.3), and potentially further spatial levels (like neighbourhoods) as well (Bell, 2014). We could also add additional explanatory variables to the fixed part of the model which may represent measured attributes of individuals, birth cohorts and periods. The random effects are then the unexplained residual differences at each level, net of the fixed effects of measured variables in the model.

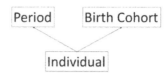

FIGURE 3.2 Multilevel structure implied by Equation 3.4

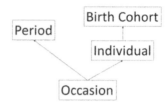

FIGURE 3.3 Multilevel structure implied by a model with panel data, extending Figure 3.2

We are, however, constrained in how many fixed classifications we can include in our model – that is, we can only include two of APC as linear effects because of the identification problem. This means that, in the model above, we are assuming that there is no continuous period trend – only discrete variation with no trend. As shown by O'Brien (2017), the choice of what variables we model as fixed effects will change the results that we find. Modelling two of APC as fixed effects will effectively set the trend of the third to zero (see also Luo and Hodges, 2019). However, as we see later in this chapter, failing to model two of APC as fixed effects can lead to apparent arbitrary apportioning of effects to random effects which (a) will mean those effects are not independently and identically distributed, but more seriously (b) will produce a solution to the identification problem that is based on the data's structure and groupings, rather than the true data-generating process. In other words, including fewer than two of APC in the fixed part of the model will not make the assumptions being made less strong – it will just make them less visible.

The Hierarchical Age–Period–Cohort model

One of a number of methods to appear in the literature in the 2000s was the Hierarchical Age–Period–Cohort (HAPC) model (Yang and Land, 2006, 2013). This is a version of the models described in the above section. It uses a specific combination of fixed continuous predictors and discrete random effects: age as a polynomial in the fixed part of the model, and period and cohort as discrete random effects (as in Figure 3.2), meaning the model can be specified as in equation 3.4 above but without the cohort fixed parameters:

$$Y_{ij} = \beta_0 + \beta_1 Age_i + \beta_2 Age_i^2 + u_p + u_c + e_i$$

$$u_p \sim N\left(0, \sigma_{up}^2\right), \quad u_c \sim N\left(0, \sigma_{uc}^2\right), \quad e_{ij} \sim N\left(0, \sigma_e^2\right) \tag{3.5}$$

The logic of the model may be apparent to the reader, given the above discussion. It makes sense to think of age as a continuously changing random effect, because discrete effects of specific ages are rarely plausible, and because it is conceptually an attribute of the individual (i in the equation above). Similarly, period and cohort are indeed contexts in which an individual resides, much like neighbourhoods, schools and other spatial contexts that are frequently modelled in this way. However, this does not mean that it solves the problems identified above, most notably the identification problem. And yet, the model has been used in a range of different social science and health disciplines as if it were a solution to the age–period–cohort identification problem (e.g., see: Dassonneville, 2013; Reither et al., 2009; Schwadel, 2010), and the authors of the method have claimed that the model does indeed solve the identification problem:

> An HAPC framework does not incur the identification problem because the three effects are not assumed to be linear and additive at the same level of analysis.
>
> *(Yang and Land, 2013:191)*

> The underidentification problem of the classical APC accounting model has been resolved by the specification of the quadratic function for the age effects.
>
> *(Yang and Land, 2006:84)*

If you have read the previous chapters, it is likely that you will already be somewhat sceptical of these claims, and that, with only one of APC specified in the fixed part of the model, it is likely that near-linear APC effects will be mis-apportioned. And indeed, simulation studies have shown that linear or near-linear APC trends can be incorrectly apportioned using the HAPC model (Bell and Jones, 2014a; Luo and Hodges, 2016). For instance, we were able to replicate Reither et al.'s (2009) study of obesity, using data generated in a quite different way from the results found by both them and us (Bell and Jones, 2014b). Follow-up commentaries have shown that, even for data that is not linearly generated, and even when there are all of APC effects present in the processes that generated the data, the model can radically mis-apportion APC effects (Bell and Jones, 2015c, 2018).

Why do multilevel APC models produce the results that they do?

We have already discussed that the choice of fixed-part APC parameters affect the results that are likely to be produced. If we include two of APC in the fixed part of the model, the third one will automatically be set to a trend of zero, and the other two trends will adjust to accommodate this constraint. For example, if the true data-generating process consists of a period trend with a gradient of 1 unit, but only age and cohort are included in the fixed part of the model, that period trend will be estimated as zero, and the cohort and age trends will be overestimated by 1 unit. That is, APC trends are tied to each other – if we constrain one to be wrong, the other two will also be wrong to the same extent to adjust the predictions of the model to be accurate.

Given the inflexibility of a model with two of APC in the fixed part of it, it might be tempting to think that including fewer than two of APC in the fixed part might be more effective. It is this that inspires the use of the HAPC model (Equation 3.5), and it could also be used to justify the use of a model along the lines of Equation 3.3, which treats all of APC as random variables. Unfortunately, this doesn't solve the problem – all it does is make it less clear precisely what assumptions the model is making. However, it is still making strong, but implicit, assumptions, meaning that misleading inference is still likely to occur.

So what does drive a model like the HAPC model, or the fully random model in Equation 3.3, to produce the results that it does? The answer lies in two things: the data collection process and resultant structure of the data being used, and the ways in which multilevel model estimators aim to maximize model fit.[1]

The vast majority of APC analysis uses data that is collected in waves. That is, data is collected for an approximately representative sample, across all age groups, on a number of occasions. The result of this is that we could plot an age-by-period diagram of our data, and that diagram would be rectangular. It might be easy to think that this is the only way data can be collected, but in reality a number of other structures are, or could be, used. For instance, cohort studies collect a sample of people born in a given year and follow them through the rest of their lives. It isn't possible to study APC effects with a single cohort (because age and period are exactly collinear, and cohort is non-varying), but we can have variation in all three by combining multiple cohort studies together. This produces a dataset that, when arranged in an age-by-cohort array, is rectangular but will be in the form of a parallelogram when arranged age-by-period (see Figure 3.4).

These differences in data structures may seem like they should be unimportant for the inference that models produce, but it turns out that they have important characteristics that can influence the results. Most notably, with repeated cross-sectional and panel data there will always be a wider range of cohorts than there will be years of measurement. For example, consider a panel dataset that runs every year between 1991 and 2008 (such as the British Household Panel Survey) with individuals aged between 18 and 70. This will have year groups spanning 18 years, but cohorts spanning from 1921 (those 70 in 1991) to 1990 (those who are 18 in 2008) – a 69-year range for birth cohorts.

Now, imagine there is a linear effect of period, of strength 1 (such that for every year that passes, we would expect an increase in the dependent variable of 1). If that were to be modelled in a multilevel model with period residuals, the size of those residuals would depend on the range of the periods – a wider range would lead to

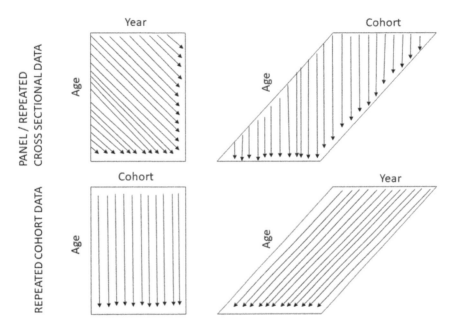

FIGURE 3.4 Data structures associated with panel/repeated cross-sectional data and repeated cohorts, when arranged age-by-year and arranged age-by-cohort. The arrows represent cohorts progressing through the life course. The large number of cohort groups that exist with panel/repeated cross-sectional data compared to the number of years should be noted

bigger residuals to account for bigger differences. Similarly, if there were a linear effect of cohort, of strength 1, that were modelled by birth cohort residuals in a multilevel model, the size of these residuals would also depend on the residuals for that data frame. This is shown in Figure 3.5 (from Bell and Jones, 2018:787).

Given the identification problem, we know that statistical models will reapportion APC linear effects in such a way to maximize model fit. In this case, high values of residuals would imply a worse model fit, since these residuals count as unexplained variance in the random part of the model. If we consider the HAPC model (Equation 3.5), we would expect it to apportion any trend to period rather than cohort, because the 'cost' of the residuals in terms of model fit is lower. If there were a linear cohort trend of magnitude 1, it would make sense for the model to reapportion this; given Cohort = Period – Age, it could reapportion this as a period trend of magnitude 1 and an age trend of magnitude –1. The age trend has no additional cost to the model's fit, since it is absorbed in the fixed part of the model, whilst the period trend is low cost in comparison to the equivalent cohort trend of the same magnitude. As such, in that situation the model is likely to find the wrong answer – it is in effect assuming there is no cohort effect and models any change over time as a period effect.

Note that, if using repeated cohort data, we would expect the results to be reversed, because the range of years would be much greater than the range of cohorts. For other multilevel models, for example that in Equation 3.3, the answer

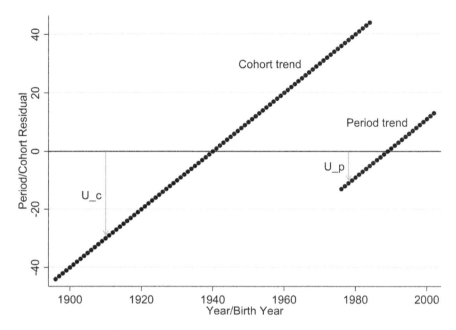

FIGURE 3.5 Estimated cohort and period residuals associated with a cohort and a period linear effect of magnitude 1. Reproduced from Bell and Jones (2018:787)

is more complex, since an age trend would also need to be modelled in the random part of the model, making the trend costly in terms of model fit. The results are likely to depend on the range of the age variable, but O'Brien (2017) finds that, at least in some cases, such a model sets the cohort trend close to zero, so would be likely to produce results similar to that produced by the HAPC model. The result is also likely to vary as a result of grouping periods and/or cohorts unevenly (Bell and Jones, 2018). The key point, however, is that these models are not apportioning effects based on actual APC processes. They are being apportioned based on the structure of the data being used.

Which multilevel APC models should researchers use?

This should make for sober reading for anyone considering using multilevel models as an automatic way of getting around the APC identification problem. Whilst these models do not always make any obvious explicit assumptions with regard to APC trends, they do always make implicit assumptions that are as strong as those made in other APC models, such as those outlined in the previous chapters.

However, this is not to say that models such as these do not have value. The ability to estimate linear (and other polynomial) long-run effects in the fixed part of the model, as well as discrete random changes in the random part, is really powerful and allows for quite nuanced analysis of how APC effects operate. However, this needs to be done with an awareness that the identification problem cannot be solved, and that we need to make explicit assumptions and justify them with theory.

Given this, a model such as that in Equation 3.4 might be a sensible one, *if* we are willing to assume that period trends have no continuous trends (i.e., whilst there are random fluctuations from one year to the next, perhaps because of economic shocks, there are no long-run changes that are a result of period trends). This is often a reasonable assumption to make, where there are theoretical reasons why we would expect change over time to be a result of successive cohort replacement rather than years passing. This is the approach taken by Bell (2014) in his analysis of APC effects on mental health, and discussed further below (see also Delaruelle et al., 2015 for a similar approach). Alternatively, if we were able to assume the opposite (that periods drive change over time), we would want to include period in the fixed part of the model, and not cohort. Theory, plausibility and research questions, accompanied by a sceptical openness, are needed to derive an appropriate model specification and analysis.

We do not have to assume a particular parameter has a linear slope of zero. We could, instead, constrain one of the fixed part parameters in the multilevel model to a particular value, potentially in a Bayesian framework, by applying a strongly informative prior to that parameter (Bell and Jones, 2015b). This could be useful if, for instance, you have a strong idea of what the age trend of a variable should look like; for medical outcomes, we might have medical reasons for being able to assume an age trend, constrain the age parameter to that value, and then estimate period and cohort trends, assuming the constraint on the age parameter is reasonable (for an example of this, see Van der Bracht and Van de Putte, 2014). It might be that we cannot know an exact constraint on a parameter, but might be able to impose some bounds on a parameter: for example, that any age effect will be positive (greater than zero). A combination of such constraints might lead to boundaries within which the true linear APC effects must lie (see Chapter 6, also Fosse and Winship, 2019). Finally, one could use a range of constraints, compare the different combinations of APC trends that those different constraints produce, and come up with an argument for which combination is the most plausible. The important point is that, in each case, the constraint that is made and the process by which it is assumed is made explicitly so that a reader can judge the validity, or otherwise, of that assumption.

Finally, in some situations we are not interested in long-run change, and only interested in discrete shocks. In this situation we can use a multilevel model like that in Equation 3.4, but ignore the fixed part estimates entirely, only interpreting the random part estimates. This detrends the residuals (in a similar manner to Chauvel et al., 2016). We can use a method like this to find, for instance, period and cohort effects related to specific years of measurement or years of birth. However, we need to be careful not to misinterpret these results by assuming that the linear effects do not exist – for instance, a non-linear trend in random effects might mean something very substantively different when a linear trend is included. We might attempt to model those non-linear continuous effects by including polynomials of two of APC. Either way, sharp discrete changes in those random effects can often be interpreted, as we will see in the second example below.

We now present two examples that take some of the approaches outlined above: first a study of mental health that assumes a zero period effect, and second a study of mortality that ignores the estimated fixed part estimates entirely and considers only discrete changes around those trends, estimated in the random part of the model. In each case, R code to guide readers in how to implement such multilevel models is provided online.

Example 1: mental health in the UK, 1991–2008

How does an individual's mental health change over their life course? There is some literature (e.g., Blanchflower and Oswald, 2008) which suggests that it takes a U-shaped pattern, with mental health worsening to midlife, and then improving into old age. However, this is often based on cross-sectional data (where the life course effect is confounded with cohort, and even when longitudinal data is used, the problem of APC identification remains).

Bell (2014) and Bell and Jones (2015a) used a multilevel model in order to attempt to find whether this U-shape really exists when cohorts are controlled, using data from the British Household Panel Survey (BHPS), which runs from 1991–2008 in the UK. They used a model like that in Equation 3.4, where Y is the score in the General Health Questionnaire (GHQ – Goldberg and Williams, 1988), a measure of mental health from 0 to 36, where high scores indicate worse mental health. The model used included age and cohort polynomials in the fixed part of the model, and so assumed that there were no period trends, on the basis that 'there is no reason to expect a continuous period trend across periods affecting all ages. Cohorts, through the nature of individuals' upbringings, more plausibly explain how changes in mental health could occur over time' (Bell, 2014:23). Because the data is panel, the structure was that depicted in Figure 3.3, with additional household and local authority levels.

The results showed that, in fact, when the assumption of no period effects is made, there is no U-shaped relationship between age and mental health – in contrast, mental health worsens throughout the life course (see Figure 3.6a). Whilst the assumption of no period effects is arguably contentious, it is no more contentious than any other assumption that would need to be made to meaningfully identify an APC model.

The model was further able to identify discrete period effects (Figure 3.6b), and both discrete and continuous cohort effects (combined in Figure 3.6c), that suggested a general trend of worsening mental health with successive cohorts.

Example 2: mortality in the UK through the 20th century

There are many things that have led to changes in mortality over the last 100+ years. First, mortality has reduced, as a result of medical and public health advances, implying

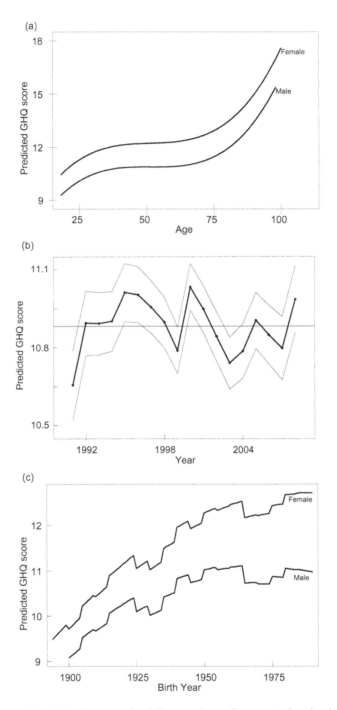

FIGURE 3.6 Predicted GHQ scores for different values of age, period and cohort.
(a) fixed part continuous age effect, (b) fixed part continuous cohort effect combined
with discrete random-part cohort effect, (c) discrete random-part period effect. From
Bell and Jones (2015a:208–210)

the presence of continuous period effects, or cohort effects, or both. There is also, of course, changes in mortality as individuals age – that is, the likelihood of death increases as an individual ages. However, these trends are likely to be subject to the identification problem and, in the absence of good theoretical reasons to constrain one of age, period and cohort, it would be impossible to find such APC effects robustly.

However, as well as these more long-run changes, we also expect to find discrete event-based period and cohort effects related to events in particular years. In particular, we would expect wars and disease epidemics to have effects both on those who lived in those times (a period effect), and also on those who were born or brought up in those times and carried on through their lives (a cohort effect). Because these are not linear or near-linear trends, they can be identified, potentially through a multilevel model.

This was the approach undertaken by Jones et al. (2018) alongside some more graphical techniques (see Chapter 5). They used a Poisson multilevel model on data from the Human Mortality Database (1922–2016) that has data on mortality across all years and all age groups (University of California and Max Plank Institute for Demographic Research). The model is thus specified as follows:

$$Log_e\left(Deaths_i\right) = Log_e\left(Exp_i\right) + \beta_0 + \beta_1 Age_i + \beta_2 Age_i^2 + \beta_3 Period_i + u_p + u_c \tag{3.6}$$

The outcome is the natural log of the number of deaths, with an offset being the natural log of the expected number of deaths (i.e., the number of deaths, given the population size, we would expect if deaths were distributed evenly). The inclusion of the offset means that, instead of modelling the outcome of the (log) number of deaths, the outcome effectively becomes the (log) mortality rate for the given age–year cell. Age and period are specified in the fixed part of the model, but any two of APC could be used, given the aim is simply to soak up the long-run APC effects. The result is that the period and cohort residuals should be free of linear trends, allowing us to model non-linear discrete changes more appropriately. We additionally included the age quadratic term to attempt to soak up more of the long-run continuous (but non-linear) trend – one could include further polynomials to attempt to control out non-linear continuous effects from the period and cohort residuals, although non-linearities that do not fit the polynomial function would remain in the residuals. The level 1 residuals are assumed to follow a Poisson distribution, whereby the variance is equal to the mean, and the period and cohort residual differentials are assumed to be normally distributed.

These period and cohort residuals are shown in Figure 3.7 for men. It can be seen that there is some non-linearity in these figures; however, this should not be over-interpreted – this is a long-run but non-linear change not fully captured by the fixed-part age and period polynomial parameters, and its meaning may well be different when combined with any linear trends that have been controlled out in the fixed part of the model. What we can consider, however, are any non-linear discrete changes that occur in this data. In this regard we can see some very clear cohort effects that appear to have produced an increased mortality for people born

(a)

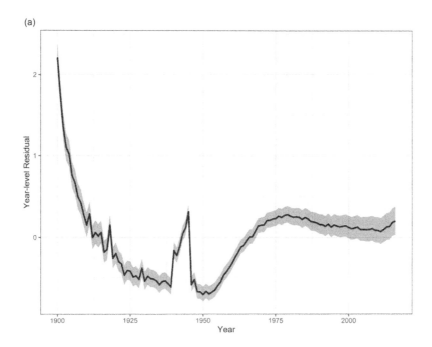

(b)

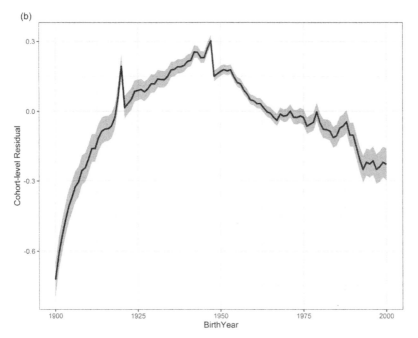

FIGURE 3.7 Cohort and period level residuals conditional on continuous trends estimated in the fixed part of the model (u_c and u_p in Equation 3.6), on male mortality

in 1919, and decreased mortality for people born in 1948. In terms of period effects, again there are potentially misleading non-linearities, but there also appears to be a significant increase in mortality associated with the early 1940s.

There are some clear reasons why such effects might have occurred: 1919 corresponds with the outbreak of the Spanish flu, which as well as causing high levels of mortality at the time, is also known to have had more long-lasting damage to young people, including children born with prenatal exposure to the disease (Almond, 2006). This corroborates the idea that a higher mortality risk associated with the Spanish flu followed individuals in that birth cohort through the rest of their lives. The opposite effect, associated with the year 1948, corresponds to the formation of the National Health Service and other post-war improvements in public health. It seems that those measures had a positive effect on those born at the time, suggesting that improvements in prenatal and antenatal healthcare were particularly valuable, and stayed with those individuals through their continuing lives. For period effects, there appears to be an effect of the Second World War – unsurprising given the large number of lives lost at that time.

Conclusion

Multilevel models present a useful tool for considering age period and cohort effects. This is because data that can be used for APC analysis is inherently multilevel, because longitudinal data always has some kind of structure. However, multilevel models do not provide a solution to the identification problem – rather a structure around which the problem can be considered and appropriate and strong assumptions made in order to make the models produce robust results if those assumptions are justified.

Whilst others have suggested multilevel models present a potential automatic solution to the identification problem, this is not the case: such multilevel models may be identifiable, but they tend to apportion APC near-linear effects on the basis of the structure of the data being analysed, rather than the true effects present in the processes that generated the data. As such, multilevel models need to make assumptions that are justified by theory and made explicit, or ensure that only discrete non-linearities are interpreted.

In sum, multilevel models present opportunities for APC analysis, but are not a magic bullet – they are not a solution to the identification problem because no such solution can exist.

Online supplementary material relating to this book can be found at www.routledge.com/9780367174439.

Note

1 A third factor is the magnitude of true non-linear APC trends in the data-generating process that occur around the APC trends (Luo and Hodges, 2019).

References

Almond D (2006) Is the 1918 influenza pandemic over? Long-term effects of in utero influenza exposure in the post-1940 U.S. population. *Journal of Political Economy* 114(4): 672–712.

Bell A (2014) Life course and cohort trajectories of mental health in the UK, 1991–2008: a multilevel age-period-cohort analysis. *Social Science & Medicine* 120: 21–30.

Bell A (2020 – in press) Cross-sectional and longitudinal studies. In Morin J, Olson C and Atikcan E (eds). *Research Methods in the Social Sciences: An A-Z of Key Concepts*. Oxford: Oxford University Press.

Bell A and Jones K (2014a) Another 'futile quest'? A simulation study of Yang and Land's Hierarchical Age-Period-Cohort model. *Demographic Research* 30: 333–360.

Bell A and Jones K (2014b) Don't birth cohorts matter? A commentary and simulation exercise on Reither, Hauser and Yang's (2009) age-period-cohort study of obesity. *Social Science and Medicine* 101: 176–180.

Bell A and Jones K (2015a) Age, period and cohort processes in longitudinal and lifecourse analysis: a multilevel perspective. In Burton-Jeangros C, Cullati S Sacker A, et al. (eds). *A Life Course Perspective on Health Trajectories and Transitions*. Cham (Switzerland): Springer, pp. 197–213.

Bell A and Jones K (2015b) Bayesian informative priors with Yang and Land's Hierarchical Age-Period-Cohort model. *Quality and Quantity* 49(1): 255–266.

Bell A and Jones K (2015c) Should age-period-cohort analysts accept innovation without scrutiny? A response to Reither, Masters, Yang, Powers, Zheng, and Land. *Social Science and Medicine* 128: 331–333.

Bell A and Jones K (2018) The hierarchical age-period-cohort model: Why does it find the results that it finds? *Quality and Quantity* 52(2): 783–799.

Blanchflower DG and Oswald AJ (2008) Is well-being U-shaped over the life cycle? *Social Science & Medicine* 66(8): 1733–1749.

Chauvel L, Leist AK and Ponomarenko V (2016) Testing persistence of cohort effects in the epidemiology of suicide: an Age-Period-Cohort Hysteresis Model. *PLOS One* 11(7): 1–20. DOI: 10.1371/journal.pone.0158538.

Dassonneville R (2013) Questioning generational replacement: an age, period and cohort analysis of electoral volatility in the Netherlands, 1971–2010. *Electoral Studies* 32(1): 37–47.

Delaruelle K, Buffel V and Bracke P (2015) Educational expansion and the education gradient in health: a hierarchical age-period-cohort analysis. *Social Science & Medicine* 145: 79–88.

Fitzmaurice GM, Laird NM and Ware JM (2011) *Applied Longitudinal Analysis*. 2nd ed. Hoboken, NJ: Wiley.

Fosse E and Winship C (2019) Bounding analyses of age-period-cohort models. *Demography* 56: 1975–2004.

Goldberg D and Williams P (1988) *A User's Guide to the General Health Questionnaire*. Windsor: NFER-NELSON.

Jones K (1991) Specifying and estimating multi-level models for geographical research. *Transactions of the Institute of British Geographers* 16(2): 148–159.

Jones PM, Minton J and Bell A (2018) Period and cohort changes in mortality risk over the twentieth century in the UK: an exploratory analysis. *OSF Preprints*. DOI: 10.31219/OSF.IO/4F7JR.

Leyland AH and Goldstein H (2001) *Multilevel Modelling of Health Statistics*. Chichester: Wiley.

Luo L and Hodges JS (2016) Block constraints in age-period-cohort models with unequal-width intervals. *Sociological Methods & Research* 45(4): 700–726.

Luo L and Hodges JS (2019) Constraints in random effects age-period-cohort models. *arXiv*. Available at: http://arxiv.org/abs/1904.07672 (accessed 19 August 2019).

O'Brien RM (2017) Mixed models, linear dependency, and identification in age-period-cohort models. *Statistics in Medicine* 36(16): 2590–2600.

O'Connell AA and McCoach DB (2008) *Multilevel Modelling of Educational Data*. Charlotte, NC: Information Age.

Reither EN, Hauser RM and Yang Y (2009) Do birth cohorts matter? Age-period-cohort analyses of the obesity epidemic in the United States. *Social Science & Medicine* 69(10): 1439–1448.

Schwadel P (2010) Age, period, and cohort effects on US religious service attendance: the declining impact of sex, Southern residence, and Catholic affiliation. *Sociology of Religion* 71(1): 2–24.

University of California Berkeley and Max Plank Institute for Demographic Research (n.d.) Human Mortality Database. Available at: www.mortality.org (accessed 2 November 2018).

Van der Bracht K and Van de Putte B (2014) Homonegativity among first and second generation migrants in Europe: the interplay of time trends, origin, destination and religion. *Social Science Research* 48: 108–120.

Yang Y and Land KC (2006) A mixed models approach to the age-period-cohort analysis of repeated cross-section surveys, with an application to data on trends in verbal test scores. *Sociological Methodology* 36: 75–97.

Yang Y and Land KC (2013) *Age-Period-Cohort Analysis: New Models, Methods, and Empirical Applications*. Boca Raton, FL: CRC Press.

4

THE LEXIS SURFACE

A tool and workflow for better reasoning about population data

Jon Minton

Introduction

This chapter will discuss how Lexis surfaces, and Lexis surface based visualisation, can help support thinking about, through and beyond questions of identifying APC effects in population data. My own perspective on the relationship between Lexis surface visualisations and APC effects has developed over the course of the last decade (Minton 2014; Minton, Vanderbloemen, and Dorling 2013), during which I've applied Lexis surfaces to a range of challenges in epidemiology, demography and public health. These applications have mainly focused on using Lexis surfaces to understand patterns in mortality data (McCartney et al. 2016a; Parkinson et al. 2017; Parkinson et al. 2018), but have also been applied to issues like understanding changing patterns in fertility, car and driving licence ownership, conviction rates and housing tenure (Matthews and Minton 2018[BIB-016] ; Minton and Clark 2018;).

Over the last couple of years, my perspective on the Lexis surface has broadened, from thinking about it mainly as a visualisation approach, to a conceptual tool that can support both the development of appropriate informal intuitions and then formal statistical modelling frameworks. After contributing Lexis surface visualisations to a number of public health papers – concerned with changing patterns and inequalities in cause-specific mortality in Scotland (McCartney et al. 2016a; Parkinson et al. 2017; Parkinson et al. 2018) – which also used more conventional APC models, including the conceptually flawed intrinsic estimator (IE) model (Bell and Jones 2014; Yang et al. 2008), and visualisations, such as time trends of summary statistics, I then wrote three more methodologically focused papers to help synthesise and articulate my thinking about how Lexis surfaces should best be used for population research.

Perhaps as each of these papers was building on the last, and they may have been too disjointed when read separately, none of them was published in academic journals, even though they are freely available as pre-prints (Minton 2017a, 2017b, 2018). I am therefore using this chapter as an opportunity to bring some of the key ideas from these individual papers together, in a way that is hopefully more accessible and coherent than it was in each single paper. However, I would encourage the reader to access these pre-prints and earlier papers if interested in the ideas presented in this chapter.

One of the modest proposals I have about Lexis surfaces is that they suggest a focus on APC effects can often lead to the 'wrong' framing of the problems, and so to the 'wrong' questions being asked. By this I mean the following: Lexis surfaces encourage thinking about population data as if it is a surface, in which all parts of the surface are connected, whereas more usual ways of analysing and interpreting such data can encourage researchers to think about the same data as comprising many discrete components and 'slices', in which the inherent connectedness between observations is simply considered to be some kind of methodological nuisance.

If geographers thought about spatial surfaces in the kind of way APC models – and questions of APC effects – encourage people to think about population data, they might not be looking at maps and talking about features like 'hills' and 'valleys', but instead concerned with the statistical significance of the 'latitude effect on elevation', and whether this 'latitude effect' is uniquely identifiable and might not also be expressible as some kind of latitude–longitude interaction.

Occasionally, this way of framing the problems of interpreting the data – looking for the effect of singular continuous variables – can be appropriate. For example, the biogeographer Jared Diamond proposed in a popular science book that civilisations spread more quickly from East to West than from North to South, due to the crops the civilisations depended on only growing effectively in certain climates (Diamond 1997). And so, in this example, the framing of an outcome in terms of 'latitude effects' and 'longitude effects' would be appropriate, and recent scientific research seems to broadly support Diamond's axial hypothesis (Laitin, Moortgat, and Robinson 2012).

However, I hope you will agree that analogues to Diamond's axial hypothesis, within population science, are the exception rather than the general rule. In most cases it makes sense to look at the map first, then attempt to identify and describe features in the map, before undertaking any further statistical analysis which imposes a particular framing on how variables are related to each other. This approach to understanding spatial maps, I argue, applies almost identically to the maps of demographic 'space' which Lexis surfaces reveal, and the broader implications of this for the challenge of thinking about age–period–cohort effects, and population structure more generally, as yet they seem to be insufficiently appreciated and understood. The overall aim of this chapter is to promote this map-like way of reasoning about population data, and the underlying population structure and processes, that Lexis surfaces support.

Key arguments

This chapter will be structured so as to advance the following propositions, in the following order:

1. We should look at population data as Lexis surfaces as a matter of routine;
2. We should look at Lexis surfaces of population data in order to produce informal models of population structure;
3. We should use our emergent knowledge of informal models to produce formal models;
4. We can and should use Lexis surfaces again at the stage of statistical model diagnostics.

Additionally, it is worth considering a fifth proposition: that we should see the uses of Lexis surfaces at various stages in the model development and testing framework as fitting together in a standard workflow for analysis, which we can go some way to defining. Some initial suggestions about how to do this are presented in the online materials.

This chapter will be structured in support of these propositions. To do this, I will mainly draw on an extended case study: that of mortality rates by age and year for Scottish populations from one of three causes: suicide, drug-related deaths (DRDs) and alcohol-related deaths (ARDs). The sources of these data, along with more conventional analyses (including those based on the conceptually flawed IE (Yang et al. 2008) model), are described in four papers published with colleagues within NHS Health Scotland (Parkinson et al. 2018, 2017; McCartney et al. , 2016a, 2016b).

The aim of this chapter, however, is to look at what the data show, on the Lexis surface, without drawing from a conventional lineage of model specifications that prioritise the identification of specific age, period or cohort effects. Instead, by starting with a Lexis surface visualisation, we can begin to develop new informal models – an informal sense of what a surface of values looks like, and how it looks in comparison with other surfaces – which can suggest powerful and novel forms of new formal models. In the extended example, two such new models are developed in order to characterise the patterns seen in three cause-specific surfaces.

The material presented then proceeds to illustrate two strategies for testing the veracity of these new models: first, through comparison with a series of generic models, not informed by visual exploration of the Lexis surface; second, through intentional misspecification of new model structures to data surfaces they are not designed to fit. The use of Lexis surfaces at the stage of model testing – through the production of predicted surfaces and residuals surfaces – will be illustrated through this example.

First, however, let's start with a simple introduction of Lexis surfaces and APC effects.

The Lexis surface and APC effects: an introduction

In 1987, Vaupel and colleagues introduced the concept of the Lexis surface (LS), named after (Lexis 1875) – an arrangement of a population attribute, like force of mortality, by age across one axis and year across the other (Vaupel, Gambill, and Yashin 1987). Despite an additional monograph in 1998 (Vaupel et al. 1998) and the use of LS in sundry papers, (e.g., Lindahl-Jacobsen et al. 2016; Schöley and Willekens 2017), LS visualisation remained relatively little used within, and even less well used beyond, the demographic community. Knowledge and application of LS remained so limited that in 2013 I had unwittingly 'reinvented' the approach as one of two 'new' graphical methods for exploring the components of international mortality trends in a paper in a top epidemiology journal (Minton, Vanderbloemen, and Dorling 2013), only discovering my lack of methodological originality a few months later (Minton 2013).

Conceptually, Lexis surfaces are maps of age–time, much as topographic maps are of latitude–longitude. The usual arrangement of a Lexis surface has years arranged horizontally, with older years on the left and newer years on the right, and age arranged vertically, with youngest ages on the bottom and oldest ages on the top. However, alternative arrangements – such as with birth cohorts on the horizontal axis instead of year – should probably still be considered Lexis surfaces too.

Figure 4.1 presents a blank Lexis surface, with some additional bands as annotation. The Lexis surface is arranged with equal projection along both axes, such that one year in time is as wide as one year in age is as tall. Because of this, cohorts run diagonally from bottom left to top right at 45-degree angles. The background of the Lexis surface marks out decades as vertical lines, decadal age groups as horizontal

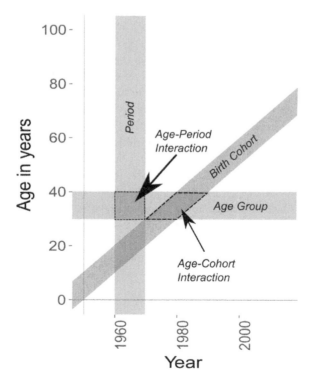

FIGURE 4.1 Age, period and cohort effects, and interactions, on the Lexis surface

lines and birth cohort decades as diagonal lines. Within this figure, a specific age band, decade band and cohort band is highlighted with green, red and blue colours, respectively.

In addition to thinking about patterns on Lexis surfaces in terms of bands of parallel horizontal (age), vertical (period) and diagonal (cohort) lines, it is also often useful to look for and identify specific regions within the surface that do not strictly run across the entirety of any of these three planes. These regions can sometimes be usefully interpreted as representing either age–period interaction effects, or age–cohort interaction effects, two examples of which are marked in the figure. However, although we *could* interpret these features as specific kinds of interactions between age, period or cohort effects, we could also simply think about these features as representations of specific types of geometric forms on the surface. It's this latter kind of thinking that Lexis surfaces can be particularly effective for promoting, and in the extended examples used throughout this chapter I show how identifying such geometric forms can be an effective basis for producing fundamentally new forms of model structure, leading to fundamentally new insights about population processes.

Within the demographic time frame of a century or longer, a common example of an age–period interaction is a war, during which the mortality risks of young adult males tend to rise sharply, before falling back more slowly. Examples of age–cohort interactions are perhaps less common, but potentially include any *additional* mortality risk experienced by 1918 birth cohorts as infants, that is, the observation of an even higher mortality rate in the first year of life for this cohort, even when the whole life-course log mortality multiplier associated with membership of this cohort is taken into account.

Particularly high mortality and morbidity risks in the first year of life can be signals of one of the main mechanisms through which persistent life-course cohort effects emerge, namely through interuterine and perinatal exposure to deleterious environments at these earliest life-course stages, often referred to as a Barker Effect (Barker 2004), after research by Barker and colleagues demonstrating links between low birthweight and a range of early onset morbidities in adulthood (Gluckman, Hanson, and Pinal 2005; Hales and Barker 1992).

The importance of later stages in the life course, beyond infancy, for either establishing or accelerating mortality and morbidity hazards at later age, has also been recognised in life-course epidemiology (Ben-Shlomo and Kuh 2002; Ben-Shlomo and Smith 1991), and ongoing research into the associations between deprivation, gender and cohort membership in Scotland seems to highlight the importance of young adulthood as an important life-course stage, and the macroeconomic conditions established young adults are exposed to at this stage, in establishing persistently elevated hazards of suicides and DRDs throughout the later life course (Minton et al. 2017; Parkinson et al. 2017, 2018). Given the role of critical stages in life-course epidemiology, the value of identifying changes in mortality risk at younger age, as potential determinants of changes in older ages, therefore seems clear.

In the first paper in which I used Lexis surfaces, I mapped age-specific mortality for selected European countries as a shaded contour map, with the contour lines tracking, as in a standard map, parts that are of the same value (Minton, Vanderbloemen, and Dorling 2013). Whereas, for a spatial map, this value would usually be elevation, for a Lexis surface, this value would typically be something like a fertility rate or, in this example, mortality rate. When the Lexis surfaces for populations in England and Wales (treated as a single country by the Human Mortality Database (HMD)) and France were visualised as a shaded contour map, many of the contour lines, which in general have a tendency to creep upwards when viewing the maps from left (oldest years) to right (newest years), instead appear 'raked downwards' for one cohort at a 45-degree angle. This meant that, for one particular cohort, many specific mortality risks (such as a 1-in-100 risk of dying in the next year) were experienced at a slightly earlier age than for cohorts born a few years later or earlier. When presented as shaded contour maps, this diagonal disruption had the appearance of a 'scar' over the surface of the map, hence the paper's name. An example of this is shown in Figure 4.2 for France, although using an aspect ratio in which period and age are fitted to the same dimensions, and so the cohort effects are not at 45 degrees.

A strength and challenge with the Lexis surface is that a single image can contain many tens of thousands of values and a large number of complex patterns and features. In the version of Figure 4.2 that is presented in Figure 4.3, a number of features on this mortality surface are labelled, largely for the female population. As well as the 1918 cohort 'scar' being labelled, so are features consistent with excess deaths through the two World Wars. These appear as a series of concentric rings when contour lines are used; there are more of these concentric rings for males than females, indicating – as we would expect – that male young adult death rates increased during war time more so than for females.

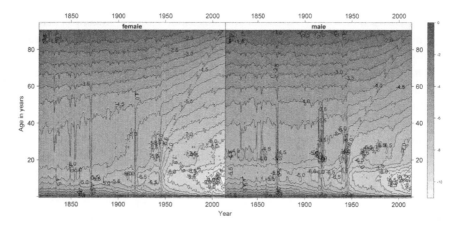

FIGURE 4.2 Log mortality Lexis surface for France, with shade and labelled contour lines

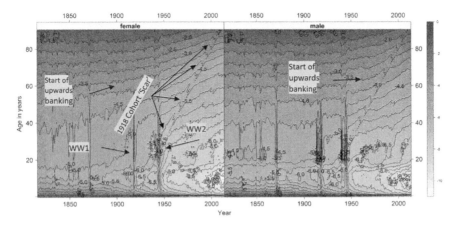

FIGURE 4.3 Annotated variant of Figure 4.2

Another feature that is labelled is that of the contour lines banking upwards from left to right. This means that the fixed risks corresponding to each of the contour lines are being faced at progressively older ages over time. Along with falling infant mortality, this long-term mortality drift on adulthood is the primary cause of increasing life expectancy overall. The start of the upward banking of these mortality hurdles in adulthood begins later for males than for females. For females, there is evidence of this continuous and gradual improvement from the late 19th century, then an accelerating rate of improvement after World War II; for males, there is no clear indication of such improvements in the first half of the 20th century, but clear upwards banking from around the 1950s onwards.

Let's now consider more carefully what we have done in being able to identify this mortality 'scar' associated with the 1918 birth cohort. Implicitly, we have compared the position of these contour lines, their 'diagonal raking downwards' towards their birth cohort, to a counterfactual, asking: Where would contour lines have been if they had not been 'raked' in this way? This counterfactual is formed by noticing continuities in the direction of travel of these contour lines from left to right, whether largely horizontal as with both sexes during the 19th century, or banking upwards as with both sexes after around the 1950s. We have a powerful analytical tool in our skulls, able to identify complex patterns and features in images and structures, and Lexis surfaces allow us to use this tool more effectively.

Having explored many dozens of Lexis surfaces of all-cause mortality like the one above, I suggest there are some fundamentally different patterns of mortality change across time by age group, of which the upwards drifting of contour lines (i.e., falling in age-specific mortality risks over time) is one of the key features. A general typology of these different age-specific features is presented in Figure 4.4.

In Figure 4.4, the upwards drifting of contour lines has been labelled 'Lee–Carter Drift', and I suggest this is most evident from the latter half of working age onwards. I've named it this because this drift of improvement over time appears to be the key

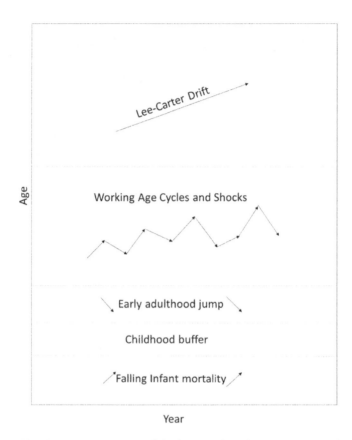

FIGURE 4.4 Heuristic representation of the key trends and patterns observed in many high income countries by broadly defined age group. Year ranges from ~1940 to ~2020

insight and assumption behind the Lee–Carter model used widely in demographic forecasting (Lee and Carter 1992). This key feature of an upwards drift is clearly not easy or intuitive to describe in distinct age, period or cohort terms, and the broad adoption – and to a large extent success – of this modelling approach in correctly forecasting life expectancy change should suggest that the initial way of framing questions of mortality change should not be in age, period or cohort terms, but in terms of the extent and continuity of this drift.

The Lee–Carter drift assumption tends to be less appropriate for the younger working age, and so I have labelled this as a different region. Age-specific mortality rates in young adulthood tend to be considerably more variable and unpredictable than those at older ages, and to be more clearly 'responsive to' changing economic and social circumstances, especially for males. A clear sex difference also tends to become apparent when looking at how much mortality rates increase when 'boys become men', that is, between the ages of 15 and 20 years, compared with corresponding increases when 'girls become women'. Throughout most of childhood, after the first year, mortality risks tend to fall particularly fast, from an already low level compared with other life-course stages.

Rates of infant-mortality decline represent another distinct phenomena, and have generally been falling at an exponential rate in richer nations, for longer than declines in any other age group. Infant death rates used to be of a similar magnitude to those of old age, and are still higher than experienced in the rest of childhood and early adulthood. Life expectancy at birth in the 1940s and 1950s was largely driven by high infant death rates, with conditional life expectancy, from around the age of five and above, much higher. If I were forced to reduce the description of long-term patterns of mortality trends to just two or three features, at least for forecasting or understanding longevity change, it would not be in terms of distinct age, period or cohort effects, but the dual phenomena of falling infant mortality and Lee–Carter-style drift throughout the latter half of the life course.

The following sections move from considering all-cause mortality, to mortality due to three specific causes: DRDs, ARDs and deaths from suicide. Two of these three causes are concentrated in the age group labelled 'working age cycles and shocks' in Figure 4.4, where changes in mortality rates from certain causes can be both caused by, and indicator of, broader forms of social and economic change experienced by that population.

Proposition one: we should look at Lexis surfaces as a matter of routine

To provide a clear motivation for why looking at Lexis surfaces of mortality data can be invaluable, before deciding on modelling strategies and so on, consider Figure 4.5. This figure shows the mortality rates for two population groups – males living in the most deprived fifth of areas in Scotland (bottom row) and males living elsewhere in Scotland (top row) – and three causes of death: ARD (left column), DRD (middle column) and suicide (right column). The data have been smoothed slightly using a Gaussian filter, in order to make the broader patterns in the data easier to identify.

Before reading ahead in this chapter, I would recommend spending a couple of minutes looking carefully at these six images in Figure 4.5 with the following questions in mind:

• What is the general relationship between these three causes of death and area deprivation (top row compared with bottom row)?
• Which causes of death predominantly affect older ages, and which younger ages?
• Which of the causes of death seems most strongly patterned by any combination of age, period or cohort effects, and which least patterned?

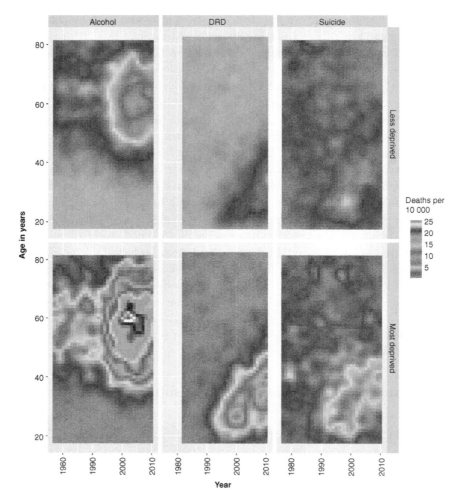

FIGURE 4.5 Smoothed level plots for the three causes of death, for males in Scotland, by deprivation category. Further analyses will focus on the most deprived quintile (bottom row)

- Of the three causes of death presented, are there three, two or one distinct patterns visible in the corresponding images?
- What might be the aetiological explanations for the patterns identified in these images, and what could be the implications of similarities and differences in these patterns?

Having spent some time thinking through what these images suggest about these three causes of death, now consider my interpretation/reading of these images below. At this stage, of 'reading' the Lexis surfaces, the interpretations provided are necessarily subjective. However, this does not mean that the interpretations drawn cannot be empirically tested, by developing and comparing statistical models which capture what we consider to be the most salient features in the Lexis surface images.

- **What is the general relationship between these three causes of death and area deprivation?** *For each of the three causes of death, the mortality hazards appear notably higher for populations living in the most deprived fifth of Scottish areas than in the more affluent four fifths of areas.*
- **Which causes of death predominantly affect older ages, and which younger ages?** *None of the three causes of death have risks that tend to increase or decrease linearly or monotonically with age. However, ARD hazards tend to be highest for people in their 50s and 60s than at other ages, whereas the hazards of DRD or suicide appear lower above approximately age 45 than below this age. So, if forced, we could say that ARD tends to affect older age groups than DRD or suicide.*
- **Which of the causes of death seems most strongly patterned by any combination of age, period or cohort effects, and which least patterned?** *By the strength of pattern, I largely mean the extent to which clear and distinct features are identifiable within a Lexis surface image. In these examples, it appears that both ARD and DRD are more clearly patterned than suicide, especially in the most deprived fifth of areas. Even the least strongly patterned cause of death, suicide, still exhibits some clear visual features; if it did not, then the corresponding image would look largely like 'noise'.*
- **Of the three causes of death presented, are there three, two or one distinct patterns visible in the corresponding images?** *Of the three causes of death, I identify two distinct patterns: one pattern that is specific to ARD; and a second pattern that is shared by both DRD and suicide. This second pattern appears more pronounced for DRD than for suicide.*
- **What might be the aetiological explanations for the patterns identified in these images, and what could be the implications of similarities and differences in these patterns?** *This is an important question to keep in mind when looking at Lexis surfaces, and in particular for seeking to explain why there may be visual similarities between any two causes of death. However, for the purposes of using Lexis surfaces to develop formal models, this question is perhaps secondary to the previous question.*

The responses to the last two questions highlight a distinction I consider important in using Lexis surfaces to better reason about population process. This is the distinction between *geometric reasoning*, as illustrated in the penultimate question, and *aetiological reasoning*, as illustrated by the last question. Both types of reasoning can, and should, be developed in tandem, with the proposal of specific geometric forms likely to spur consideration of likely causal mechanisms that might give rise to the forms proposed and aetiological considerations likely to spur questions of which geometric forms would likely be observed if the causal mechanisms under considerations were true.

Proposition two: we should look at Lexis surfaces of population data in order to produce informal models of population structure

Within the previous section, I proposed that, for either of the populations under consideration (male Scots in either high deprivation or other areas), there were effectively two types of geometric form present for the three causes of death under consideration. DRD and suicide both exhibit one of these forms, and ARD exhibits the other of these two forms.

But what do these forms look like? Verbally, I would describe them as follows:

- **Form one**: the truncated triangle (shared by DRD and suicide);
- **Form two**: a horizontal band and an ellipse (ARD).

Graphically, I would sketch out each of these forms as shown in Figure 4.6.

So far, neither of these proposed forms represents anything further than the researcher's subjective impressions as to what they thought they saw, or didn't see, in a particular image. A different researcher, or the same researcher on a different day, may look at these Lexis surface images and see something different. What separates this exercise from, say, seeing faces in clouds, or fortunes in used tea leaves? Why might this proposed exercise, of looking for features in Lexis surface images, possibly add anything to population science that would be missed if we either visualised the data in a simpler way or used a standard model specification for APC analysis – such as the IE (Yang et al. 2008) or Hierarchical APC (HAPC) (Bell and Jones 2017; Yang 2006) models – without first looking at and thinking about what the data show as Lexis surfaces?

To answer the first of these objections – Why not just use simpler visualisations? – consider what might have been missed if we had, say, only looked at the crude death rates over time for each of these three causes. This is shown in Figure 4.7. Amongst other features, this plot shows death rates from all three causes rising from the mid-1980s onwards, more rapidly so – in the case of DRD, from the early 1990s onwards. The fall in ARD from the early/mid-2000s is also visible.

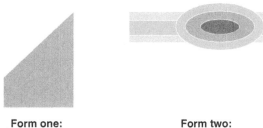

Form one:
Truncated triangle

Form two:
Band and ellipse

FIGURE 4.6 Stylised representations of key geometric features identified in Lexis surfaces

Crude death rates per 100 000 population, by cause of death
Population: Males living in most deprived fifth of areas in Scotland

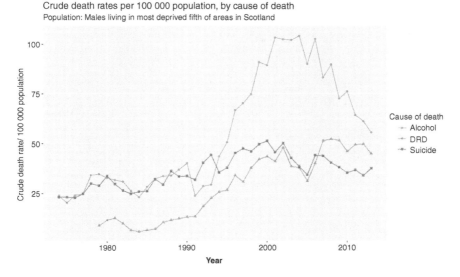

FIGURE 4.7 Crude death rates for three causes of death in Scotland

However, by design, nothing about the age structure is revealed by this figure. To start to explore variation by age, additional figures are then required. Figure 4.8 shows one such example, plotting the mean age of death from each of these causes by year. This figure suggests that, in terms of this summary statistic, there has been little change over time for ARD, with a mean age of death of around 55 years, whereas the mean age of death for DRD fell and rose again, becoming more dissimilar into the 1990s, then more similar again from the late 1990s/early 2000s, largely due to an increasing age of death for DRD.

By looking at these figures in combination, and likely in combination with many additional figures – such as death rates for many separate age groups – it may eventually become possible to get a sense of what the underlying forms of the Lexis surfaces image might be. However, attempting to interpret the population structure in this way, through a series of descriptive statistics, is a fairly oblique and inefficient approach to using the population data effectively. This seems analogous to the parable of a team of blind people trying to collectively understand an elephant through their own local, tactile, sense data. Whereas one person reports feeling a fan, another reports feeling a snake, another a wall, another a snake, and so on. Each individual's experience of the same phenomenon appears qualitatively dissimilar and difficult to reconcile, because no member of the team has access to the visual sense data that shows how each of these perspectives connect.

Such challenges in interpretation are not addressed by starting with a statistical model, either. In the online Appendix I present the results of applying some of the standard model and model diagnostic functions from the R package 'apc' (Nielsen 2015) to this data. Such an approach produces a table that ranks around a dozen

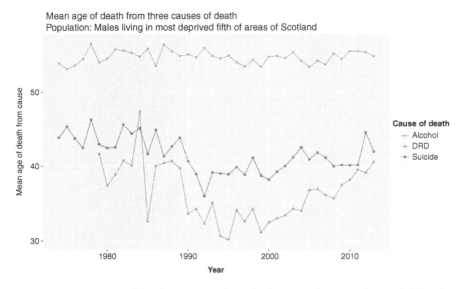

Mean age of death from three causes of death
Population: Males living in most deprived fifth of areas of Scotland

FIGURE 4.8 Mean age of death over time for males living in the most deprived fifth of areas for three causes of death

different model specifications using the Akaike Information Criterion (AIC), as well as default model diagnostic and output plots labelled, by default, 'APC canonical parameters and detrended representation'. This figure is presented in the Appendix for reference; I hope the reader will agree that these model diagnostics and outputs do not shed a great deal of light on what the data itself shows. The 'truncated triangle' and 'belt-and-ellipse', for example, are not at all easy to identify from the model outputs, and without looking at the data structure as Lexis surfaces, and beginning by running a group of 'off-the-shelf' models, then picking the model with the lowest AIC, the useful structural insights which the data contain will not be realised.

Proposition three: we should use our emergent knowledge of informal models to produce formal models

In the previous section, exploration of the Lexis surfaces of mortality rates for three causes of death was able to identify two distinct shapes or forms to the data: a 'truncated triangle' and a 'band plus ellipse'. These are our 'informal models', and in this section we will consider how the emergence of these models can now be used to start to develop new formal models which can be specified algebraically, and fitted and tested statistically.

Algebra is a precise and rarified language for describing proposed relationships and assumptions. It allows us to say things precisely. But in order for this to be valuable, we first need to have something insightful to say. The first stage, of developing the 'informal models', is therefore a necessary first step in this process. To start to turn the informal models into formal models, the features in the forms proposed need to be

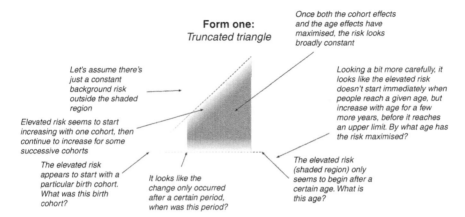

FIGURE 4.9 Refinement of heuristic representation of form one: truncated triangle

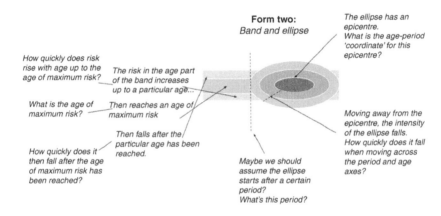

FIGURE 4.10 Refinement of heuristic representation of form two: band and ellipse

described and defined more clearly. Figures 4.9 and 4.10 illustrate how the process of refining the informal model specifications into something that can be expressed algebraically can take place, firstly for the truncated triangle, then for the band plus ellipse.

As each of these questions (and others) are identified and addressed, we move ever further along the path from informal model to formal statistical model. Again, the process of refining the informal and formal models can be iterative and recursive. For example, in the truncated triangle case I refined my informal model somewhat, while thinking about how to formalise it by adding in an 'ageing in effect', that is, assuming the region of elevated risk is not constant across all affected ages, but increases for a few years of age first. I therefore changed the lower end of the truncated triangle from a step to a ramp. Perhaps this additional detail is unnecessary, but this specific question – A step or a ramp? – is now specific and tractable. It can be addressed as a statistical question, rather than an interpretive question.

The process of operationalising the initial informal model into a statistical model – or family of closely related statistical models – forces us to be even more precise as to the underlying structures we are claiming the mortality surfaces exhibit. Once we have done so to such an extent that the model structure can be algebraically defined, comprising a series of parameters that can be determined from the data, we can move onto the next stage: finding best fits of new models against the data, comparing these model fits against each other and against a series of simpler models, and further exploring patterns in the model fit to see if further structural requirement may be required.

As this chapter is intended to be a relatively light introduction to the use of Lexis surfaces in this way, I will not go into further detail as to how the two new models – the truncated triangle and the band and ellipse – have been defined and fitted. (Readers interested in this process should refer to the online Appendix for further details.)

Proposition four: we can and should use Lexis surfaces again at the stage of statistical model diagnostics

In the previous three sections, the Lexis surface has been used as a tool for hypothesis generation. Visual exploration of Lexis surfaces helped identify some patterns and featured in the data that would likely be difficult to identify if the data were visualised in a more conventional way. Looking at the Lexis surfaces allowed some informal models – proposed geometric features or patterns – to be developed, and further reflection and refinement of these informal models allowed new formal models, new model specification structures, to be developed. Though the final stages, of defining these proposed model structures algebraically and fitting them, have not been covered in any detail, they can be and have been fitted. This section will describe how Lexis surfaces can be used again, at the model testing and comparison stage, to better understand what is being claimed when a particular model specification is being used, and how plausible these claims are compared with those embedded in alternative model specifications.

There are two proposed uses for Lexis surfaces at this stage in the research process: to visualise model prediction surfaces and to visualise model residuals surfaces. By model prediction surfaces, I mean the predicted values of a model for each combination of age and year shown on a Lexis surface. And by model residuals surfaces, I mean the differences between the values predicted by the model and the values observed, for each age–year combination shown in the Lexis surface. This latter use is, in effect, a surface of the difference between the two surfaces: the prediction surface and the observed surface.

I propose using Lexis surfaces for two broad classes of models:

- 'Naive' models, not informed by any prior visualisation of the Lexis surface;
- 'Smart' models, which represent the researcher's best attempt to express, algebraically, what they think they observed in the Lexis surface of the data.

The 'naive'/'smart' dichotomy is not necessarily related to the number of parameters a model has, or the statistical or computational challenges involved in fitting it. Instead, it relates to whether the model could or would likely have been considered by the researcher in the absence of any additional information or insight provided through use of the Lexis surface to visualise the data. If the model could have been proposed without first looking at the data as a Lexis surface, it is 'naive'; otherwise, it is 'smart'.

The aim of including the 'naive' models is to try to understand how smart the 'smart' models really are. If a 'naive' model, not informed by any insight developed from looking at the data first, fits the data better than the 'smart' model, then perhaps the 'smart' model is not so smart after all. Perhaps the researcher's eyes deceived them and, like seeing faces in clouds, they saw patterns in the data that weren't really there. Without including some 'naive' models, the risk of using Lexis surfaces to fool ourselves can be too great.

A good model is one that effectively balances model fit against model complexity. This trade-off can be assessed – albeit not definitively – by using a measure of penalised model fit, such as the AIC (Akaike 1974) and Bayesian Information Criterion (BIC) (Schwarz 1978). For all three causes of death, a total of 17 'naive' model specifications were fitted, each structured primarily along age, period and cohort effects and interactions. These models varied between two and over a hundred parameters, ranging from models assuming simple linear relationships between risk and either age, period or cohort, through to models that included various forms of interaction terms and non-linearities within and between age, period and cohort effects. For both ARD and DRD, only the six best performing model specifications, in terms of AIC and BIC, were then visualised as Lexis surfaces of model predictions and model residuals. These are discussed in more detail below.

Prediction and residual surfaces for ARD

In Figure 4.11, the prediction surfaces of the top-six performing 'naive' models are shown on the left-hand side. These models tend to include age terms in preference to cohort terms, with the best performing models tending to assume that the relationship between age and mortality risk is non-linear.

To complement the prediction surfaces, the right-hand side of the figure shows the Lexis surfaces of residuals – differences between modelled and observed death rates for each age–year combination – for each of these six best-performing 'naive' models. Within these residual surfaces, blue colours indicate over-estimation of death rates, red colours under-estimation of death rates, with stronger colours (bluer blues or redder reds) indicating larger differences between predicted and observed values.

When looking at the prediction surfaces we should keep in mind the smoothed data surfaces (Figure 4.5); we are interested in the extent to which the modelled surfaces are qualitatively similar or dissimilar to the data surfaces, in terms of whether the most salient patterns and features identified in the data surfaces are also present in the modelled surfaces. The residual surfaces help to identify systematic deviations between the data surfaces and modelled surfaces, and so make for a more nuanced identification of model misspecification than summary statistics alone – such as root-mean-squared (RMS) error – would allow.

Whereas in the Lexis surfaces of the observations we are hoping to be able to identify patterns and features in the images produced, for the Lexis surfaces of residuals we are hoping for the exact opposite: to *not* see any clear patterns or features in the data. This is because we are hoping that any systematic variation over the Lexis surface will have been captured in the model specification, so only purely random variation remains. We are looking, in effect, for something like multi-coloured static.

For example, the top left sub-figure on the left half of Figure 4.11 shows the prediction surface for the model 'age_lin', which just assumes that risk of ARD increases with age; the top left sub-figure of the right half shows the Lexis surface of residuals for the same model. By looking at the residuals surface for this model, we can see that it over-predicts (dark blue in the online version) the ARD risks at older ages (men in their 70s and 80s), whereas it under-predicts (dark red cloud in the online version) the mortality risks between around age 40 and 70 years after the mid/late 1990s. Most of the other models do not tend to exhibit this first feature in the residuals surfaces – that of over-predicting elderly mortality – but do still exhibit this latter feature of under-predicting mortality from around age 40 to 70 after the mid/late 1990s. For the more complex models – such as 'ccpp', in which cohort and period effects are each allowed to be non-linear, and to interact – the visibility of any features in the residuals surface tends to decrease, and the surfaces look 'noisier', but such features do not seem to be entirely absent.

Prediction and residual surface for DRD

The same exercise, of showing both the prediction and residuals surfaces for six of the best performing 'naive' models, for the DRD data, is shown in Figure 4.12.

Whereas with the ARD data the best performing models within each category tended to preference age over cohort effects, the best performing models within the DRD data tend to include cohort effects instead.

Again, the more complex models tend to fit the data somewhat better than the less complex models, though as for alcohol mortality all models show clear patterns of bias on the residuals surface. A further discussion of the comparative fit of models is presented in the Appendix.

For both the DRD and ARD datasets, the same 'naive' model has a better fit (as assessed through AIC and BIC) than any of the others: this is referred to as ccpp, which includes cohort and period terms, allows both to be non-linear, and allows interactions between both the linear and non-linear components of both cohort and period terms. This model should be considered the 'naive benchmark' against which the 'smart' models will now be compared.

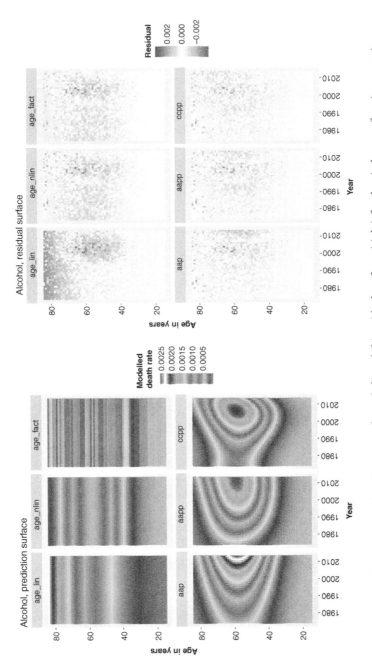

FIGURE 4.11 (a) Comparison of prediction surfaces (left) and (b) residual surfaces (right) for the six best performing generic models for ARD data. (See colour version online.)

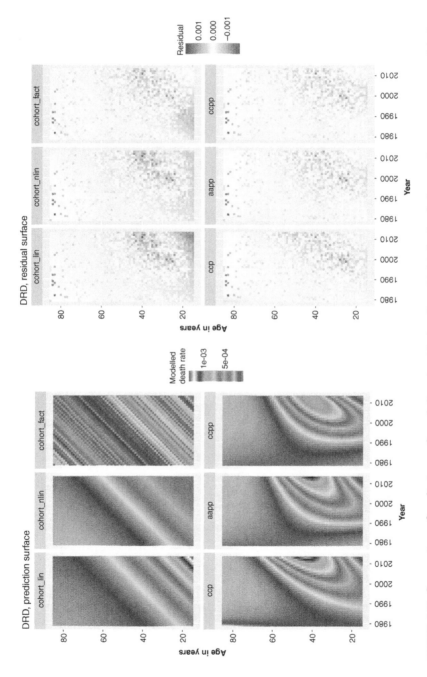

FIGURE 4.12 Comparison of prediction surfaces (left) and residual surfaces (right) for the six best performing generic models for DRD data. (See colour version online.)

Beyond the 'naive' benchmark: fitting 'smart' models naively and smartly

Earlier in this chapter, I suggested that there were two distinct features visible in the three sources of data, which are not easy to describe in APC terms, and which we would likely not have thought of if we had simply looked at the statistical significance of model coefficients. Initially, these suggestions seemed quite subjective. However, we first were able to formally define these features, allowing them to be turned into new model structures. Then, we were able to produce a series of 'naive' models and assess their penalised model fit against the data. One of these naive models, ccpp, has a better penalised model fit (according to both AIC and BIC) than the other model specifications. This will then form our 'best naive benchmark' model. The 'smart' models should, ideally, have model fits similar to, or better than, this naive benchmark model. This is one of two ways we want to test our smart models.

The other way of trying to test our smart models is to fit it 'naively', that is, to the datasets for which it was not designed. We are therefore looking to see not just whether the smart model fits well to the dataset for which it was designed to fit, but also whether it fits the dataset for which it was not designed to fit poorly. In this case study, this means we are expecting to see the following:

- The truncated triangle fits the DRD and suicide data better than the ARD data;
- The band and ellipse fits the ARD data better than the DRD and suicide data;
- The truncated triangle fits the DRD and suicide data better than, or similarly to, the best 'naive' benchmark model (ccpp), and much better than most of the 'naive' models;
- The band and ellipse fits the ARD data better than, or similarly to, the best 'naive' benchmark model (ccpp), and much better than most of the 'naive' models.

To start this comparison of smart models, let's use the Lexis surfaces once again. Figure 4.13 shows the prediction surfaces (left) and residuals surfaces (right) for each of the two model specifications by row, and each of the three causes of death by column.

Given differences in the incidences of the causes of death, the legend is not shown for either the prediction or residuals surfaces; instead what matters is the visual impression about whether, for the prediction surfaces, the models produce something qualitatively similar to the patterns seen in the data surfaces; and for the residuals surfaces whether, firstly, the model developed to fit a particular dataset tends to fit it better than other model specifications, and secondly, whether the patterns of residuals tend to appear random rather than clearly clustered.

The top row shows the alcohol model ('belt and ellipse') as applied to each of the three causes of death. The left-hand side shows the modelled surface for each of these three causes, and the right-hand side the surface of residuals. To allow

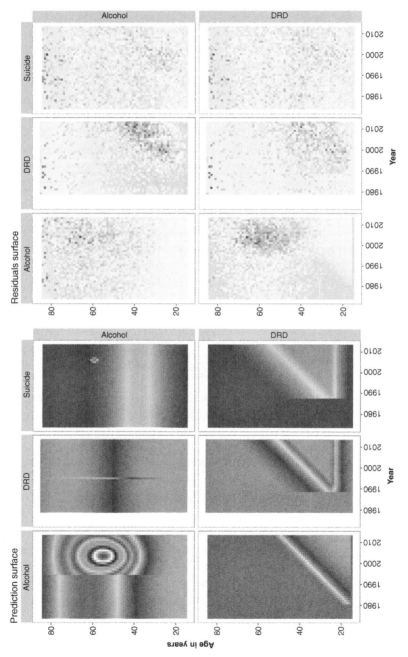

FIGURE 4.13 Prediction surfaces (left) and residuals surfaces (right) from the smart models. (See colour version online.)

comparability between causes of death these residuals have been scaled by cause by dividing each residual value by the maximum absolute residual value observed for that particular cause. Because of this, rescaling the legends have been omitted.

The impression that the alcohol (belt and ellipse) model fits the alcohol data relatively well, and the other datasets relatively poorly, is supported by looking at the AIC and BIC values, and comparing them against the best performing 'generic' model presented previously (ccpp). For the alcohol data, the AIC of the alcohol model is 8750, compared with 8869 for the ccpp model; for BIC, which penalises additional parameters more heavily, the improvement over the ccpp model is even greater, with values of 8773 for the alcohol model and 8928 for the ccpp model. For DRD and suicide, by contrast, the alcohol model does not outperform the ccpp models: for DRD the alcohol model has an AIC of 7122 and a BIC of 7145, compared with 6180 and 6238 respectively for the ccpp model. For suicide, the alcohol model has an AIC of 9210 and a BIC of 9234, compared with 9061 and 9121 respectively for the ccpp model.

Looking at the residuals surfaces, the evidence of misspecification when using the alcohol model is strongest in the case of the DRD data, in which the model tends to systematically over-estimate risks for the older, less affected cohorts, and systematically under-estimate risks for those in latter cohorts. A qualitatively similar, but much slighter, pattern is also evident for the suicide data. Exploring the residuals surface for alcohol also indicates some systematic misspecification, a slight under-estimation of risk in men aged around 60 and above up to around 1995, followed by over-estimation in this age group after this period. A faint red 'cloud' is also evident between the ages of 50 and 60 years approximately, after around 2000, suggesting the model in its current form slightly over-estimates the risk over this period and age group. Both allowing for a more skewed rather than symmetric distribution, and allowing for covariance in the bivariate normal distribution – i.e., for the off-diagonal terms to be non-zero – could therefore improve the fit of the model still further. However, it already outperforms other models for this data.

The AIC for the DRD (truncated triangle) model when applied to the DRD data is 6033, which is lower than the best performing generic ccpp model with an AIC of 6180. For suicide, the DRD model's AIC is 9065, which is close to but slightly worse than the ccpp model's AIC of 9061. The AIC when applied to the alcohol data is by far the worst performing, with an AIC of 11,844, as compared with 8869 for the ccpp model. Visually, the comparatively poor fit of this model specification is apparent for the alcohol data by noting the high background mortality value, the purple shade outside of the triangular part of the surface, by noting that the gradient of the edge of the ramp associated with cohort is negative (i.e., the gradient of the shades along the top section of the triangle ranges from purple to blue), and that the bottom part of the ramp, indicating 'ageing in', is not present.

Overall, the smart models have performed well. Both in terms of AIC, and in terms of visual exploration of prediction and residuals surfaces, they appear to fit the data they are designed to fit, and (perhaps as importantly) not to fit data they are not designed to fit. Both of these smart model specifications are, to my knowledge, novel and result from attempting to operationalise and formalise insights derived from using Lexis surfaces to explore the data, and thinking about how to simply describe what the Lexis surface images show in terms of simple or more complex geometric form. In the final section, I will discuss how the above process can be generalised into a broader research workflow that uses Lexis surface visualisations for both model development and model testing.

What does formal modelling add?

Some questions I have been explicitly asked to address in this chapter are: What does the modelling add substantively to the original Lexis plots? What is to be gained from modelling something that you can see in the data anyway? These are important questions, whose answers are likely to depend on both individual and collective considerations.

Firstly, it should be noted that, sometimes, the answer to the question, What does (formal) modelling add substantively? is 'nothing', or at least 'nothing that justifies the effort involved'. When the aim of the researcher is to efficiently explore complex data, and to make a quick-and-dirty judgement about what the data appear to be suggesting about the data generating process that causes it, then it may simply not be worth making the effort to develop and fit a formal model based on what one thinks one sees in the data. LS visualisations are an effective tool for generating insight and knowledge, even where that knowledge comprises informal reckonings rather than formal algebraic specifications. The opportunity cost of developing and testing a formal model specification is the additional informal reckoning that could otherwise have been undertaken about additional sources of data, populations and outcomes.

There are also audiences who will expect more than informal reckonings to a researcher's argument, and the formal modelling strategy presented above allows this additional evidence and rigour to be provided. The seductive appeal of statistical models, combined with Neyman–Pearson hypothesis testing (Neyman and Pearson 1933) of their outputs, is that they can give at least the appearance that the researcher's pronouncements are based on something more than purely subjective judgement. Though the reliance on statistical modelling in many of the sciences can have a cult-like mindlessness to it (Ziliak and McCloskey 2008), there is something to be said for describing the patterns, structures and forms one sees in a Lexis surface precisely, and algebra and computer code are likely the clearest means for such precise expression.

Within the examples presented above, it is the precise formulation of two distinct model structures that provides a means of clearly and carefully addressing appropriate forms of scepticism about the researcher's claims. In this example, the claim being made is that two of the three causes of death (DRD and suicide) are more alike than the third cause (ARD). Intuitively, a prior assumption might be that ARD and DRD would be more similar to each other than suicide, because alcohol is a drug and suicide is not. This means that there are grounds for assuming some scepticism about the above claim. Stronger claims require stronger evidence, and the finding that intentionally fitting either of the models to the 'wrong' data – the truncated triangle to the ARD data, and the band plus ellipse data to the DRD and suicide data – produces particularly *poor* model fit, should help to address some of this scepticism, in a way that additional descriptive analyses, or rhetorical strategies, either will not or should not.

Amongst those parties who should be expected to be sceptical are included the person or people doing the research. It is all too easy to fool oneself into seeing patterns in data that are not there, especially when these data are presented as images, as they are in Lexis surface visualisations. To the extent that formal statistical hypothesis testing, at least in the frequentist tradition, can bias the researcher towards false negatives – in particular the equation of 'not statistically significant' with 'not substantively significant' – so data visualisation can bias the researcher towards false positives. One reason for modelling as well as data visualising is therefore that broad biases of each approach can be complementary.

Discussion

Lexis surfaces, combined with a commitment to the as-if-spatial reasoning it supports, allow for population processes to be both seen and understood as three-dimensional phenomena, and given this to be modelled appropriately. The new, smart models presented here are illustrations of the kinds of models that could be developed if as-if-spatial reasoning were applied more to such data.

Examples of such developments include the application of modified spatial models to population data, in which neighbouring values (nearby periods and ages) are represented as non-independent through the use of neighbourhood matrices to specify spatial contiguity, as without doing this hypotheses tests may be biased (Besag, York, and Mollie 1991; Lee and Mitchell 2013). Additionally, the inherently hierarchical nature of the models developed suggest that developing them within a Bayesian framework, using appropriate software like BUGS or Stan, may also be appropriate. If both spatiality and hierarchy of parameters can be appropriately modelled, then more formal tests to identify common structure in data surface patterns – such as appears to be the case for DRD and suicide – can be performed.

Additionally, appropriate smart models could be developed to interrogate ancillary questions of substantive importance. For example, it appears that both male gender and high area deprivation multiply the risk of DRD throughout the life course in Scotland for affected cohorts, with these two risks multiplying rather than simply adding to each other for males in the most deprived areas, as compared with females from less deprived areas. A similar multiplication or interaction of risk factors also appears present for suicide. Therefore, three important questions to ask are whether these additional risk multipliers are fixed through the life course, whether they are of similar magnitude for both causes, and whether they are multiplicative (in interactions) rather than simply additive. Additionally, it appears that the first cohorts to be affected by rising suicide and DRD risks were slightly older cohorts in more deprived areas than elsewhere: so, not only was the magnitude of the cohort-led change greater, it began earlier too. All of these hypotheses could be explored more formally by developing, fitting and comparing a series of nested models, and through doing so a number of substantively important questions, with important policy and public health implications, can be formally addressed. However, the first step to answering such questions is to know to ask them, and this is what initially exploring the data using LS visualisations allows.

The strategy of using Lexis surfaces both for the development of hunches and ideas about what the data show and tell, and for testing these hunches, might be considered questionable because it both 'trains' and 'tests' a model on the same data, creating a risk that the model is overfitted. This is a valid objection in many ways, and I would welcome more widespread objection to this kind of approach on these grounds. However, within the academic social sciences this issue is under-recognised, whereas in cognate disciplines like machine learning both clear articulations of the problem already exist, along with proposed solutions that are relatively straightforward to implement.

Along with emerging best practice in machine learning, one solution may be to perform an a priori split of the data used to produce the Lexis surface first presented to the researcher into a 'training set' (typically 80% of the data) and a 'test set' (the remaining 20%). Visually, this would produce a Lexis surface image in which 20% of the pixels are missing at random. Given such an image, would the researcher still suggest the same structural features exist in the data as if they were given the complete image? How would the confidence of the researcher in proposing a new model structure vary if 5% of the data were missing, compared with 10%, 20% or 40%? Though it might be somewhat contrived to intentionally look at only some proportion of the data first, in this way it could be done. Following standard practice in the training-test data split paradigm, the accuracy of the proposed model could be assessed on the training set, using metrics like root mean squared error (RMSE) and so on.

Similarly, which data are missing from the training data could be non-random rather than random. For example, the model could be trained on the first 80% of years, and tested on the remaining 20%. Similarly, trends at older ages could be predicted from the data in younger ages, and vice versa. However, in both of these cases the questions being asked of the model at the validation stage are different to that being asked when a random split is used. In the period example, the validation effectively becomes a forecasting exercise, and in the age example, it becomes a question of how trajectories across some ages continue into other ages. Although being able to forecast future trends is useful, it is not identical to the question of whether the researcher has been able to correctly identify and formally describe a genuine feature in the data. For features that appear initiated by events that are unlikely to reoccur with any predictable regularity – such as wars or pandemics – the forecasting accuracy of a model based on such features may be modest, but the value of being able to describe the structure of such events' effects on population outcomes can be more broadly valuable.

It is hoped this description and illustration of the workflow, and argument for an adoption of as-if-spatial reasoning about population data, will encourage more research about population processes to look at population data as Lexis surfaces, and for new insights and findings to be identified and developed more quickly and effectively.

Online supplementary material relating to this book can be found at www.routledge.com/9780367174439.

References

Akaike, H. 1974. "A new look at the statistical model identification." *IEEE Transactions on Automatic Control* 19 (6): 716–723. https://doi.org/10.1109/TAC.1974.1100705.

Barker, D J P. 2004. "The developmental origins of adult disease." *Journal of the American College of Nutrition* 23 (6 Suppl): 588S–595S. https://doi.org/10.1080/07315724.2004.10719428.

Bell, Andrew, and Kelvyn Jones. 2014. "Another 'futile quest'? A simulation study of Yang and Land's Hierarchical Age–Period–Cohort model." *Demographic Research* 30 (11): 333–360. https://doi.org/10.4054/DemRes.2014.30.11.

Bell, Andrew, and Kelvyn Jones. 2017. "The hierarchical age–period–cohort model: Why does it find the results that it finds?" *Quality & Quantity* 52 (2): 1–17. https://doi.org/10.1007/s11135-017-0488-5.

Ben-Shlomo, Yoav, and Diana Kuh. 2002. "A life course approach to chronic disease epidemiology: conceptual models, empirical challenges and interdisciplinary perspectives." *International Journal of Epidemiology* 31 (2): 285–293. https://doi.org/10.1093/ije/31.2.285.

Ben-Shlomo, Yoav, and G D Smith. 1991. "Deprivation in infancy or in adult life: which is more important for mortality risk?" *The Lancet* 337 (8740): 530–534.

Besag, Julian, Jeremy York, and Annie Mollie. 1991. "Bayesian image restoration, with two applications in spatial statistics." *Annals of the Institute of Statistical Mathematics* 43 (1): 1–20. https://doi.org/10.1007/BF00116466.

Diamond, J. 1997. *Guns, Germs, and Steel*. 1st ed. New York : W.W. Norton.

Gluckman, Peter D, Mark A Hanson, and Catherine Pinal. 2005. "The developmental origins of adult disease." *Maternal & Child Nutrition* 1 (3): 130–141. https://doi.org/10.1111/j.1740-8709.2005.00020.x.

Hales, C N, and D J Barker. 1992. "Type 2 (non-insulin-dependent) diabetes mellitus: the thrifty phenotype hypothesis." *Diabetologia* 35 (7): 595–601. https://doi.org/10.1007/bf00400248.

Laitin, David D, Joachim Moortgat, and Amanda Lea Robinson. 2012. "Geographic axes and the persistence of cultural diversity." *Proceedings of the National Academy of Sciences of the United States of America* 109 (26): 10263–10268. https://doi.org/10.1073/pnas.1205338109.

Lee, D, and R Mitchell. 2013. "Locally adaptive spatial smoothing using conditional autoregressive models." *Journal of the Royal Statistical Society Series C* 62: 593–608.

Lee, Ronald D., and Lawrence R Carter. 1992. "Modeling and forecasting U.S. mortality." *Journal of the American Statistical Association* 87 (419): 659–671. https://doi.org/10.1080/01621459.1992.10475265.

Lexis, Wilhelm. 1875. *Einleitung in die Theorie der Bevölkerungsstatistik*. Strasburg: Karl J Trobner.

Lindahl-Jacobsen, Rune, Roland Rau, Bernard Jeune, Vladimir Canudas-Romo, Adam Lenart, Kaare Christensen, and James W Vaupel. 2016. "Rise, stagnation, and rise of Danish women's life expectancy." *Proceedings of the National Academy of Sciences of the United States of America* 113 (15): 4015–4020. https://doi.org/10.1073/pnas.1602783113.

Matthews, B, and J Minton. 2018. "Rethinking one of criminology's 'brute facts': the age-crime curve and the crime drop in Scotland." *European Journal of Criminology*, 15(3), 296–320.

McCartney, G, J Bouttell, N Craig, P Craig, L Graham, F Lakha, J Lewsey, et al. 2016a. "Explaining trends in alcohol-related harms in Scotland 1991–2011 (II): policy, social norms, the alcohol market, clinical changes and a synthesis." *Public Health* 132 (March): 24–32. https://doi.org/10.1016/j.puhe.2015.12.012.

McCartney, G, J Bouttell, N Craig, P Craig, L Graham, F Lakha, J Lewsey, et al. 2016b. "Explaining trends in alcohol-related harms in Scotland, 1991–2011 (I): the role of incomes, effects of socio-economic and political adversity and demographic change." *Public Health* 132 (March): 13–23. https://doi.org/10.1016/j.puhe.2015.12.013.

Minton, Jon. 2013. "Featured graphic. Logs, lifelines, and lie factors." *Environment & Planning A* 45 (11): 2539–2543. https://doi.org/10.1068/a130208g.

Minton, Jon. 2014. "Real geographies and virtual landscapes: exploring the influence on place and space on mortality Lexis surfaces using shaded contour maps." *Spatial and Spatio-temporal Epidemiology* 10 (July): 49–66. https://doi.org/10.1016/j.sste.2014.04.003.

Minton, Jon. 2017a. "Lexis surface visualisation workflow." *Open Science Framework*. https://doi.org/10.17605/osf.io/ntz72.

Minton, Jon. 2017b. "The shape of the troubles: visualising and modelling conflict-attributable trends in mortality in young adult males in Northern Ireland." (Unpublished). Open Science Framework. Available at: https://doi.org/10.31219/osf.io/hqd95.

Minton, Jonathan. 2018. "Mapping mortality: using Lexis surfaces to identify complex patterns in age-year specific mortality rates within and between populations." Open Science Framework. Available at: https://doi.org/10.31219/osf.io/6anwy.

Minton, Jon, and Julie Clark. 2018. "Driving segregation: age, gender and emerging inequalities." In *Geographies of Transport and Ageing*, edited by Angela Curl and Charles Musselwhite, 25–50. Cham: Springer International. https://doi.org/10.1007/978-3-319-76360-6_2.

Minton, Jonathan, Laura Vanderbloemen, and Danny Dorling. 2013. "Visualizing Europe's demographic scars with coplots and contour plots." *International Journal of Epidemiology* 42 (4): 1164–1176. https://doi.org/10.1093/ije/dyt115.

Minton, Jonathan, Mark Green, Gerry McCartney, Richard Shaw, Laura Vanderbloemen, and Kate Pickett. 2017. "Two cheers for a small giant? Why we need better ways of seeing data: A commentary on: 'Rising morbidity and mortality in midlife among White non-Hispanic Americans in the 21st century'." *International Journal of Epidemiology* 46 (1): 356–361. https://doi.org/10.1093/ije/dyw095.

Neyman, J, and E S Pearson. 1933. "On the problem of the most efficient tests of statistical hypotheses." *Philosophical Transactions of the Royal Society A: Mathematical, Physical and Engineering Sciences* 231 (694–706): 289–337. https://doi.org/10.1098/rsta.1933.0009.

Nielsen, Bent. 2015. "apc: an R package for age-period-cohort analysis." *The R Journal* 7 (2): 52. https://doi.org/10.32614/RJ-2015–020.

Parkinson, Jane, Jon Minton, James Lewsey, Janet Bouttell, and Gerry McCartney. 2017. "Recent cohort effects in suicide in Scotland: a legacy of the 1980s?" *Journal of Epidemiology and Community Health* 71 (2): 194–200. https://doi.org/10.1136/jech-2016-207296.

Parkinson, Jane, Jon Minton, James Lewsey, Janet Bouttell, and Gerry McCartney. 2018. "Drug-related deaths in Scotland 1979–2013: evidence of a vulnerable cohort of young men living in deprived areas." *BMC Public Health* 18 (1): 357. https://doi.org/10.1186/s12889-018-5267-2.

Schöley, Jonas, and Frans Willekens. 2017. "Visualizing compositional data on the Lexis surface." *Demographic Research* 36 (21): 627–658. https://doi.org/10.4054/DemRes. 2017.36.21.

Schwarz, Gideon. 1978. "Estimating the dimension of a model." *The Annals of Statistics* 6 (2): 461–464. https://doi.org/10.1214/aos/1176344136.

Vaupel, James W, B A Gambill, and A I Yashin. 1987. *Thousands of Data at a Glance: Shaded Contour Maps of Demographic Surfaces.* Laxenburg, Austria: International Institute for Applied Systems Analysis.

Vaupel, James W, Kirill F. Andreev, Wang Zhenglian, and Anatoli I. Yashin. 1998. *Population Data at a Glance: Shaded Contour Maps of Demographic Surfaces over Age and Time.* Odense, Denmark: University Press of Southern Denmark.

Yang, Yang. 2006. "Bayesian inference for Hierarchical Age–Period–Cohort models of repeated cross-section survey data." *Sociological Methodology* 36 (1): 39–74. https://doi. org/10.1111/j.1467-9531.2006.00174.x.

Yang, Yang, Sam Schulhofer-Wohl, Wenjiang J. Fu, and Kenneth C. Land. 2008. "The intrinsic estimator for age-period-cohort analysis: what it is and how to use it." *American Journal of Sociology* 113 (6): 1697–1736. https://doi.org/10.1086/587154.

Ziliak, Stephen Thomas, and Deirdre N. McCloskey. 2008. *The Cult of Statistical Significance: How the Standard Error Costs Us Jobs, Justice, and Lives.* Ann Arbor: University of Michigan Press.

5

DETECTING THE 'BLACK HOLE' OF AGE-PERIOD EXCESS MORTALITY IN 25 COUNTRIES[1]

Age–period–cohort residual analysis

Louis Chauvel, Anja K. Leist and Herbert L. Smith

Introduction

In a time of worldwide availability of annual age-specific mortality data, we lack basic tools for detecting and graphing, from a comparative perspective, fine-grained deviations from mortality trends. The Global Burden of Disease Study has undertaken large efforts to collect high-quality mortality information by country, age, gender and cause of death, and life expectancy tables provide helpful guidance on where public health response is adequate and where it could be improved (Lozano et al. 2012). In this chapter, we show how a systematic presentation of mortality trends by period and cohort is desirable to understand the long-term effects of health policies. A fine-grained analysis of deviations from trend helps us understand better where policies have failed (or succeeded), and which age groups at which periods in time suffered to a greater or lesser extent. The graphic visualization tool presented here allows a long-term comprehensive assessment of changes in (all-cause or cause-specific) mortality rates, and thus the success of responses to public health crises. Take for example the current opioid crisis in the U.S. and other countries (Rudd et al. 2016). While this crisis needs a complex response, involving healthcare, neighborhood emergency services, poverty reduction and so on, we will only in hindsight be able to evaluate the reach and success of these measures. Applying the 'Black Hole' methodology elaborated here enables us to understand better the scale, period and age range of those individuals affected by this crisis.[2]

We build on a line of work dedicated to distinguishing the additive effects of age, period and cohort, given the deterministic linear relationship among them (Fienberg and Mason 1979; Mason and Fienberg 2012; Mason and Smith 1985). Applied research to date has struggled to distinguish period from cohort mortality *trends*. Indeed, there is little to choose between period and cohort representations (see also Chapter 9 of this volume). Research efforts that have been successfully ruling out period effects in mortality without APC methodology usually need a reference population to quantify cohort effects (Lindahl-Jacobsen et al. 2016). Our method overcomes these limitations since we focus here on residuals derived from the parameterizations of age, period and cohort effects. We use a combination of age-period (AP) and APC-detrended (APCD) methodology (Chauvel and Schröder 2014, 2015) to develop a graphical visualization tool to plot mortality by year and age per country. This tool helps to assess comprehensively datasets characterized by time-series data points across age and period, in order to detect excess mortality.

The chapter has two parts. In the first part, we introduce the new method and plot male mortality for selected countries based on data from the Human Mortality Database (data obtained through the HMD, www.mortality.org on July 7, 2016). This multi-country fine-grained single-year by single-year period and age group database offers unique opportunities for detailed description. We detect abnormalities in the sense of localized mortality increases (Black Holes) of young-adult cohorts in the early 1990s in several countries. In the second part of the chapter, we analyze those mortality deviations in more detail. More specifically, additional analyses are guided by the hypothesis that mortality increases during that time may be attributable to HIV/AIDS mortality. We confirm this assumption with data from the WHO Mortality Database.

Part I: introducing the new method

Our method consists of three steps. First, we analyze mortality patterns across age (25–60) and calendar years (1975–2010) by plotting one-year AP mortality (derived from HMD) for 25 countries in an equilateral Lexis diagram (Keiding 2011; see Table 1, Figure 2 in the Appendix of Lexis 1875; Riffe 2011). The equilateral Lexis is widely known among epidemiologists and demographers and provides an intuitive representation of mortality trends as a cohort (lower-left to upper-right diagonal) or period effect (lower-right to upper-left diagonal) or an interaction of both. Figure 5.1 and online Appendix Figures 5.1 and 5.2 give an overview of information contained in this diagram and how mortality patterns can be interpreted.

We use the spgrid and spmap Stata ado file (Pisati 2004) to draw these equilateral Lexis diagrams. We graph the resulting (A, P) residuals to detect Black Holes of excess mortality, an abnormality expressed as a specific AP interaction that points to localized increases from expected mortality patterns for one or more birth cohorts in one or more calendar years. The opposite of Black Holes, say some 'White holes', which denote localized *decreases* in expected mortality patterns of around 5%, are less relevant for this analysis of mortality crises.[3] This notion opens a technical point on using residuals (i.e., residual values after subtracting predicted from observed values). The sum of residuals are zero by definition, so in any given Lexis diagram, we cannot expect black depicted mortality increases without white spots or areas. These white areas of decreases in mortality mathematically compensate for the increases captured by the Black Hole methodology. In most of the countries used

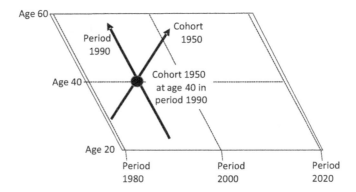

FIGURE 5.1 A theoretical equilateral Lexis diagram containing AP mortality coefficients by age and period, illustrating a Black Hole which would indicate here localized 10% elevated mortality patterns of 1950-born individuals in 1990

for analysis here, the white areas are diffused and extend over larger areas; only very few strong White Holes of reduced mortality can be detected.

We provide, for the sake of completeness, the earlier work carried out by the first author that led to the development of the visualization tool. The reader less interested in the technical details may directly move to the next section.

Earlier work considered deviations from the linear age, period and cohort trends. Here, the use of residuals of APCD mortality analyses was presented, first on income (Chauvel and Schröder 2014) and then in different contexts of ecological behavior, political participation and suicide (Chancel 2014; Chauvel, Leist, and Ponomarenko 2016; Chauvel, Leist, and Smith 2016; Chauvel and Schroeder 2015). The APCD model acknowledges that linear trends in APC models cannot be definitively attributed to age, period or cohort (Mason and Smith 1985): it is impossible to know whether linear change stems from a cohort or from an age plus period effect. Therefore, the model focuses on fluctuations (non-linearity) of the effects of age, period and cohort around a linear trend. Thus, the model absorbs linear trends by appropriate coefficients to focus on accelerations and decelerations in age, period and cohort trends:

$$y^{apc} = \alpha_a + \pi_p + \gamma_c + \alpha_0 rescale(a) + \gamma_0 rescale(c) + \beta_0 + \left(\sum_j \beta_j x_j\right) + \varepsilon \ (APCD)$$

where α_a, π_p , γ_c are sum zero and trend zero; α_0 and γ_0 absorb age and cohort trend.

The conventional way of using APC models is to express coefficients (at first, for birth cohorts) to contrast protected or advantaged versus unprotected or disadvantaged cohorts. This means the residuals of the (A, P) models, without a cohort, are expected to present upward right lines following a cohort (Figure 5.2).

a. Equilateral Lexis of Russia

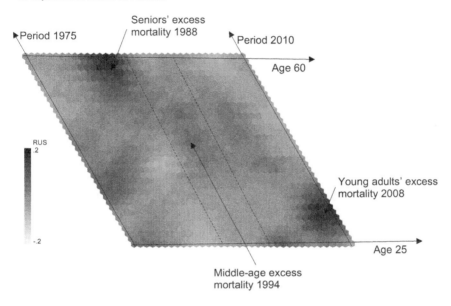

b. Equilateral Lexis of the USA

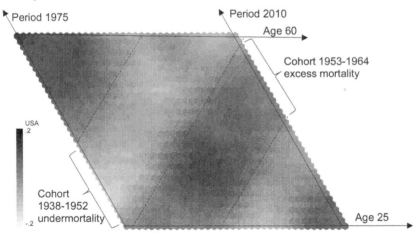

FIGURE 5.2 Equilateral Lexis diagrams for (a) Russia and (b) the U.S.

A less usual way in APCD is to focus on the APCD residuals as something other than unstructured noise. Our approach shows that residuals from APC models, be they two-way or of a higher order, help us to understand how social phenomena are beginning, developing and ending across time and across cohorts. The fact that we see commonalities across countries, which we are able to relate to domain-specific knowledge on mortality crises in the relevant countries, add credibility to the soundness of this approach. Indeed, these residuals can be strategic information that equilateral Lexis will expose (Figure 5.2a) with a focus on the $+/-$ 10 years around the point age 32 in period 1992 (Figure 5.2b).

The residuals that are the foundation for the visualization of excess mortality indicate mortality variance not captured by the additive terms (in time) in any of the just-identified age–period–cohort models. The residuals are plotted on an equilateral Lexis diagram, thereby using information on the center of the Black Holes of the AP mortality analysis. In order to facilitate understanding and more clearly convey the message of excess mortality, we employ a smoothing algorithm. We focus this analysis on the Black Holes only (a full diagram would contain the same but also much irrelevant information), by plotting only ten birth and calendar years around the Black Hole; think of a magnifying lens only focusing on the area of interest. This graphic illustration of APCD residuals gives an impression of the magnitude of the age–period interaction (with black color indicating again highest magnitude).

Last, to complement the identification of mortality crises, we rerun AP mortality analyses by suppressing the Black Hole: we use the residuals of APCD analysis (Figure 5.3) as a *covariate* of the (A,P) model, that is, the values of the residuals inside the 10 years circle around the point age 32 in period 1992, and zero elsewhere. This is an additional feature for researchers interested in the technical working of the method. The suppression of the Black Hole, when for example evaluating health policies, is not recommended, for example, in a presentation to a lay audience. However, researchers interested in the method may want to visualize the evolution of the mortality increase: Did the excess mortality appear abruptly, that is, in a very specific period of a very specific cohort, or was there a longer-term evolvement leading to a peak for a particular period and cohort? This additional step of analysis needs to consider that with a sum zero of residuals we must expect areas or spots of lower mortality in the same cohort. Plotting the residuals, net of the elevation detected in the first step of the analysis, enables us to detect if the mortality crisis of a birth cohort came 'with a warning', that is, if it results from a long-term disadvantage of birth cohorts, or if the mortality crisis appeared abruptly. At the same time, *plotting* the Black Hole enables us to detect localized mortality crises resulting from period–cohort interactions, whereas *suppressing* the Black Hole enables us to even better detect cohort effects in APCD analysis (Figure 5.4 a and b). This is particularly helpful for cohorts that have experienced strong deviations in an outcome at a given age. Suppressing the Black Hole puts singular deviations into perspective and helps re-evaluate the cumulative experiences of that cohort; it is analogous to similar approaches to dealing with higher-order interactions discussed previously in the literature (Mason and Fienberg 2012; Mason and Smith 1985).

Data

We use data from the HMD and choose age groups 25 to 60 in the years 1975 to 2010 (i.e., cohorts born between 1915 and 1985) as our window of observation for

12 countries. Some countries are selected for their intrinsic interest– indeed, mortality crises of the 1990s that resulted in elevated HIV/AIDS mortality of affected cohorts are known for Spain, the U.S. and some southern European countries (Granizo, Guallar, and Rodriguez-Artalejo 1996; Valdes and George 2013). For some countries, data for the full-time range under investigation are not available (Israel, Greece). We also do not report results for countries without any substantial mortality deviations, for example, Belgium, although we note here that it is relevant that such countries (and such situations) do exist (i.e., that departures from trend are *not* ubiquitous, hence that when and where they do occur, they may well be documenting something of substantive interest).

Results

In the first step of detecting additive cohort effects as patterned departures from an (A,P) representation, AP coefficients are used to illustrate mortality patterns. We do this for Russia and the U.S. for a closer look (Figures 5.2a and 5.2b), then for 25 countries (Figure 5.3). Diagonals from lower-left to upper-right delineate cohort effects, diagonals from lower-right to upper-left delineate period effects. For Russia, the visualization detects a period of excess mortality of older people around 1988 in the upper-left corner, a period of excess mortality of people in middle age around 1994 in the middle of the Lexis graph, and a third period of excess mortality around 2008 in the lower-right corner (Figure 5.2b). For the U.S., we observe rather different patterns. In the beginning of the period of investigation in the lower-left corner, we see 'under'-mortality of the cohorts born in 1938–1952, and excess mortality of the later-born cohorts in 1953–1964 in the upper-right corner (Figure 5.2b).

In the presentation of the 25 countries, a few country cases stand out (Figure 5.3). See, for example, the Danish cohort of 1950 with elevated mortality patterns across the window of observation. Focusing on Black Holes, that is, age–period interactions that indicate age and period-defined mortality crises, we detect notable mortality increases for young-adult cohorts (more specifically, the birth cohort of 1961 and those adjacent) in the early 1990s in Spain, the U.S., France, Portugal, Switzerland, Canada, the Netherlands and Denmark.

In a second step, in order to assess the magnitude of the detected age–period interaction, we run an APCD analysis and plot the resulting residuals, again in an equilateral Lexis diagram (Figure 5.4a); see the mortality crises depicted as Black Holes particularly for Spain, Italy and France. These countries, and also Switzerland and Russia, show compensations to those dramatically elevated mortality patterns as age and period-defined white areas, thus pointing to rather sudden onset and ending of the detected mortality crisis. This is a well-known finding of earlier epidemiological analyses on HIV/AIDS mortality of groups of younger adulthood in the 1990s (Valdes and George 2013). We provide first evidence here that this elevated mortality is not restricted to these countries, but also extends to other countries that have received less public health focus on HIV/AIDS mortality during

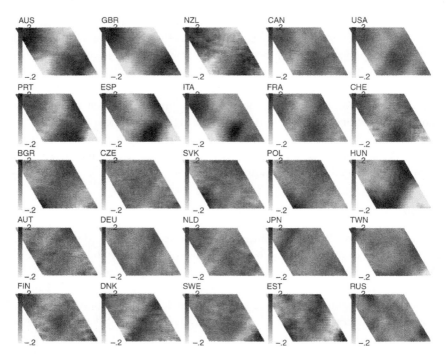

FIGURE 5.3 Residuals of (A, P) model, excess mortality in black. Mortality with strong birth cohort components appear when clear upward-right diagonals are figured (Hungary, Denmark, Japan). Period-related mortality trends are characterized by left-upward diagonals (Spain, Russia). Country codes per row: 1 AUS, GBR, NZL, CAN, USA; 2 PRT, ESP, ITA, FRA, CHE; 3 BGR, CZE, SVK, POL, HUN; 4 AUT, DEU, NLD, JPN, TWN; 5 FIN, DNK, SWE, EST, RUS. *See the supplemental material* (http:// orbilu.uni.lu/handle/10993/40983) *for the color graphs that present excess mortality as Big Red Spots rather than Black Holes.*

that period, such as Switzerland (cf. Rehm et al. 2005) and Russia (cf. Donoghoe, Lazarus, and Matic 2005). In order to omit irrelevant information, we select a ten-year interval around this spot (i.e., cohorts of 1951 to 1971 and calendar years 1983 to 2003) for a magnifying lens illustration. Figure 5.4a illustrates that the magnitude of the detected mortality crisis varied considerably across countries, with Spain, France, Portugal and Switzerland having a larger increase in mortality of cohort 1961 in calendar year 1993 than the U.S., Canada, the Netherlands and Denmark.

In a last step, we consider the extent to which Black Holes, defined by certain age and period ranges, occur in a larger context of cohorts being disproportionally disadvantaged throughout the window of observation and are also differentially affected by mortality crises. In other words, have some cohorts been worse off across their lives than those born before and after them, or do the mentioned mortality crises in the affected cohorts occur with an element of surprise? In order to arrive at the *net* cohort effects, we rerun the APCD analysis after suppressing the Black Hole, that is, age–period interaction. We thus not only improve the quality of

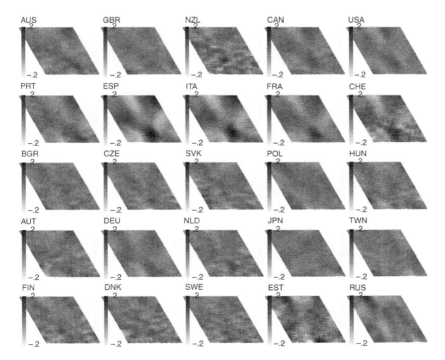

FIGURE 5.4A Residuals of APCD model, excess mortality in black. APCD residuals help detect abnormalities. Apart from the strong Russian/Estonian end of 1980s seniors' excess mortality, the European Latin countries (Spain, Italy, France, etc.) show a Black Hole of those aged 30+ in the early 1990s as an unexpected singularity. Country codes per row: 1 AUS, GBR, NZL, CAN, USA; 2 PRT, ESP, ITA, FRA, CHE; 3 BGR, CZE, SVK, POL, HUN; 4 AUT, DEU, NLD, JPN, TWN; 5 FIN, DNK, SWE, EST, RUS

the APCD analysis as a 'cohort bump detector' (Chauvel, Leist, and Ponomarenko 2016), but also gain information regarding whether some cohorts may have disproportionally worse outcomes across their life course, or are instead affected by worse outcomes at defined periods, that is, stages of their life course. We plot the resulting APCD residuals in an equilateral Lexis diagram (Figure 5.4b). Most cohorts in those countries affected by a Black Hole can be classified as unlucky cohorts with longer-term mortality increases from the overall trend. The suppression of the Black Hole (and the A and P fluctuations and trends) enables us to better detect cohort effects in APCD analysis with strong upward-right oriented fluctuations (Figure 5.5).

Part II: explaining the mortality increases in Spain, southern Europe and the U.S.

To provide a fuller picture on what such a Black Hole of elevated mortality levels may contain, we take the case of Spain and provide background to the specific public health crisis of the early 1990s. Spanish young adults in the 1980s faced a

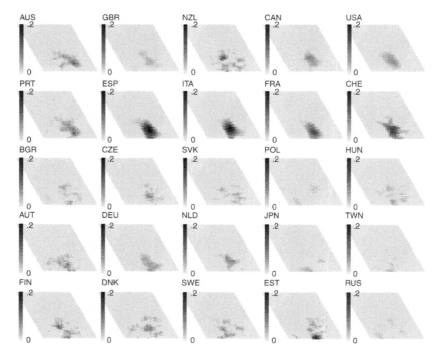

FIGURE 5.4B Residuals of APCD model, excess mortality in black/focus on the Black Hole (age 32 in period 1992/cohort 1960). APCD residuals are displayed only for the ten-year circle around cohort 1960 at age 32. The strongest examples are Spain, Italy, France, and Switzerland; several further countries such as the U.S. and Canada show the same singularity, whereas others do not show excess mortality for that cohort and time at all. Country codes per row: 1 AUS, GBR, NZL, CAN, USA; 2 PRT, ESP, ITA, FRA, CHE; 3 BGR, CZE, SVK, POL, HUN; 4 AUT, DEU, NLD, JPN, TWN; 5 FIN, DNK, SWE, EST, RUS

'perfect storm' of political and structural crises, economic downturns and associated diminished aspirations, alcohol and drug abuse and other risky health behaviors (Gómez-Redondo and Boe 2005). This socioeconomic and health context was reinforced by the HIV outbreak, transmitted in Spain first mainly through shared use of (heroin) injection needles and leading to rather dramatic losses in life expectancy, mainly due to higher mortality at young ages (Valdes and George 2013). Indeed, AIDS mortality increased in the early 1990s, with a peak for male AIDS incidence in 1994, male AIDS mortality in 1995, and with the cohorts of the early 1960s being the most affected for both genders (Valdes and George 2013). Other causes of mortality such as traffic accidents and drug and alcohol abuse were also contributing to the increased mortality of the cohorts in young adulthood at that time (Cleries et al. 2009). There was also a marked rise at that time in suicide mortality for young cohorts (Granizo, Guallar, and Rodriguez-Artalejo 1996). We recently showed that the elevated suicide mortality patterns of the 1965–1975

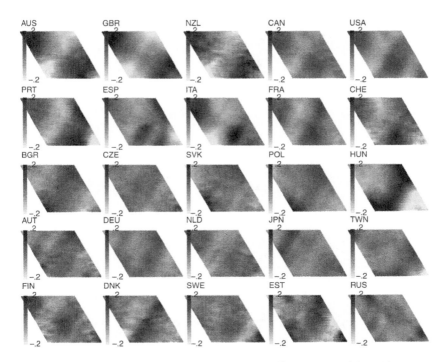

FIGURE 5.5 Residuals of (A, P) with the Black Hole effect suppressed (age 32 in p = 1992/cohort 1960 +/−10 years). Note: Net of the Black Hole, the mortality structures are much more diagonally shaped in many countries and are better able to show healthier cohorts (e.g., U.S. residents born in 1945 or 1975) and unhealthier ones (those born in 1915, 1955, 1985). Country codes per row: 1 AUS, GBR, NZL, CAN, USA; 2 PRT, ESP, ITA, FRA, CHE; 3 BGR, CZE, SVK, POL, HUN; 4 AUT, DEU, NLD, JPN, TWN; 5 FIN, DNK, SWE, EST, RUS

cohort in Spain diminished over time and returned to normal levels again in the following decades (Chauvel, Leist, and Ponomarenko 2016).

The following analysis assumes that the Black Holes of similarly occurring mortality crises in Spain, other southern European countries and, on a smaller scale, the U.S., Canada, the Netherlands and Denmark, may be driven by increases in HIV/AIDS mortality. The Spanish case in particular (Valdes and George 2013) has demonstrated the magnitude of the AIDS epidemic, leading to quite severed losses in life expectancy. For our purposes, an exact re-running of analyses with WHO cause-specific mortality data is not possible, as deaths and population are only available in five-year intervals after age five.[4] We therefore choose an aggregate correlation analysis by country relating the log of the average value of the Black Hole residual for ages 30–34 in 1992–1997 (y-axis in Figure 5.5) to the log-HIV/AIDS mortality rate in WHO (x-axis in Figure 5.5). WHO provides HIV/AIDS mortality for 17 countries in the window of observation, of which we exclude four countries where values are very small (logs below a value of −10). In our selection

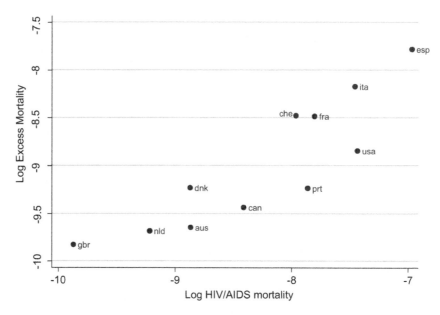

FIGURE 5.6 Correlation between Y = HMD intensity of (log-)excess mortality and X = WHO log-HIV/AIDS mortality for 13 countries, age group 30–34 and period 1992–1997

of 13 countries (Australia, Austria, Canada, Denmark, France, Italy, the Netherlands, New Zealand, Portugal, Spain, Switzerland, the U.K. and the U.S.) the correlational analysis shows that all-cause mortality increases are strongly related to increases in HIV/AIDS mortality, with 73% of the variance in those measures explained (Figure 5.6). This is a rather high fraction, considering that AIDS may not have always been reported as the underlying cause of death, but rather other causes of death, such as suicide or accidents.

There is some evidence for HIV/AIDS incidence that other European countries have been affected by public health crises during this time as well (Houweling et al. 1999), with a geographic divide into southern European countries (France, Switzerland, Spain, Portugal) and northern European countries (the Netherlands, Belgium, Germany and the U.K.) (Valdes and George 2013). Our method is the first to point out that Spain was not the only country experiencing a public health crisis in the early 1990s, but also Switzerland, France, Italy and Portugal, and – on a smaller scale – the U.S., Canada and Denmark.

Discussion

We provide a tool to analyze and graph mortality trends per birth cohort and calendar year, in order to detect deviations from the overall mortality trends, and to determine to which extent those deviations are a cohort or a period effect or both.

Strengths and limitations

The strength of our method is that it is able to analyze and intuitively graph fine-grained mortality data per birth cohort and calendar year, and that it is able to give evidence of the magnitude of mortality deviations, especially with regard to the Black Hole, the age–period interaction.

Important for the interpretation of the graphs is that the method detects public health crises with a certain delay. This means that for all health behavior-related mortality, for example, alcohol and drug abuse, and all conditions like HIV, hepatitis and war trauma, with an incubation, the latency or unawareness period is only visible years and sometimes even decades after their outbreak. Indeed, the detection of the mortality increases in the early 1990s in this chapter points to a large increase in rates of HIV infection and related improper public health management in the years and decades *before* the increase in mortality.

More detailed analyses on why unlucky birth cohorts with (unspecified) longer-term mortality disadvantages faced sudden increases in mortality need to be complemented with other data sources, in particular mortality by cause, to obtain hints at possible causes for mortality crises as done in this chapter. Micro-level data are helpful in order to investigate which population groups (education, ethnicity, marital status or migrant status) were most affected in terms of unfavorable economic and social outcomes. As an illustration, we recently showed that Easterlin's hypothesis, that size of birth cohort matters, holds for suicide mortality of the late U.S. baby boomers (Chauvel, Leist, and Smith 2016). Using micro-level information from the Centers for Disease Control and Prevention (CDC) mortality data, we were able to show that increases in suicide of that cohort in 2010 were mostly attributable to white, low-educated, non-married men (Chauvel, Leist, and Smith 2016).

Conclusions

Our method is the first to systematically analyze and intuitively plot period–cohort interactions of elevated mortality relative to trend, and to detect localized mortality crises of one or more birth cohorts in one or more calendar years. Our findings suggest that APC analysis should always be complemented by exploiting residuals information from APCD analysis. We show that Spain was not the only country affected by a perfect storm of multiple health challenges for young adults, but that Switzerland, France and Portugal faced similar situations, as well as the U.S., Canada, the Netherlands and Denmark, albeit on a smaller scale. Additional analyses show that most of the increase in overall mortality can be attributed to increases in HIV/AIDS in those countries. The method of detecting Black Holes can be applied to mortality-by-cause and to other dichotomous economic and social outcomes for virtually any aggregated or micro-level dataset to detect and estimate deviations from period and cohort trends.

Funding

This work was supported by the Fonds National de la Recherche Luxembourg (FNR/P11/05 and FNR/P11/05bis, PI: L. Chauvel).

Notes

1 Readers are encouraged to consult supplemental material to this book chapter online (http://orbilu.uni.lu/handle/10993/40983).
2 The Black Hole analogy serves here a mainly educational purpose of communicating findings to a lay or less-informed audience. Code is available at http://orbilu.uni.lu/handle/10993/40983, so the freely available mortality and other data (diseases and other dichotomous outcomes) can be used – for age ranges and periods that make sense for analysis of the relevant outcomes – to visualize graphically how mortality is evolving differentially.
3 Note that in this cross-country comparison we depart from different mortality levels, i.e., low early age mortality in many European countries in the 1980s and 1990s, but rather high early age mortality at that time in the U.S., driven by extremely high homicide rates of young adults related to the crack cocaine epidemic (Dahlberg 1998).
4 In general, all-cause mortality can be considered as more robust than cause-specific mortality for a general depiction of mortality trends, since no bias due to questions of validity and reliability of medical death certificates needs to be considered. Especially for AIDS mortality it is known that unawareness of the disease in the beginnings of the outbreak as well as reporting other causes of death related to AIDS and other causes most likely led to a conservative reporting of the magnitude of the AIDS epidemic (Valdes and George 2013).

References

Chancel, Lucas. 2014. "Are Younger Generations Higher Carbon Emitters than Their Elders? Inequalities, Generations and CO2 Emissions in France and in the USA." *Ecological Economics* 100: 195–207.
Chauvel, Louis, Anja K Leist, and Valentina Ponomarenko. 2016. "Testing Persistence of Cohort Effects in the Epidemiology of Suicide: An Age-Period-Cohort Hysteresis Model." *PloS One* 11 (7): e0158538.
Chauvel, Louis, Anja Leist, and Herbert Smith. 2016. "Cohort Factors Impinging on Suicide Rates in the United States, 1990–2010." *Paper for the 2016 Meeting of the Population Association of America.* http://orbilu.uni.lu/handle/10993/25339.
Chauvel, Louis, and Martin Schröder. 2014. "Generational Inequalities and Welfare Regimes." *Social Forces* 92 (4): 1259–83.
Chauvel, Louis, and Martin Schroeder. 2015. "The Impact of Cohort Membership on Disposable Incomes in West Germany, France, and the United States." *European Sociological Review* 31 (3): 298–311.
Cleries, R, Martínez, J. M., Valls, J., Pareja, L., Esteban, L., Gispert, R., Moreno, V., Ribes, J., and Borràs, J. M. 2009. "Life Expectancy and Age-Period-Cohort Effects: analysis and projections of mortality in Spain between 1977 and 2016." Public Health 123 (2): 156–62.
Dahlberg, Linda L. 1998. "Youth Violence in the United States: Major Trends, Risk Factors, and Prevention Approaches." *American Journal of Preventive Medicine* 14 (4): 259–72.

Donoghoe, Martin C, Jeffrey V Lazarus, and Srdan Matic. 2005. "HIV/AIDS in the Transitional Countries of Eastern Europe and Central Asia." *Clinical Medicine* 5 (5): 487–90.

Fienberg, Stephen E, and William M Mason. 1979. "Identification and Estimation of Age-Period-Cohort Models in the Analysis of Discrete Archival Data." *Sociological Methodology* 10: 1–67.

Gómez-Redondo, Rosa, and Carl Boe. 2005. "Decomposition Analysis of Spanish Life Expectancy at Birth: Evolution and Changes in the Components by Sex and Age." *Demographic Research* 13: 521–46.

Granizo, Juan J, Eliseo Guallar, and Fernando Rodriguez-Artalejo. 1996. "Age-Period-Cohort Analysis of Suicide Mortality Rates in Spain, 1959–1991." *International Journal of Epidemiology* 25 (4): 814–20.

Houweling, Hans, Lucas G Wiessing, Françoise F Hamers, Fabian Termorshuizen, O Noël Gill, and MJ Sprenger. 1999. "An Age-Period-Cohort Analysis of 50,875 AIDS Cases among Injecting Drug Users in Europe." *International Journal of Epidemiology* 28 (6): 1141–48.

Keiding, Niels. 2011. "Age-Period-Cohort Analysis in the 1870s: Diagrams, Stereograms, and the Basic Differential Equation." *Canadian Journal of Statistics* 39 (3): 405–20.

Lexis, Wilhelm Hector Richard Albrecht. 1875. *Einleitung in Die Theorie Der Bevölkerungsstatistik.* KJ Trübner.

Lindahl-Jacobsen, Rune, Roland Rau, Bernard Jeune, Vladimir Canudas-Romo, Adam Lenart, Kaare Christensen, and James W Vaupel. 2016. "Rise, Stagnation, and Rise of Danish Women's Life Expectancy." *Proceedings of the National Academy of Sciences* 113 (15): 4015–20.

Lozano, Rafael, Mohsen Naghavi, Kyle Foreman, Stephen Lim, Kenji Shibuya, Victor Aboyans, Jerry Abraham, Timothy Adair, Rakesh Aggarwal, and Stephanie Y Ahn. 2012. "Global and Regional Mortality from 235 Causes of Death for 20 Age Groups in 1990 and 2010: A Systematic Analysis for the Global Burden of Disease Study 2010." *The Lancet* 380 (9859): 2095–2128.

Mason, William M, and Stephen Fienberg. 2012. *Cohort Analysis in Social Research: Beyond the Identification Problem.* Springer Science & Business Media.

Mason, William M, and Herbert L Smith. 1985. "Age-Period-Cohort Analysis and the Study of Deaths from Pulmonary Tuberculosis." In *Cohort Analysis in Social Research*, 151–227. Springer.

Pisati, Maurizio. 2004. "Simple Thematic Mapping." *The Stata Journal* 4 (4): 361–78.

Rehm, Jürgen, Ulrich Frick, Christina Hartwig, Felix Gutzwiller, Patrick Gschwend, and Ambros Uchtenhagen. 2005. "Mortality in Heroin-Assisted Treatment in Switzerland 1994–2000." *Drug and Alcohol Dependence* 79 (2): 137–43.

Riffe, Tim. 2011. "Equilateral Lexis Triangles?" *Demog Blog* (blog). November 25. https://sites.google.com/site/timriffepersonal/DemogBlog/equilaterallexistriangles.

Rudd, Rose A, Noah Aleshire, Jon E Zibbell, and R Matthew Gladden. 2016. "Increases in Drug and Opioid Overdose Deaths—United States, 2000–2014." *American Journal of Transplantation* 16 (4): 1323–27.

Valdes, Béatrice, and Karen George. 2013. "Demographic Analysis of AIDS Mortality in Spain." *Population* 68 (3): 473–85.

6

LEARNING FROM AGE–PERIOD–COHORT DATA

Bounds, mechanisms, and 2D-APC graphs

Ethan Fosse, Christopher Winship and Adel Daoud

"The formulation of the problem is often more essential than its solution."

Albert Einstein

"A problem well put is half solved."

John Dewey

Introduction[1]

Social scientists have long sought to explain social change by using age–period–cohort (APC) models, attempting to estimate the unique contributions of age, period and cohort effects on a particular outcome. A major obstacle, however, has been the issue of model identification that arises from the linear dependence among age, period and cohort. Many solutions have been proposed to the identification problem, but none have gained wide acceptance. The lack of consensus, along with limited understanding of seemingly complicated models, has greatly hindered both methodological development and the application of APC methods to substantive analyses of social change.

As the quotes above suggest, solving a problem may require redefining it. In this chapter we present a set of related strategies in which the goal is to determine the unique contributions of age, period and cohort on an outcome. In doing so, we argue that the challenge is to not to achieve point identification but rather to determine what and how much can be learned from a particular APC dataset. In some instances, it may be possible to identify or nearly identify point estimates for APC causal effects using weak theoretical assumptions, but in others not. However, even if point identification is not possible, a great deal can often be learned from the data.

As we show below, the great advantage of redefining the goal of an APC analysis in this way is that it is possible to carry out a series of analyses using techniques that have a solid methodological foundation, something that has eluded the great majority of past efforts and arguably is the much more fundamental problem. Our claim is not that we have 'solved' the APC identification problem, but rather that, by changing the definition of the problem, we have developed ways to rigorously analyze APC data involving transparent assumptions that can be clearly defended using substantive theory.

Central to our approach is the belief that there is an inherent trade-off between theoretical assumptions and what can be learned from data. The fewer the assumptions, the less is revealed. More assumptions mean that more can be learned, but what is learned will depend directly on the assumptions made. Given this trade-off, researchers need to demonstrate what can be learned with different assumptions. This is ultimately no different from any causal inference problem, which always requires information external to the data to justify a causal story.

Our suggested strategy for analyzing APC data consists of three general stages, each containing more detailed steps. The first stage (Analysis without assumptions) consists of two parts: an analysis of the nonlinear effects and different combinations of the linear effects.[2] As we discuss below, the nonlinear effects are identified under the standard assumption that there are no interactions between the APC variables. The nonlinearities may be of considerable interest in their own right and worthy of detailed analysis. Furthermore, in many cases it may be reasonable to assume that the absence of nonlinear effects for one or more of the three APC variables implies the likely absence of their related linear effects. We call this the Coupled Temporal Effects assumption (CTE).[3] If there are no nonlinear effects for one of the APC variables and the CTE assumption seems reasonable, identification then can be achieved by dropping that variable from the model and standard methods can be used.

The second step in the first stage is to carry out an analysis of the linear effects that are consistent with the data. This is done using what is called a 2D-APC graph that indicates that set of parameter values for the three APC variables that are consistent with the data. These values always fall on a one-dimensional line, what we term the canonical solution line.

What has not been previously recognized is that the location of the solution as determined by the data potentially rules out various combinations of linear effects. For example, there might be no point on the solution line where the linear age effect was positive and both the linear period and cohort effects are negative. Thus even in the total absence of assumptions, the data may rule out certain combinations of effects.

In the second stage (Partial Identification Using Bounds) we propose carrying out a bounds analysis. In many cases there may good theoretical reasons for assuming that the overall effect (i.e., the combined linear and nonlinear effects) of an APC variable is monotonically increasing or decreasing over some range of the variable. By monotonically increasing we mean that as the APC variable of interest increases, the outcome increases or at least remains constant. By monotonically decreasing we mean that as the APC variable of interest increases, the outcome decreases or at least remains constant. For example, there is established biological theory as to why immunity to many diseases increases from infancy to childhood to adulthood, but then decreases at older ages. Similarly, theories of the human brain with regards to the development of the prefrontal cortex imply that an individual's attraction to risk will decrease as they transition from adolescence to adulthood.

Assumptions about whether or not ordered outcome values are monotonically increasing or decreasing are important in that they have the potential to bound the effects of the APC variables. As discussed below, fixing the value of any one APC value determines the values of the other two. Analogously, it is the case that bounding one variable potentially bounds the values of the other two variables. For instance, depending on the data, a monotonically increasing age effect might imply a monotonically decreasing period effect or a monotonically increasing cohort effect. The resulting bounds one obtains for each of the three APC variables may be wide or narrow. In our experience, it is often possible to achieve quite narrow bounds resulting in approximate point estimates for the effects of each of the three APC variables.

In the third and last stage (Mechanism-based models of APC effects), we recommend incorporating into one's analysis, when available, measured mechanisms (or mediators) of the bundles of causal effects thought to be related to the APC variables. As explained below, key here will be the assumption that the mechanism is affected by at most two of the APC variables. Mechanisms have the potential to explain the effects of the APC variables on an outcome. For example, below we examine the potential for educational attainment to explain age-related differences in religious disaffiliation in the United States. Importantly, whether one or more mediating variables explains the nonlinear effects of an APC variable is testable. If the nonlinear effects of an APC variable are explained and it is reasonable to assume that this implies its linear effect is also explained (as discussed in the CTE assumption above), then the APC model is fully identified and a full set of point estimates for each of the three APC variables can be obtained.

We suggest that researchers learn from APC data by carrying out their analysis following the three stages above. Each successive stage represents an analysis built on successively stronger assumptions. The first stage involves no assumptions. However, a researcher in finding the absence of nonlinear effects for one of the three APC variables may drop that variable invoking the CTE assumption, namely, that the absence of nonlinear effects of an APC variable implies the same for its linear effect. In this case, analyses can proceed using conventional methods. The second stage involves carrying out a bounds analysis in which assumptions about whether or not an APC variable is monotonically increasing or decreasing over some range of an APC variable is used to bound the effects of other APC variables. The third stage involves the inclusion of mediators and the assumption that they are affected at most by two of the APC variables. This last stage is often the most challenging, in that the researcher needs data on mechanisms to estimate the causal pathways.

The remainder of the chapter is organized as follows. In the next section we provide a very brief history of APC analysis before providing the logic of APC analyses.

In the following section we formally discuss how to organize temporal data, the relationship between models of temporal effects, and the nature of the identification problem. In the next sections we discuss the three stages of APC analysis.[4] We focus in particular on describing the usefulness of 2D-APC graphs and the importance of theoretical arguments in developing APC models. In each section we illustrate how these methods can be used by analyzing changes in religious disaffiliation. Specifically, we examine changing patterns of religious intensity from 1977 to 2018 as measured in the General Social Survey (GSS).

Background of APC analysis

Brief history

The history of APC analysis goes back to at least the 1860s, pre-dating Wilheim Lexis's introduction of the Lexis diagram in his book *Introduction to the Theory of Population Statistics* in 1875 (for a review, see Keiding 2011). In his well-regarded essay, written in the 1920s, the German sociologist Karl Mannheim demonstrated the importance of generations indicating how a population could change without individuals changing as a result of cohort replacement (Pilcher 1994). Wade Hampton Frost's analysis in the 1930s changes in tuberculosis rates marks the modern period of APC analysis in epidemiology (Frost 1995). Norman Ryder's classic (1965) paper on cohorts similarly delineates this for demography and sociology.

Over the decades social and behavioral scientists have researched a wide variety of topics using APC methods. Two general types of outcomes have been studied. Both epidemiologists and demographers have examined changes in rates of disease and other health-related behaviors, (Chen et al. 2003; Kerr et al. 2004; O'Malley, Bachman, and Johnston 1984;Vedøy 2014), obesity (Diouf et al. 2010; Fu and Land 2015), cancer (Clayton and Schifflers 1987; Liu et al. 2001) and mental health (Lavori et al. 1987;Yang 2008). Sociologists, demographers and others have examined a variety of outcomes related to social change, including verbal ability (Alwin 1991; Hauser and Huang 1997;Wilson and Gove 1999), social trust (Clark and Eisenstein 2013; Putnam 1995; Robinson and Jackson 2001; Schwadel and Stout 2012), party identification (Hout and Knoke 1975; Tilley and Evans 2014) and religious affiliation (Chaves 1989; Firebaugh and Harley 1991).

APC effects as bundles of unmeasured causes

In the APC literature, researchers have typically viewed age, period and cohort as indicators of distinct sets of unmeasured causes (e.g., see Mason and Fienberg 1985; Rodgers 1990). The notion that the APC variables are causal variables themselves is hard to support since it is not possible through manipulation to change an individual's age, the year they were born, or the current year. To quote Clifford Clogg (1982): 'age, period, and cohort are merely indicators of other variables which actually "cause" the observed variation in the dependent variable under study. The age–period–cohort framework is properly interpreted as an accounting scheme, not a "causal model'" (460). Mason and Fienberg (1985) make the same point: 'these models do not explain so much as they provide categories with which to seek explanation. For accounting models to have value, the parameterizations of the general framework must be linked to phenomena presumed to underlie the accounting categories' (46–47).

If age, period and cohort can be understood as indices, what are they indices of? Generally, the APC literature describes the 'effects' of the three APC variables as consisting of a set of underlying causal processes each associated with one or more of the three APC variables.[5] For example, consider a study examining temporal effects in happiness. Age might be an indicator for the stress associated with having children of different ages. Period might reflect changes in the employment and political environment. Cohort might reflect differences in opportunities over the entire life course.

Figure 6.1 represents the general logic of the APC model with each of the three APC variables being associated with some underlying causal mechanism (MA, MP and MC), which are unobserved. The double-headed lines denote associational linkages between the three time scales and unobserved causal mechanisms. The directed arrows indicate causal relations between the unobserved mechanisms and the outcome. The logic represented by Figure 6.1 now clarifies what one might mean when one says that age, period or cohort have an 'effect': such a statement is just shorthand for the longer statement that the causal variables associated with each of the three APC have a causal effect on the outcome.

If the APC variables are simply indices, what then are the regression parameters associated with the three APC variables? The most basic way to understand a regression model is as a conditional expectation or conditional mean operator

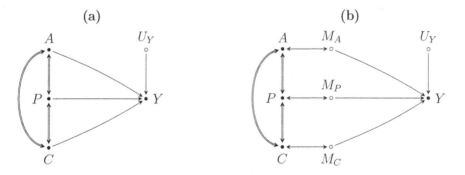

FIGURE 6.1 Graphical models of temporal variables
Notes: Panel (a) shows the simplified APC graphical model for age (A), period (P) and cohort (C). The double-line arrows denote the linear dependence among the three time scales. Filled circles denote observed variables, while hollow circles denote unobserved variables. Panel (b) shows the graphical model with a full set of mechanism variables (MA, MP and MC), which are unobserved. The double-headed lines denote associational linkages between the three time scales and unobserved causal mechanisms.

(Goldberger 1991). That is, a regression equation if properly specified indicates the mean of the outcome variable for individuals with fixed values for a specific set of X's. Thus, under this noncausal interpretation, a regression parameter indicates the difference in the conditional means for two groups with equivalent X's except that they differ by one unit with respect to the X whose parameter is of interest. For example, in a linear regression model where education is the outcome if the regression parameter for cohort is 0.25, this would indicate that a cohort born one year later, all the other X's being the same, would have 0.25 more years of education.

The logic of the APC identification problem

The APC identification problem, as it has become known, is simply the fact that if we know a person's age in years and the year in which their outcome was measured, then we know their birth year. That is, we know:

$$\text{cohort} = \text{period} - \text{age} \tag{6.1}$$

Suppose we have collected data on a set of individuals and have measured each person's birth year, age, year of measurement and their value on some outcome. An intuitive way to understand this problem is to use age, period and cohort variables as inputs in a multiple linear regression model:

$$Y = \mu + \alpha(\text{age}) + \pi(\text{period}) + \gamma(\text{cohort}) + \varepsilon \tag{6.2}$$

where Y is the outcome variable to be explained; μ is the intercept; age, period and cohort are measured in years; α, π and γ are the slopes for age, period and cohort, respectively; and ϵ is random error. For simplicity we have dropped the subscripts indexing each row (i.e., individual) of the dataset.

In Equation 6.2, we are attempting to estimate the effect of each variable holding the other variables constant. What provides information for estimating the effect of the variable of interest is the extent to which Y varies with that variable holding the control variables constant (i.e., varies within the levels of the control variables). Without loss of generality, assume that we want to estimate the linear effect of cohort (γ in Equation 6.2) holding age and period constant. Now consider only individuals of a certain age measured at a specific point of time: because of the perfect linear dependency among the three temporal variables, these individuals are not only the same age at the same period, but they also have the same birth year. There is no variance in cohort holding age and period constant, and as such it is impossible to estimate its linear effect.

For example, if we know a person was born in 1900 and that person's outcome was measured in 1950, then we know that person's age is 50. Then we are estimating the following equation for this person:

$$Y = \mu + \alpha(50) + \pi(1950) + \gamma(1950 - 50) + \varepsilon \tag{6.3}$$

Once we control for this person's age (50) and period (1950), then there is no information to estimate the linear cohort effect, γ, because the cohort is just the difference between period and age (1950 − 50).[6]

Modeling APC effects

Organizing temporal data

Previously in Equation 6.2 we outlined a simple linear regression model based on data in which each row is a different individual with columns consisting of the variables age, period, cohort and the outcome. More commonly, data on temporal effects is arranged in a rectangular age–period array of observations,[7] with age and period aggregated into intervals of equal width (Holford 1983: 311–318; Mason and Fienberg 1985: 67–68).[8] For example, Table 6.1 displays the data structure of an age–period array with five age groups and three period groups, both aggregated into five-year intervals. The number of cohort groups equals one less than the sum of the age and period groups, so there are 3 + 5 − 1 = 7 cohorts in Table 6.1. The number of observations on the outcome equals the number of cells in the array, which is simply the number of age groups multiplied by the number of period groups. Thus, in Table 6.1 there are $3 \times 5 = 15$ observations.

Cohort groups are labeled in the cells, calculated by cross-referencing corresponding age and period groups.[9] For instance, the cohort interval 1956–1964 is derived from the range of possible birth years for those observed during the period interval 2000–2004 and age interval 40–44. The history of each cohort can be traced along the diagonals of the table, moving forward in time from the upper-left to the lower-right. For example, the shaded diagonal set in Table 6.1 refers to the cohort born during the years 1956–1964. Following from the upper-left shaded cell to the lower-right shaded cell, we can track the cohort of people born in 1956–1964 as they advance in age from 40–44 to 50–54 and move through time from 2000–2004 to 2010–2014.

TABLE 6.1 Structure of a Lexis table with interval values of equal width for age and period groups

Age groups	2000–2004	2005–2009	2010–2014
30–34	1966–1974	1971–1979	1976–1984
35–39	1961–1969	1966–1974	1971–1979
40–44	1956–1964	1961–1969	1966–1974
45–49	1951–1959	1956–1964	1961–1969
50–54	1946–1954	1951–1959	1956–1964

Notes: Age and period aggregated into five-year intervals, with corresponding nine-year cohort intervals labeled in the cells. Shaded cells track the history of the cohort born in 1956–1964.

Classical APC model

It is common in the APC literature to use index notation to keep track of the dimensions of a temporal data structure such as that shown in Table 6.1 (Mason and Fienberg 1985: 67–71). We will let $i = 1,..., I$ represent the age groups, $j = 1,..., J$ the period groups, and $k = 1,..., K$ the cohort groups with $k = j - i + 1$ and $K = I + J - 1$.[10] Using this index notation, temporal effects in an age–period array can be represented using the classical APC (C-APC) model, also known as the multiple classification model (Mason, Mason, et al. 1973: 243) or accounting model (Mason and Fienberg 1985: 46–47, 67), which has the following form (Mason and Fienberg 1985: 67–68; Yang and Land 2013: 61):

$$Y_{ijk} = \mu + \alpha_i + \pi_j + \gamma_k + \varepsilon_{ijk} \tag{6.4}$$

where Y_{ijk} is the outcome variable to be explained, μ is the intercept, α_i represents the ith age effect, π_j represents the jth period effect, γ_k represents the kth cohort effect, and ε_{ijk} is the error term. To avoid overparameterization, we apply the so-called usual constraints that the parameters sum to zero, such that $\sum_{i=1}^{I} \alpha_i = \sum_{j=1}^{J} \pi_j = \sum_{k=1}^{K} \gamma_k = 0.$[11]

The parameterization shown in Equation 6.4 is very flexible, allowing the age, period and cohort effects to be highly nonlinear because there is one parameter for each age, period and cohort category (Mason, Mason, et al. 1973: 246). However, like Equation 6.2, the C-APC suffers from a fundamental identification problem due to perfect linear dependence in the columns (Yang and Land 2013: 63). The linear dependence can be difficult to spot visually, but what it means in practice is that at least one of the temporal variables must be dropped.

Linearized APC model

To clarify the nature of the identification problem with the C-APC, it is useful to provide an alternative representation of the C-APC that orthogonally decomposes the linear from the nonlinear components (Holford 1983, 2006). We can accordingly specify a linearized APC (L-APC) model with the form:

$$Y_{ijk} = \mu + \alpha\left(i - i^\star\right) + \pi\left(j - j^\star\right) + \gamma\left(k - k^\star\right) + \tilde{\alpha}_i + \tilde{\pi}_j + \tilde{\gamma}_k + \varepsilon_{ijk} \tag{6.5}$$

where the asterisks denote midpoint or referent indices and are

$$i^\star = \left(\frac{1+1}{2}\right), j^\star = \left(\frac{J+1}{2}\right), \text{ and } k^\star = \left(\frac{K+1}{2}\right)$$

As before, we refer to the linear effects as α, π and γ for age, period and cohort. However, we now introduce $\tilde{\alpha}$, $\tilde{\pi}$ and $\tilde{\gamma}$ to represent age, period and cohort nonlinearities, respectively. The L-APC model is based on setting up APC data so that the linear and nonlinear components are orthogonal to each other (see Fosse and Winship 2018).

The C-APC and L-APC are equivalent representations of the temporal data shown in Table 6.1. As with the C-APC, each cell in an age–period array is modeled by a unique combination of parameters under sum-to-zero constraints. For example, the ith age effect in the C-APC is represented in the L-APC by the overall linear age effect along with a unique parameter for the ith age non-linearity: $\alpha_i = \left(i - i^*\right)\alpha + \tilde{\alpha}_i$. That is, each age effect α_i is decomposed into the sum of a common parameter α representing the (linear) age slope for the entire array, with a value shifting across rows (or age categories) as a function of the age index $_i$, and a unique parameter $\tilde{\alpha}$ which is a nonlinearity specific to each row (or age category) of the array. We can similarly decompose the period and cohort effects into linear and nonlinear components.

The importance of the L-APC model is that, by explicitly separating the slopes from their deviations, it clearly shows that the identification problem is limited to the linear effects.[12] When the nonlinear terms are zero in the population, the L-APC is equivalent to the basic linear model:

$$Y_{ijk} = \mu + \alpha\left(i - i^*\right) + \pi\left(j - j^*\right) + \gamma\left(k - k^*\right) + (0) + (0) + (0) + \varepsilon_{ijk}$$

$$= \mu + \alpha\left(\text{age}_i\right) + \pi\left(\text{period}_j\right) + \gamma\left(\text{cohort}^k\right) + \varepsilon_{ijk} \tag{6.6}$$

where age$_i$, period$_j$ and cohort$_k$ are the midpoint values for each of the categories (see Table 6.2), which are simply the indices recentered and rescaled, and the nonlinearities are zeroed out.[13] A useful way to understand the nonidentifiability

TABLE 6.2 Structure of a Lexis table with midpoint values for age, period and cohort

	Period		
Age	2002	2007	2012
32	1970	1975	1980
37	1965	1970	1975
42	1960	1965	1970
47	1955	1960	1965
52	1950	1955	1960

Notes: Age and period values are midpoints of five-year intervals, while cohort values are midpoints of nine-year intervals calculated by cross-referencing age and period intervals. Shaded cells track the history of the cohort with a midpoint birth year of 1960.

problem is to note that for any particular APC model we can specify the linear effects as (Rodgers 1982: 782):

$$\alpha^* = \alpha + v$$

$$\pi^* = \pi - v \tag{6.7}$$

$$\gamma^* = \gamma + v$$

where the asterisk ($\star$) indicates an arbitrary set of estimated slopes from an APC model and v is a scalar fixed to some value. As Equation 6.7 demonstrates these parameters are simple additive rescalings of the true unobserved slopes α, π and γ shifted by a single arbitrary scalar, v.

A three-stage approach to analyzing APC data

We are now in a position to discuss how to actually analyze APC data using our three-stage approach. We illustrate our approach by examining changes in religious disaffiliation from 1977 to 2018 using the GSS. The outcome is religious intensity, which measures the respondent's strength of religious affiliation on a scale from 1 to 4, where 1 = no religious affiliation, 2 = not very strong religious affiliation, 3 = somewhat strong religious affiliation, and 4 = strong religious affiliation.[14] After subsetting to respondents born in the United States, this gives us a sample of 48,598 respondents. Age and period are grouped into five-year intervals. To deal with the complex sampling of the GSS, estimates are adjusted using the appropriating sampling weights.

Because the predicted values of an APC model are identified under any particular constraint, we can estimate the expected average religious intensity for various age, period and cohort groups using the full linearized APC model.[15] These results are shown in Figure 6.2. Although it might be tempting to informally 'eyeball' the unique contributions of the temporal effects from this graph, it is important to note that each of the expected averages in Figure 6.2 are based on the combined effects of age, period and cohort. The patterns in this graph simply tell us that religious intensity is generally lowest among younger individuals measured during the most recent periods who are also members of the most recent birth cohorts, while religious intensity is highest among older individuals measured in earlier periods who are also members of earlier cohorts. To determine the unique effects of age, period and cohort, we need a more formal approach, which we outline below in three stages.

Stage 1: analysis without assumptions

The APC literature has generally failed to recognize that data are informative about the three APC effects, even in the absence of any assumptions.[16] The data are informative in two ways. First, as discussed previously, the nonlinear APC effects are identified. This means that they can be estimated and graphed. Furthermore, it is possible to test whether or not these effects are zero. If various tests or visual

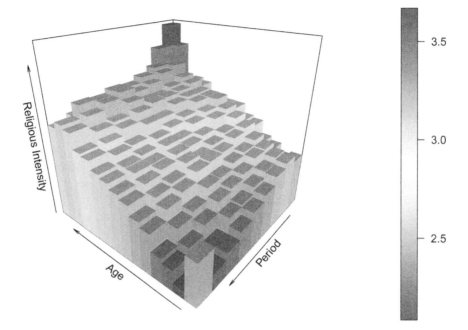

FIGURE 6.2 3D Lexis histogram of religious intensity
Notes: Results are based on a full linearized APC model with the period linear
effect fixed to zero. Each cell gives the expected average religious intensity on a
scale from 1 to 4, where 1 = no religious affiliation, 2 = not very strong religious
affiliation, 3 = somewhat strong religious affiliation, and 4 = strong religious affiliation.
Estimates are adjusted using appropriate sampling weights. Estimates based on 59,573
respondents in the United States GSS.

inspection suggest that it is reasonable to assume that one or more of the APC
nonlinear effects are zero, then it may reasonable to assume that there is no linear
effect as well (the CTE assumption) and drop these variables from the model, thus
suggesting a fully identified analysis is appropriate.

Second, particular combinations of linear effects are identified, which define a
set of solutions. Moreover, as discussed in detail below, because the set of solutions
lie on a line, certain combinations of effects are ruled out. This means that particular
theories may be shown to be inconsistent with the data. In general, the data are
likely to be consistent with multiple patterns of effects, but not all combinations of
APC effects. As such, the data, in the absence of any assumptions, may well provide
evidence against certain theoretical claims.

Nonlinear effects: no assumptions needed

Because the nonlinear effects are identified, we can get point estimates of their
values. The corresponding figure shows the nonlinear effects for age, period and
cohort on religious disaffiliation.

As can be seen in Figure 6.3, there are clear nonlinear fluctuations in the data for all three temporal variables.[17] In Table 6.3 we present a set of tests for helping to ascertain whether or not the nonlinear effects for age, period or cohort should be dropped. For example, the AP Model in Table 6.3 refers to a model in which the nonlinear effects for cohort have been dropped. Both visual inspection of the graphs for the nonlinear effects as well as these results allow the researcher to determine whether or not – in terms similar to those outlined by Yang and Land – all three APC dimensions are operative. If, based on these tests, one is willing to assume that one or more effects are not operating, one can drop the corresponding nonlinear components. Accordingly, one can fit the sub-model rather than the full APC model.[18] Table 6.3 includes the model log-likelihoods, AIC and BIC fit statistics, as well as chi-square statistics from Wald tests comparing the candidate model with the full APC model. The AIC favors the model with period and cohort nonlinear effects, suggesting that it might be reasonable to favor a model in which the age linear effect is zero. In contrast, BIC, which prefers parsimonious models, suggests one should just fit a model with period nonlinear effects, implying that the age and cohort linear effects could be fixed to zero. In this case, we would want to be careful about making assumptions about any of the effects, because model results (not shown here) indicate that they are all statistically significant at conventional levels, notwithstanding the imprecision of the estimates for the cohort effects due to the unbalanced nature of the data.[19]

Constraints on linear effects absent assumptions

Without data, the age, period and cohort parameters can take on any combination of values in a three-dimensional space. The data, however, constrains all of the effects to lie on a line determined by the unidentified linear parameters. This implies that if we fix anyone of the three linear effects, the values of the other two are determined.

The canonical solution line

To appreciate how the data constrains the linear effects, one needs to understand the geometric representation of the linear dependence problem. Let $\theta_1 = \alpha + \pi$ and $\theta_2 = \gamma + \pi$. Figure 6.4(a) shows the age–period plane defined by the identified quantity for hypothetical data where $\theta_1 = 3$, while Figure 6.4(b) shows the period–cohort plane defined by the identified quantity $\theta_2 = -2$. Intersecting these two planes defines a line, as shown in Figure 6.4(c) and Figure 6.4(d). This is what is known as the *canonical solution line* as all points on it represent parameter estimates for α, π and γ that are equally consistent with the data.[20] As such, this visually represents the APC identification problem. If the age, period and cohort parameters were identified, the planes would intersect at a single point in the parameter space. Here the intersection consists of all points along a line. The scalar v in Equation 6.7 essentially moves the possible estimates up and down the canonical solution line.

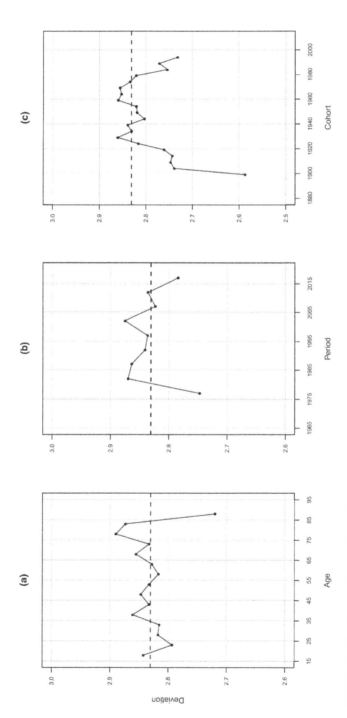

FIGURE 6.3 Nonlinear effects: religious intensity

TABLE 6.3 Fit statistics for various APC models: religious intensity

	Log-likelihood	AIC	BIC	Chi-square	P-value
Full APC Model	56,343.81	56,466,78	56,818,63		
PC Model	56,403.80	56,452,78	56,698,78	16.70	0.213
AC Model	56,403.80	56,505.65	56,785.81	39.86	<0.0001
AP Model	56,411.18	56,474.52	56,647.26	49.59	0.0004
A Model	56,482.29	56,524.13	56,622.24	97.24	< 0.0001
P Model	56,440.18	56,467.81	56,528.50	67.46	0.0005
C Model	56, 425.38	56,491.92	56,666.70	57.31	< 0:0001

Notes: All models include the same set of linear effects, which are estimated under the constraint that the period linear effect is zero. Chi-square statistics and p-values based on Wald tests comparing the full APC model with the specified candidate model.

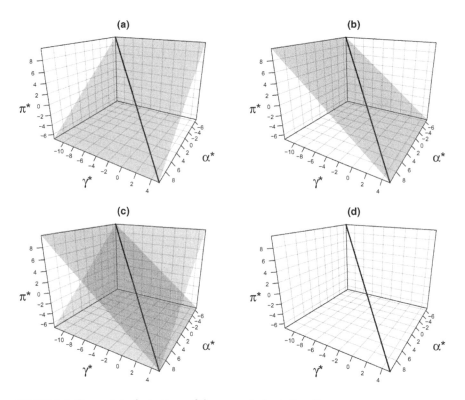

FIGURE 6.4 Geometric derivation of the canonical solution line

What is important to appreciate is what is accomplished when data are used in an APC model. If there are only linear effects, the data has taken us from a situation where all parameter values in a three-dimensional space are possible to one where only estimates lying on a one-dimensional line are consistent with the data. This same reduction also occurs if our model has nonlinear effects as they are fully identified.

As Fosse and Winship (2018) demonstrate, the solution line always sits in a three-dimensional subspace of the overall space of possible parameter values. Thus, the data has substantially reduced the possible estimates for the linear effects of age, period and cohort to values that lie on a single one-dimensional line. The data are quite informative about parameter values, just not informative enough to give us point estimates for the linear effects. That said, the data, by constraining values to a single line, contains considerable information about the possible values of the APC parameters.

2D-APC graphs

There is a useful way to simplify the representation of the solution line in the previous section. Because of the linear relationships $\alpha + \pi = \theta_1$ and $\pi + \gamma = \theta_2$, our three-dimensional representation can be reduced to just two. A way of doing this is by having the horizontal axis represent the period slope, the left vertical axis the age slope and the right vertical axis the cohort slope. Fosse and Winship (2019) call this a 2D-APC graph.

The 2D-APC graph clarifies an important, unrecognized fact in the APC literature that, by fixing the location of the solution line, the data also determines which of the eight combinations of positive and negative age, period and cohort linear effects are empirically possible. Because the offset between the age and cohort slopes must be either positive or negative as determined by the difference between the θ's, only six combinations can exist. Then, depending on the location of the canonical solution line, as few as two and as many as four remaining combinations may be possible. Figure 6.5 shows an example of a 2D-APC graph using simulated data, where $\theta_1 = 3$ and $\theta_2 = -2$. There are six regions of the parameter space defined by the signed combinations of the slopes (α, π, γ). In the figure these are labeled as regions **I** $(+,-,+)$, **II** $(+,+,+)$, **III** $(+,-,-)$, **IV** $(+,+,-)$, **V** $(-,-,-)$ and **VI** $(-,+,-)$. Note first that there is no region representing either the $(-,+,+)$ or $(-,-,+)$ patterns of effects. This is due to the fact that $\theta_2 - \theta_1 < 0$. Thus, any theory that posits a negative age slope and positive slopes for period and cohort can be ruled out by the data alone. Similarly, we can rule out any theory that assumes that age and period have negative slopes while cohort has a positive slope. Furthermore, the canonical solution line runs through only four out of the six regions, so we can also rule out any social or biological theory that posits that the linear age, period and cohort effects are all positive (region **II**) or all negative (region **V**). Thus, despite the linear dependence problem, the data can eliminate a number of possibilities based on theorizing just about the direction of the slopes.

Turning to our empirical example, Figure 6.6 shows the bounding regions in the 2D-APC graph for religious intensity. The data, via the values of θ_1 and θ_2, determines the location of the solution line in the parameter space. The estimates of these parameters for religious intensity are displayed in Table 6.4. Also note that the data determines which of the signed plotting regions are even possible. This graph shows the various signed plotting regions: **I** $(+,-,+)$, **II** $(+,+,+)$, **III** $(-,-,+)$, **IV** $(-,+,+)$, **V** $(-,-,-)$ and **VI** $(-,+,-)$. Unlike the previous example with simulated data, with the religious disaffiliation data there is no region representing either the

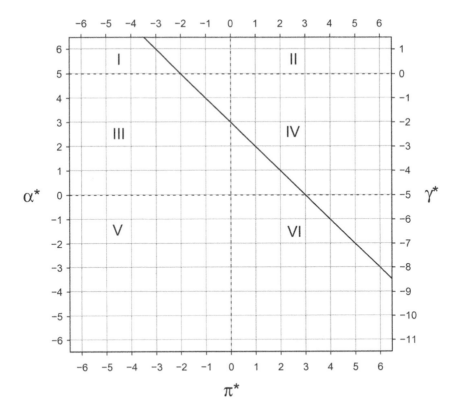

FIGURE 6.5 Example of a 2D-APC graph

Notes: This graph shows the various signed plotting regions: **I (+,–,+)**, **II (+,+,+)**, **III (+,–,–)**, **IV (+,+,–)**, **V (–,–,–)** and **VI (–,+,–)**. Note first that there is no region representing either the **(–,+,+)** or **(–,–,+)** patterns of linear effects.

TABLE 6.4 Intercept and combined linear effects: religious intensity

Parameter	Est.	SE	t-ratio	P-value
Intercept	2.8307	0.0129	219.49	< 0.0001
θ_1 or $(\alpha + \pi)$	0.1538	0.0351	4.38	< 0.0001
θ_2 or $(\gamma + \pi)$	–0.4760	0.0377	–12.6379	< 0.0001
$\theta_1 - \theta_2$ or $(\alpha + \gamma)$	–0.6298	0.0308	–20.46	< 0.0001
$\theta_2 - \theta_1$ or $(\gamma + \alpha)$	0.6298	0.0308	20.46	< 0:0001

Notes: Coefficients and standard errors based on the full linearized APC model.

(+,–,–) or (+,+,–) patterns of slopes. We can rule out any theory that makes the assumption that the age slope is positive while both the period and cohort slopes are negative. Likewise, we can rule out any theory that claims that the cohort slope is negative while both the age and period slopes are positive. Furthermore, note that

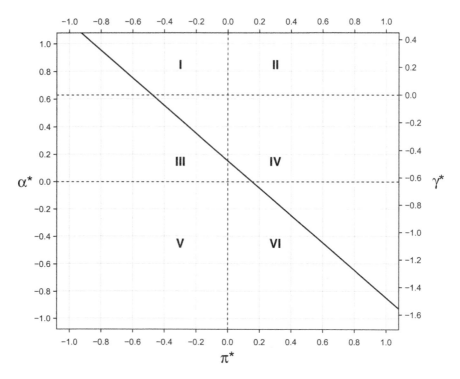

FIGURE 6.6 2D-APC graph: religious intensity
Notes: This graph shows the various signed plotting regions: **I** (+,−,+), **II** (+,+,+),
III (−,−,+), **IV** (−,+,+), **V** (−,−,−) and **VI** (−,+,−). Note first that there is no region
representing either the (+,−,−) or (+,+,−) patterns of linear effects. Solid points
denote zero-slope models, while hollow dots denote the age-period and cohort-
period origins (i.e., where the age and period slopes are both zero as well as where the
cohort and period slopes are both zero).

the canonical solution line does not go through regions **III** or **V**. In other words, we
can reject any theory that assumes that the cohort slope is positive while both the
age and period slopes are negative; additionally, we can reject any theory that assumes
that all three slopes are negative. Another way of stating the above is that only the
combinations of slopes in regions **I, II, IV** and **VI** are consistent with the data.

Combining the linear and nonlinear effects

If we had estimates of both the linear and nonlinear effects we could combine these
to get the total effects of the three APC variables. Understanding how to do this
is a useful preliminary to understanding how to combine point estimates of the
nonlinear effects with bounds on the linear effects. We show how to do so using a
hypothetical example.

Previously we have outlined how the C-APC model is related to the L-APC
model. The advantage of using the L-APC is that we can focus on those parts of the

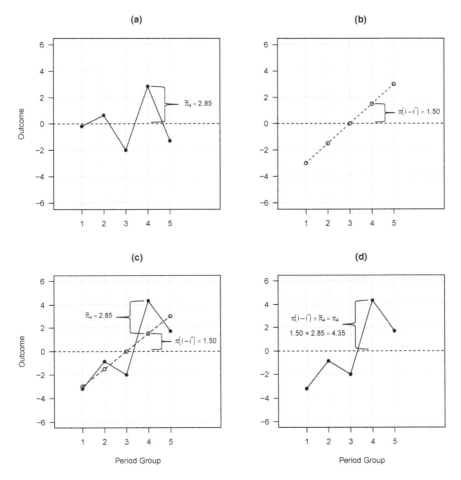

FIGURE 6.7 Combining linear and nonlinear APC effects

Notes: Panel (a) shows the nonlinear effects for a period variable (solid line). Panel (b) shows the assumed value of the period slope (dashed line). Panel (c) visualizes the combination of the linear and nonlinear effects as a solid line. Panel (d) shows the combined linear and nonlinear effects, resulting in the overall effects (solid line).

APC effects that are not identified in the standard model – that is, the linear effects. Once we use a 2D-APC graph to obtain a range of values for the linear effects, we can combine these effects with the nonlinear effects to obtain the overall effects. To illustrate how we can use the separate linear and nonlinear effects to obtain the overall effects, see Figure 6.7.

It is relatively simple to determine the total effects: we just need to add the nonlinear and linear effects together. In this hypothetical example, we have a set of nonlinear period effects that are identified: $\pi_1 = -0.20$, $\pi_2 = 0.65$, $\pi_3 = -2.00$, $\pi_4 = 2.85$, $\pi_5 = -1.30$. We also have a set of linear effects that are not identified, which can be represented generically as $\pi(j - j^*)$. With $J = 5$ period groups and $\pi = 1.5$, assume the following values for the period groups: $\pi(1 - 3) = -3$,

$\pi(2-3) = -1.5, \pi(3-3) = 0, \pi(4-3) = 1.5, \pi(5-3) = 3$. Adding the linear and nonlinear effects together gives us the overall effects: $\pi_1 = -3.20, \pi_2 = -0.85, \pi_3 = -2.00, \pi_4 = 4.35, \pi_5 = 1.70$. Figures 6.7(a) and (b) show the overall effects and how they are the simple sum of the linear and nonlinear effects. For example, the fourth period group has an overall effect of $\pi_4 = 4.35$, which is simply the sum of the period linear and nonlinear effect for that group, or $1.50 + 2.85$.

The above illustration is vital for understanding our overall approach to APC models. By splitting the unidentified temporal effects of the C-APC into identified and unidentified linear effects, we can focus on that portion of these effects that can be estimated from the data. This idea of combining the linear and nonlinear effects extends easily to actual data. In Figure 6.8, we examine religious disaffiliation effects under the assumption that the age linear effect is zero. Specifically, these results are based on first estimating the nonlinear effects, assuming that the age linear effect is zero, and then using the estimated values of θ_1 and θ_2 to calculate the values of the period and cohort linear effects. Because we have obtained a single set of estimates, we have achieved what is called *point identification*. However, in practice one will want to specify a range of values of the effects, reflecting the inherent uncertainty of the linear effects, thereby achieving *partial identification*. We cover this topic in the next section on bounding analyses of APC effects.

Stage 2: partial identification using bounds

Bounding analyses entail restriction on the parameter space of the 2D-APC graph (or, equivalently, fixing a constraint). With bounding analyses, no direct measures of U_A, U_P or U_C are included in the model. Rather, constraints are added that entail assumptions about the effect of these underlying causes on the outcome of interest. One new approach is to specify bounds based on the sign, size or shape of one or more of the temporal effects. It is crucial to underscore that in many cases by constraining the direction of one temporal slope we can make conclusions about the direction and magnitude of at least one of the other slopes. To illustrate this, consider Figure 6.9(a)–(d). The graphs show various bounds on the canonical solution line using data on religious intensity.[21] Figure 6.9(a) shows that we can reject any theory that claims that the age and period slopes are both negative; this is easily falsified by the data. In other words, either age or period has a positive linear effect. Likewise, Figure 6.9(b) illustrates that it is impossible for there to be a positive age slope and a negative cohort slope. There is no point on the canonical solution line in which this combination of linear effects exists.

The above discussion mirrors our previous overview of the signed regions of the parameter space in a 2D-APC graph. However, we can go a step further and use a 2D-APC graph to obtain finite bounds (i.e., bounds that do not entail positive or negative infinity). In general, any particular APC dataset should have at least two combinations of slopes that, with a minimal assumption about the direction of the slopes, should result in finite bounds. Figure 6.9(c) shows that we can obtain narrow bounds by assuming that the age and period slopes are both positive. This assumption results in a relatively narrow bound on the cohort slope. Similarly,

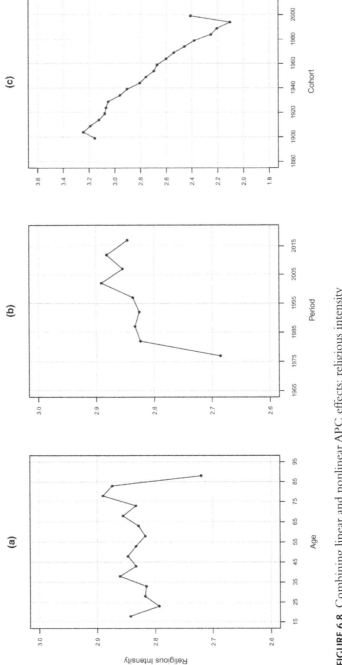

FIGURE 6.8 Combining linear and nonlinear APC effects: religious intensity

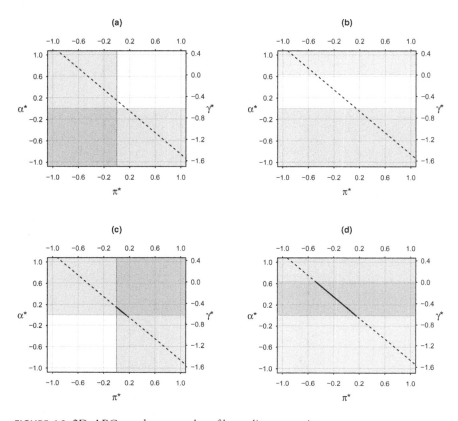

FIGURE 6.9 2D-APC graphs: examples of bounding strategies

Figure 6.9(d) illustrates the bounds, assuming that the age slope is negative and the cohort slope is positive. Given these assumptions, we can conclude that the period slope must be positive within a relatively narrow range of values.

The above bounds are based only on assumptions about the sign (or direction) of the linear effects. This is overly restrictive, because in practice we have data not only on the linear effects but the nonlinear effects as well. As a result, we can restrict not just the sign but the size of the slope by making assumptions about the shape of the temporal effects. For example, assume that we have strong theoretical reasons to believe that the overall set of effects in age is monotonically increasing. A set of simulated age nonlinear effects is displayed in Figure 6.10. As can be seen in Figure 6.10(a), the set of effects is at some groups increasing and at other groups decreasing. We want to specify a value for the linear age effect that ensures that, between any two adjacent age categories, the pair of effects is flat. To do so we need only find that pair of age adjacent categories in which the downward trend is most negative. This can be computed using the following equation: $\alpha_{m.i.} = (-1) \times min(\Delta\alpha_{I-1})$. The Δ notation indicates forward differences (i.e., $\alpha_{i+1} - \alpha_i$), and the subscript $m.i.$ indicates the linear effect is monotonically increasing. We can use this equation to calculate the lower bound for a monotonically increasing set of effects.

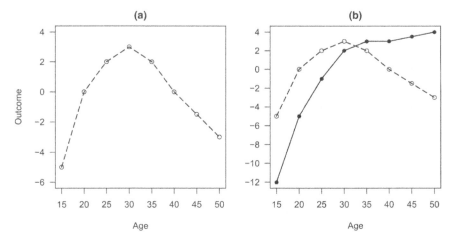

FIGURE 6.10 Specifying monotonicity constraints

The forward differences for the age nonlinearities are $\Delta\alpha_{l-1} = \{5,2,1,-1,-2,-1.5,$ $-1.5\}$. The minimum of these differences is -2, which is between ages 35 and 40. To counter this downward deviation, the parameter value for the linear age term must be greater than or equal to $+2$. In Figure 6.10(b) we show what happens to the set of age effects when the slope is set to $+2$, which is illustrated by the solid line. As can now be seen the overall set of age effects is monotonically increasing. Any slope less than $+2$ will result in an overall effect that is neither monotonically increasing nor decreasing over the full set of age groups. Alternatively, any slope greater than $+2$ will be monotonically increasing; $+2$ is the minimum monotonically increasing age slope consistent with our data.

By incorporating nonlinearities, we are able to make weaker assumptions about the sign of the slopes. For example, for the age slope we can specify the range as $-\infty$ $\leq \alpha_{m.d.} \leq 0 \leq \alpha_{m.i.} \leq +\infty$. The range $\alpha_{m.d.} \leq 0 \leq \alpha_{m.i.}$ is a weaker version of assuming a zero slope for age, since it takes into account some deviations above and below so long as the deviations are neither monotonically increasing nor decreasing. Similarly, instead of assuming the age slope is positive, we can say that $\alpha_{m.d.} \leq 0 \leq +\infty$. Finally, rather than assuming the age slope is negative, we can say that $-\infty \leq 0 \leq \alpha_{m.i.}$, which allows for any set of effects except those that are monotonically increasing.

Turning to our empirical example, we can consider placing bounds over one or more of the temporal effects using monotonicity constraints. Based on the fit statistics presented earlier, we might assume not that the age linear effect is zero, but rather that the age effects are neither monotonically increasing nor decreasing for some set of age groups. In Figure 6.11, we display the upper and lower bounds for the APC effects under the assumption that the age effects are neither monotonically increasing nor decreasing during middle age, defined here as the age groups 28–32 to 63–67. These constraints restrict the age linear effect within the range -0.4536 to 0.2772. We can conclude that, under this assumption, the great decline in religious intensity is mainly attributable to cohort effects.

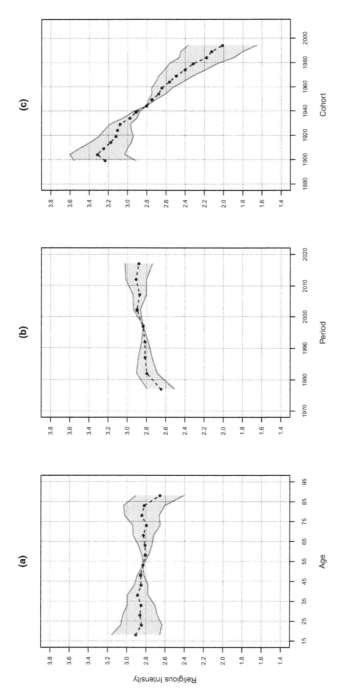

FIGURE 6.11 Specifying bounds with monotonicity constraints: religious intensity

To summarize, we can restrict the range of plausible estimates using a variety of bounding strategies, especially those about the sign, size and/or shape of the temporal effects. These should, at a minimum, reflect social or biological theories about the true causal effects thought to underlie the temporal variables. Although just-identified models fit the data equally well (and are thus observationally equivalent), some parameter values can be deemed as more plausible than others based on sociological or biological theory.

Stage 3: mechanism-based models of APC effects

Bounding analyses are based on the idea that we do not have measured mechanisms linking the APC variables to the outcome. However, in many instances we have causal mechanisms available. Such mechanisms can greatly aid in the identification of temporal effects. The mechanism-based approach identifies the causal effect of APC variables on an outcome by specifying at least one of the pathways between the temporal variables and the outcome (Winship and Harding 2008).

Incorporating observed mechanisms in an APC analysis

The first instance of the mechanism-based approach is Duncan's (1985) model shown in Figure 6.12, but it is relatively undeveloped and the causal assumptions are not fully specified. However, we present Duncan's example here because it helps to reveal the nature of the assumptions. In Duncan's basic model, M is a mechanism linking cohort, denoted by C, to the outcome, given by Y. In Duncan's particular instance, M is education and the outcome Y is a measure of generational attitudes.[22] This model identifies the putative effect of C on Y as long as M is the

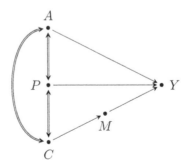

FIGURE 6.12 Duncan's basic model of APC effects
Notes: This figure displays Duncan's graphical model in which there is a mechanism between cohort and the outcome. Unobserved idiosyncratic causes of the mechanism and outcome are omitted for simplicity. The double-headed, double-lined arrows denote the inherently deterministic relationship among the three temporal variables. Filled circles indicate observed variables.

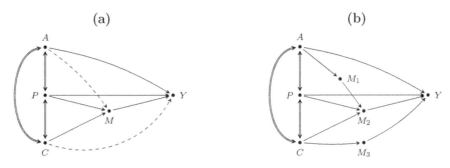

FIGURE 6.13 Omitted pathways in mechanism-based models
Notes: Panel (a) shows an extension of Duncan's APC model with omitted pathways
A → M and **C → Y**. Panel (b) shows the same model with the pathway **P → M**
specified and mechanisms added for the other omitted pathways.

only mechanism associated with C. The model also assumes that neither A nor P are
associated with M. These assumptions are visualized as dashed lines in Figure 6.13(a).

It is worth emphasizing that a richer, more detailed set of data can deal with
expected violations of these assumptions. Figure 6.13(b) shows the same graphical model except M is now labeled M_2 and we have included two additional
mechanisms, M_1 and M_3. As indicated in Figure 6.13(b), one can specify the pathway
between P and M directly and then include an additional mechanism, M_1, between
A and M_2. Likewise, if it is thought there are additional pathways not modeled
by M_2 between C and Y, one can include them in the model. Here we weaken
the assumption that the relationship between C and Y is entirely mediated by M_2
by including an additional mechanism, M_3. Even when these mechanisms are not
available in a given dataset, theorizing about likely omitted pathways is helpful for
orienting what new variables should be measured in future data collection efforts
(Winship and Harding 2008).

Two points are worth emphasizing about the mechanism-based approach. First,
the Duncan model is relatively simple in that it includes just one mechanism.
However, as discussed by Fosse and Winship (2019) as well as Winship and Harding
(2008), the mechanism-based approach is compatible with a very diverse set of
models with multiple mechanisms. Second, so far we have said little about linear
and nonlinear effects in a mechanism-based analysis. The nonlinear effects can be
estimated directly, because they are identified. That is, one can specify the full set
of nonlinear effects for the outcome as well as all mechanisms. In practice, we recommend controlling for all of the nonlinear effects when estimating the linear
effects. Under the CTE assumption mentioned previously, the idea is that one can
be relatively confident that the linear effect is zero if the corresponding nonlinear
effects are zero after adjusting for one or more mechanisms. In our example, this
would mean that, if the nonlinear effects of C on Y on A and M are zero, then
we can be confident under the CTE that the linear effects of C on Y as well as A
on M are zero. In those cases in which the CTE assumption is not met, then we

recommend specifying bounds on the linear effects using the procedures outlined in the previous steps.

Mechanism-based analysis of religious intensity

To illustrate the mechanism-based approach, we use years of education (ranging from 0 to 20) as a mechanism between the age linear component and the outcome, religious intensity. This reflects the argument that attaining higher levels of education will cause, in general, individuals to turn away from organized religion. We also posit that education is associated with the cohort linear component. Because they are identified, we assume that the nonlinear components for all three variables are associated with years of education as well as religious intensity. The corresponding graphical model is visualized in Figure 6.14. Note that this graphical model represents our assumptions about the linear components only. Because the mechanism and outcome are both continuous, we can use the product rule to obtain the estimated APC effects (Winship and Mare 1983). The mechanism-based models produce point estimates of $\alpha = 0.010$, $\pi = 0.144$ and $\gamma = -0.620$.

We could stop our analysis here. However, it is likely that several mechanisms are missing from our models (Chaves 1989; Firebaugh and Harley 1991). For example, we do not include variables that capture one's political identity, life course transitions or subjective health, all of which are likely associated with age and might cause religious disaffiliation. Under the CTE we would expect the nonlinear effects of age on the outcome to be zero after adjusting for education. However, statistical significance tests indicate that the CTE is not satisfied: specifically, after adjusting for education, there are still statistically significant nonlinear cohort effects on the

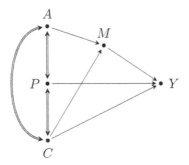

FIGURE 6.14 Mechanism-based model of religious intensity
Notes: This figure displays the graphical model used in the analysis of religious intensity. Unobserved idiosyncratic causes of the mechanism and outcome are omitted for simplicity. The double-headed, double-lined arrows denote the inherently deterministic relationship among the three temporal variables. Filled circles indicate observed variables. It should be noted that this graphical model applies to the linear components. All nonlinear components are included in the corresponding regression models.

outcome. Accordingly, we proceed to conduct a bounding (or sensitivity) analysis. To do so, we assume that the estimate of the mechanism-based age linear effect is an underestimate. Specifically, we assume that the influence of a set of unobserved mechanisms is no greater in absolute value than 20 times the size of the estimated age linear effect operating through education (denoted as the pathway from A to Y via M in Figure 6.14). This assumption is equivalent to claiming that the age linear effect is no less than -0.1857 and no greater than 0.2053. The bounds from this assumption are shown in Figure 6.15. These results reveal that cohort effects dominate in explaining changes in religious disaffiliation, with relatively minor effects of age and period.

Conclusion

Over a century ago, the sociologist Karl Mannheim attempted a reformulation of the problem of generations. In doing so, he outlined a distinctly sociological approach to the problem, rather than one based on what he termed 'positivist' or 'humanist' formulations, neither of which he thought were entirely satisfactory. In this chapter we have attempted a similar reformulation of the problem in its contemporary form, namely, APC analysis. Rather than using a just-identifying constraint to achieve a particular set of APC estimates or advocating for a particular statistical model, our goal has been to outline a general three-stage procedure for conducting APC analysis focused on examining what can be learned from the data without assumptions, using theory to specify bounds and, when variables are available, modeling mechanisms. Our approach is inherently sociological in that it requires thinking about theoretical assumptions at every stage of the analysis.

To summarize our approach, we recommend the following three stage process when conducting an APC analysis, each of which involves a set of smaller steps:

- **Stage 1** (Analysis without assumptions): Learn as much as possible from the data without making assumptions. Determine whether all three APC variables are operative.
  1. *Linearized APC model*: Separate the linear from the nonlinear components using the L-APC model. Using the L-APC, fit a model with the period linear effect fixed to zero.
  2. *Nonlinear effects*: Report the full set of nonlinear effects (e.g., α, π and γ). Because the nonlinear effects are point-identified, they can be visualized using traditional graphical techniques. Conventional significance tests and fit statistics can be applied. If it seems reasonable to conclude that the nonlinear effects for one of the three APC are zero and the CTE assumption seems reasonable, then that variable may be dropped from the model and analysis can proceed using conventional methods.
  3. *Linear effects*: Report the identifiable combinations of linear effects $\theta_1 = \alpha + \pi$ and $\theta_2 = \gamma + \pi$ that determine the location of the canonical solution line in the parameter space. Visualize the canonical solution line using a 2D-APC

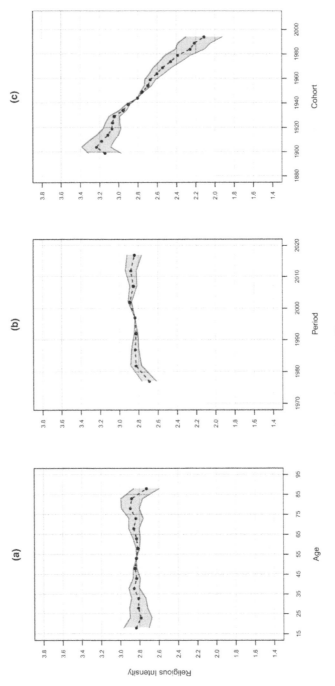

FIGURE 6.15 Religious intensity: upper and lower bounds on APC effects

graph. Consider what combinations of linear APC effects are ruled out by the 2D-APC graph and the location of the canonical solution line.

- **Stage 2** (Partial identification using bounds): Specify a series of bounds using explicit theoretical assumptions about the size, sign and/or shape of the temporal effects. In specifying bounds, one should ask whether there is value in making stronger assumptions to obtain more precise estimates. If not, one is done and should proceed to the next step.

  1. *Constrained 2D-APC graph*: Using the 2D-APC graph, analyze the effects of one's theoretical assumptions on the constraints imposed on the solution line. Are a broad set of parameter effects still plausible? If so, are there additional assumptions that can be defended that might be used to narrow the bounds? Note that it is possible for a set of assumptions to be inconsistent, leading to the whole solution line being excluded.

  2. *Bounds on overall effects*: Plot the bounded total effects for the three APC variables. Are the bounds sufficiently narrow to draw meaningful substantive conclusions? Are additional assumptions needed for this to be the case?

- **Stage 3** (Mechanism-based models of APC effects):

  1. *Mechanism-based models*: Using the observed measures of causes, fit one or more mechanism-based models to obtain point estimates of the temporal effects. Test whether any of the remaining nonlinear effects for the three APC variables are zero.

  2. *Sensitivity analyses*: After fitting mechanism-based models, one should consider conducting a sensitivity analysis with a 2D-APC graph to assess the robustness of findings in the presence of unobserved causal pathways.

The goal of our approach is to clarify what can be learned from the data itself and what can be concluded from data with the incorporation of various theoretical assumptions about the temporal effects. Mechanism-based models are promising in that they can be tested against the data and in many cases are overidentified. We view our approach as an attempt to redefine the problem of APC analysis away from a single identifying constraint to learning as much as possible using the weakest assumptions possible.

The approach outlined here is general, flexible and renders transparent many of the otherwise hidden assumptions of conventional APC models. As is generally the case with new methodologies, there is the question as to whether past substantive findings will be sustained or overturned. This is a critical task for future APC analysis given that many of the methods used have often rested on untested or untestable assumptions. We conjecture that the results will be mixed: when analyses have been driven by strong theory and/or conclusions are primarily based on nonlinear effects, new methods are likely to sustain old findings; when theory is lacking and/or conclusions are based on linear effects then it will be little more than luck if previous findings are not overturned. The important point, however, is that with the ongoing development of new methods, a broad set of new empirical analyses are needed.

Online supplementary material relating to this book can be found at www. routledge.com/9780367174439.

Notes

1 A Shiny program that allows replicating this work and analyzing new data can be found at https://github.com/adeldaoud/WhatIfAPC

2 A linear effect refers to a straight-line relationship, while a nonlinear effect refers to any deviation around this straight-line relationship. For example, a nonlinear effect might appear as an upside-down 'U' shape. The combination of linear and nonlinear effects we refer to as the total effect.

3 We have yet to identify a compelling case where CTE is unlikely to hold, that is, a case where there are linear effects, but no nonlinear effects. The converse situation – in which there is a nonlinear effect, but no linear effect, or what might be called 'trendless fluctuation' – does seem possible.

4 As noted above, numerous solutions to the APC identification problem have been offered over the years. These are not a concern of the present chapter. Detailed discussions can be found in Fosse and Winship (2018; 2019) as well as O'Brien (2015).

5 This conceptualization is close to that of Sen and Wasow's (2016) idea of race (and also gender) as a bundle of underlying causal processes.

6 Critical, although it has been under appreciated in the literature, the APC identification problem is restricted to the linear effects. As Fienberg (2013) has stated: 'The APC problem is a linear effects problem (1982).' We provide intuition for this point below. For a formal proof, see Fosse and Winship (2018).

7 For detailed reviews on the variety of temporal data structures and their associated problems, see the chapters by Yang and Land (2013: 15–53) as well as Mason and Fienberg (1985: 59–67).

8 Additional complications arise when the age and period intervals are not equally spaced, since this can generate artifactual cyclical patterns. For approaches to estimating temporal effects when age and period intervals are unequal, see Holford (2006).

9 Note, however, that calculating the cohorts from an age–period array introduces some ambiguity, since adjacent cohorts will overlap partially (Holford 1983: 311–312). This ambiguity is present even when the age and period groups are of equal width. For example, in Table 6.1 the 1956–1964 cohort overlaps partially with the cohort born during 1961–1969. Narrower age and period intervals will produce a finer grid of cells in the age–period array, but neighboring cohorts will nonetheless overlap to some extent. For instance, if age and period are tabulated into two-year intervals (Tarone and Chu 1996), then those in age 31–32 and period 2000–2001 will be in cohort 1968–1970, while those in age 30–31 and period 2000–2001 will be in the adjoining cohort 1969–1971. The inexactness can be mitigated when all three temporal variables are measured at the individual level, since this will allow for aggregation into nonoverlapping groups, but few datasets include all three variables.

10 Note that 1 is added to $j-i$ so that the cohort index begins at $k = 1$. This ensures that, for example, $i = j = k = 1$ refers to the first group for all three temporal measures. One could just as easily index the cohorts using $k = j - i$, but this identity would be lost.

11 Alternatively, one could fix the parameters at one of the levels to zero. By convention researchers typically fix the first set of levels (e.g., $\alpha_{i=1} = \pi_{j=1} = \gamma_{k=1} = 0$) or the last set (e.g., $\alpha_{i=I} = \pi_{j=J} = \gamma_{k=K} = 0$), although another set could be chosen to satisfy the constraints.

12 This is reflected in the null vector of the L-APC, which consists of $[1, -1, 1]$ for the age, period and cohort slopes, respectively, and a set of zeros for the nonlinearities. In fact, the basic linear model of Equation 6.2 is just a special case of the L-APC model. Referring to our example, note that we can replace the intervals in Table 6.1 with single values, such as the midpoint of each category, to obtain the array shown in Table 6.2. For

example, we can replace the 30–34 age interval with the midpoint 32, the 2000–2004 period interval with the midpoint 2002, and the 1966–1974 cohort interval with the midpoint 1970.

13 A simple linear transformation can be used to convert age_i to $i - i*$, since $i - i* = (age_i - age*)/(\Delta age)$, where $age*$ is the midpoint for all age groups and Δage is the fixed difference between the midpoints. For example, referring to Table 6.2 we have $age_1 = 32$, $age_2 = 37$, $age_3 = 42$, $age_4 = 47$ and $age_5 = 52$. The midpoint across all age groups is 42 and the fixed difference for the groups is 5. Thus, for example, we can calculate that for $age_1 = 32$, the transformed $age_1 = (32 - 42)/5 = -2$ which is equivalent to $i - i* = 1 - 3 = -2$.

14 For simplicity of exposition we treat this as a continuous variable and thus our estimates are based on classical linear regression models. We obtain similar results using ordinal or multinomial logistic regression models.

15 We fix the period linear effect to zero when estimating the predicted values of the outcome.

16 We note that there are, in fact, assumptions involved regarding sum-to-zero constraints and the additive nature of the classical APC model. However, these assumptions are relatively minor.

17 For visualization purposes we have dropped the first two cohort groups and last cohort group from the graphs. These groups are sparse, each consisting of 120 or fewer respondents.

18 Note that there is still an identification problem in the sense that one must assume, based on the principle of CTE, that the linear effect of the dropped variable is not operative. This assumption about the linear effects cannot be tested due to the identification problem.

19 Note that the cohort categories are unbalanced in two senses: first, there are fewer individual-level observations in the tails of the cohort categories; second, there are fewer age-period categories in the corners of the Lexis table. Both of these can result in greater imprecision of the cohort categories despite relatively large effect sizes of the nonlinearities.

20 The same dataset of APC variables can have any number of solution lines depending on how the variables are coded (Fosse and Winship 2018). However, in general these various solution lines can be expressed in their most basic form in terms of three dimensions, or what we call the canonical solution line.

21 Note that this discussion provides another way of thinking about the signed regions described in the previous section.

22 The question is as follows: "Which statement do you agree more with?" The answer consisted of two choices. The first choice is: "The younger generation should be taught by their elders to do what is right." The second choice is: "The younger generation should be taught to think for themselves even though they may do something their elders disapprove of."

References

Alwin, Duane F. (Oct. 1991). "Family of Origin and Cohort Differences in Verbal Ability". *American Sociological Review* 56 (5), pp. 625–638.

Chaves, Mark (1989). "Secularization and Religious Revival: Evidence from US Church Attendance Rates, 1972–1986". *Journal for the Scientific Study of Religion* 28 (4), pp. 464–477.

Chen, Xinguang et al. (2003). "Secular Trends in Adolescents Never Smoking from 1990 to 1999 in California: An Age-period-cohort Analysis". *American Journal of Public Health* 93 (12), pp. 2099–2104.

Clark, April K. and Marie A. Eisenstein (2013). "Interpersonal Trust: An Age–Period–Cohort Analysis Revisited". *Social Science Research* 42 (2), pp. 361–375.

Clayton, D. and E. Schifflers (1987). "Models for Temporal Variation in Cancer Rates. II: Age–period–cohort models". *Statistics in Medicine* 6 (4), pp. 469–481.

Clogg, Clifford C. (1982). "Cohort Analysis of Recent Trends in Labor Force Participation". *Demography* 19 (4), p. 459.

Diouf, Ibrahima et al. (2010). "Evolution of Obesity Prevalence in France: An Age-Period-Cohort Analysis". *Epidemiology* 21 (3): 360.

Duncan, Otis Dudley (1985). "Generations, Cohorts, and Conformity". In Mason, William M and Gienberg, Stephen E (eds), *Cohort Analysis in Social Research*. New York: Springer: 289–321.

Fosse, Ethan and Christopher Winship (2018). "Moore–Penrose Estimators of Age–Period–Cohort Effects: Their Interrelationship and Properties". *Sociological Science* 5 (14), pp. 304–334.

Fienberg, Stephen E. (2013). "Cohort Analysis' Unholy Quest: A Discussion". *Demography* 50 (6), pp. 1981–1984.

Firebaugh, Glenn and Brian Harley (1991). "Trends in U.S. Church Attendance: Secularization and Revival, or Merely Lifecycle Effects?" *Journal for the Scientific Study of Religion* 30 (4), pp. 487–500.

Fosse, Ethan and Christopher Winship (2019). "Analyzing Age-Period-Cohort Data: A Review and Critique". *Annual Review of Sociology* (45), pp. 467–492.

Frost, Wade Hampton (1995). "The Age Selection of Mortality from Tuberculosis in Successive Decades". *American Journal of Epidemiology* 141 (1), pp. 4–9.

Fu, Qiang and Kenneth C. Land (2015). "The Increasing Prevalence of Overweight and Obesity of Children and Youth in China, 1989–2009: An Age–Period–Cohort Analysis". *Population Research and Policy Review* 34 (6), pp. 901–921.

Goldberger, Arthur Stanley (1991). *A Course in Econometrics*. Cambridge, MA: Harvard University Press.

Hauser, Robert M. and Min-Hsiung Huang (1997). "Verbal Ability and Socioeconomic Success: A Trend Analysis". *Social Science Research* 26 (3), pp. 331–376.

Holford, Theodore R. (1983). "The Estimation of Age, Period and Cohort Effects for Vital Rates". *Biometrics* 39 (2), p. 311.

——— (2006). "Approaches to Fitting Age-Period-Cohort Models with Unequal Intervals". *Statistics in Medicine* 25 (6), pp. 977–993.

Hout, Michael and David Knoke (1975). "Change in Voting Turnout, 1952–1972". *Public Opinion Quarterly* 39 (1), pp. 52–68.

Keiding, Niels (2011). "Age-Period-Cohort Analysis in the 1870s: Diagrams, Stereograms, and the Basic Differential Equation". *Canadian Journal of Statistics*, 39 (3), pp. 405–420.

Kerr, William C. et al. (2004). "Age, Period and Cohort Influences on Beer, Wine and Spirits Consumption Trends in the US National Alcohol Surveys". *Addiction* 99 (9), pp. 1111–1120.

Lavori, Philip W. et al. (1987). "Age-Period-Cohort Analysis of Secular Trends in Onset of Major Depression: Findings in Siblings of Patients with Major Affective Disorder". *Journal of Psychiatric Research* 21 (1), pp. 23–35.

Liu, S. et al. (2001). "Increasing Thyroid Cancer Incidence in Canada, 1970–1996: Time Trends and Age-Period-Cohort Effects". *British Journal of Cancer* 85 (9), p. 1335.

Mason, Karen Oppenheim, William M. Mason, et al. (1973). "Some Methodological Issues in Cohort Analysis of Archival Data". *American Sociological Review* 38 (2), p. 242.

Mason, William M. and Stephen E. Fienberg, eds. (1985). *Cohort Analysis in Social Research.* New York, NY: Springer New York.

O'Brien, Robert (2015). *Age-Period-Cohort Models: Approaches and Analyses with Aggregate Data.* Boca Raton, FL: CRC Press.

O'Malley, Patrick M., Jerald G. Bachman, and Lloyd D. Johnston (1984). "Period, Age, and Cohort Effects on Substance Use among American Youth, 1976–82." *American Journal of Public Health* 74 (7), pp. 682–688.

Pilcher, Jane (1994). "Mannheim's Sociology of Generations: An Undervalued Legacy". *The British Journal of Sociology* 45 (3), pp. 481–495.

Putnam, Robert D. (1995). "Tuning in, Tuning out: The Strange Disappearance of Social Capital in America". *PS: Political Science & Politics* 28 (4), pp. 664–683.

Robinson, Robert V. and Elton F. Jackson (2001). "Is Trust in Others Declining in America? An Age–Period–Cohort Analysis". *Social Science Research* 30 (1), pp. 117–145.

Rodgers, Willard L. (1982). "Estimable Functions of Age, Period, and Cohort Effects". *American Sociological Review* 47 (6), pp. 774–787.

——— (1990). "Interpreting the Components of Time Trends". *Sociological Methodology* 20, p. 421.

Ryder, Norman B. (1965). "The Cohort as a Concept in the Study of Social Change". *American Sociological Review* 30 (6), pp. 843–861.

Schwadel, Philip and Michael Stout (2012). "Age, Period and Cohort Effects on Social Capital". *Social Forces* 91 (1), pp. 233–252.

Sen, Maya and Omar Wasow (2016). "Race as a Bundle of Sticks: Designs that Estimate Effects of Seemingly Immutable Characteristics". *Annual Review of Political Science* 19, pp. 499–522.

Tarone, R. E. and K. C. Chu (1996). "Evaluation of Birth Cohort Patterns in Population Disease Rates". *American Journal of Epidemiology* 143 (1), pp. 85–91.

Tilley, James and Geoffrey Evans (2014). "Ageing and Generational Effects on Vote Choice: Combining Cross-sectional and Panel Data to Estimate APC Effects". *Electoral Studies* 33, pp. 19–27.

Vedøy, Tord F. (2014). "Tracing the Cigarette Epidemic: An Age-Period-Cohort Study of Education, Gender and Smoking Using a Pseudo-panel Approach". *Social Science Research* 48, pp. 35–47.

Wilson, James A. and Walter R. Gove (1999). "The Age-Period-Cohort Conundrum and Verbal Ability: Empirical Relationships and Their Interpretation: Reply to Glenn and to Alwin and McCammon". *American Sociological Review* 64 (2), pp. 287–302.

Winship, Christopher and David J. Harding (2008). "A Mechanism-Based Approach to the Identification of Age–Period–Cohort Models". *Sociological Methods and Research* 36 (3), pp. 362–401.

Winship, Christopher and Robert D. Mare (1983). "Structural Equations and Path Analysis for Discrete Data". *The American Journal of Sociology* 89 (1), pp. 54–110.

Yang, Yang (2008). "Social Inequalities in Happiness in the United States, 1972 to 2004: An Age-Period-Cohort Analysis". *American Sociological Review* 73 (2), pp. 204–226.

Yang, Yang and Kenneth C. Land (2013). *Age-Period-Cohort Analysis: New Models, Methods, and Empirical Applications.* Boca Raton, FL: Chapman and Hall/CRC.

7

MODELING FACTORS AFFECTING AGE, PERIOD AND COHORT TRENDS

The effect of cigarette smoking on lung cancer trends

Theodore R. Holford

Introduction

Temporal disease trends are driven by causal factors that are themselves changing over time. A time scale is measured in reference to a starting point, so the choice of scale should be based on the mechanism for the causal agent affecting outcome. Age, for example, measures time from birth so that changes in disease risk that result from the aging process can be captured to some extent by introducing age into a model used for analysis. If there are also exposure changes that affect all ages in much the same way, then we might expect these to be manifested as period effects on trend. Likewise, if the changes only affect individuals of an age group and not the entire population, then these effects can be represented as birth cohort effects.

Age–period–cohort models are useful at the early stages of trying to understand the causes of an outcome. If the trend is primarily due to a period effect, then we would primarily consider factors that affect all ages at the same time. Likewise, if trend is more closely related to birth cohort then better candidates for causal agents would be generational exposures that are often set early in life. These scenarios occur early in the research process when little is known about causes of the trends observed for an outcome. However, it is also useful to consider these trends after knowledge has advanced so that one can quantify the extent to which an identified factor can account for the observed trends. In this chapter I describe how age–period–cohort models can be extended to include the effect of exposure on the outcome that has been determined from analytical studies and assess the extent to which this knowledge accounts for the observed trends. This can not only suggest further areas of study to understand better what is not known, but it can also provide a framework that can be used to quantify programs intended to control the outcome.

Lung cancer provides an example of the use of age–period–cohort ideas to first get clues to a growing epidemic and then to use that knowledge to plan for controlling it. By the mid-1900s, lung cancer rates had been steadily growing, but the reasons for that growth were not well understood. Evidence emerged for a strong association with cigarette smoking. The Surgeon General of the U.S. produced a report bringing together evidence for this effect, one of the first being a demonstration of trend being more plausibly associated with birth cohort and not period (Surgeon General's Advisory Committee on Smoking and Health 1964). This was not the result of fitting a statistical model, but an interpretation of a graphical display. Nevertheless, it indicated a factor that affected birth cohorts differently, which was consistent with the way in which cigarettes were introduced to the population. In men, for instance, cigarettes were distributed for free to those enlisted for military service. This was a birth cohort effect because enlistees were the appropriate age for enlistment because of their date of birth. The Surgeon General's Report further documented the research showing the link between smoking and lung cancer risk, and the evidence now is well established (Surgeon General's Advisory Committee on Smoking and Health 1964; Doll and Peto 1981; US Department of Health and Human Services 2014).

Fitting age–period–cohort models to lung cancer incidence or mortality data has confirmed the conclusions of a predominate cohort effect on these trends for lung cancer (Roush, Schymura, Holford et al. 1985; Roush, Holford, Schymura, and White 1987; Zheng et al. 1994). The trends that are observed are consistent with smoking initiation occurring in the late teens or early 20s which results in trends with birth cohort that have resulted from effective promotions by cigarette manufacturers. In U.S. men, large changes in smoking resulted from free distribution of cigarettes to the military during World Wars I and II, and in women by advertising directed at those seeking gender equality during the 1960s and 1970s. Although period effects were much smaller, they were not entirely absent, and they could have resulted from anti-smoking campaigns or changes in the manufacturing process. These inferences provided a qualitative rationale for observed trends, but they do not make use of the vast literature of analytical studies that have quantified the association between cigarette smoking and lung cancer mortality risk.

In this chapter we explore ways to use the knowledge gained in quantifying the effect of exposure trends on the disease. This will be illustrated using lung cancer as the outcome and cigarette smoking as the primary exposure affecting those trends. The effect of smoking on cancer can emerge years after exposure. Hence, it is essential to obtain details of exposure, including when the practice was started, what dose was used, and when a person quit. This can be a challenge in that surveys typically obtain status cross-sectionally and not longitudinally. One must reconstruct the experience of individuals as best one can using survey data that are available. The data are then used in a carcinogenesis model to generate estimates of the effect of exposure on the outcome.

Estimates of the outcome expected from exposure trends and a carcinogenesis model can be compared to observed trends using the age–period–cohort framework. This can point to limitations that may result from imperfections in the exposure data, or the carcinogenesis model. In addition, it provides a method for calibrating the estimates, so that they are consistent with what is observed in the population.

Method for describing the effect of exposure in a population

To quantitatively describe the relationship between exposure and disease risk it is essential to have a model that includes the relevant exposure characteristics and to also have necessary detail in exposure history for the population. I first describe a model for the relationship between smoking and lung cancer risk, and in the following section I describe an approach for estimating the smoking history characteristics required to use this model.

Disease model

Using data from Cancer Prevention Study-1 (CPS-1) conducted by the American Cancer Society, Garfinkel (1985) and Knoke, Burns, and Thun (2008) developed a model for the effect of smoking on lung cancer risk. As a follow-up study, the model provided estimates of lung cancer mortality rates as a function of age at initiation, age at cessation and smoking intensity. The model described death rates from lung cancer for never (N), current (C) and former (F) smokers as a function of age, age at initiation and age at cessation.

For never smokers, the death rate in males at age t is given by

$$\lambda_N(t) = \alpha_N t^{\beta_N} \tag{7.1}$$

Parameters were estimated using a log transformation of the rate, giving rise to a log-linear model in which the number of deaths was assumed to have a Poisson distribution, yielding $\hat{\alpha}_N = 9.21 \times 10^{-13}$ and $\hat{\beta}_N = 4.60$.

A current smoker who began smoking at age τ_0 will have smoked for $(t - \tau_0)$ years, and the smoking intensity is d. The increase in risk of lung cancer mortality over never smokers is given by

$$\Delta\lambda_C(t, \tau_0, d) = \alpha_C t^{\beta_C} d^{\gamma_C} (t - \tau_0)^{\delta_C}$$

Estimates of model parameters are $\hat{\alpha}_C = 1.51 \times 10^{-13}$, $\hat{\beta}_C = 2.38$, $\hat{\gamma}_C = 0.867$ and $\hat{\delta}_C = 2.87$. The overall death rate for current smokers is then given by

$$\begin{aligned} \lambda_C(t, \tau_0, d) &= \lambda_N(t) + \Delta\lambda_C(t, \tau_0, d) \\ &= \alpha_N t^{\beta_N} + \alpha_C t^{\beta_C} d^{\gamma_C} (t - \tau_0)^{\delta_C} \end{aligned} \tag{7.2}$$

Former smokers did not reveal strong evidence of an association with smoking intensity, so this was not included in the analysis. The model used for this group was for the proportional change in the excess rate for current smokers, which was found to depend on the age an individual quit, τ_1, and time since quitting, $(t - \tau_1)$. This function is given by

$$\phi_F\left(t, \tau_1\right) = \exp\left\{-\left(\alpha_F + \beta_F \tau_1\right)\left(t - \tau_1 - 2\right)\right\}$$

with parameter estimates $\hat{\alpha}_F = 0.274$ and $\hat{\beta}_F = -0.00279$. Thus, the mortality rate for former smokers is given by

$$\lambda_F\left(t, \tau_0, \tau_1\right) = \lambda_N\left(t\right) + \phi_F\left(t, \tau_1\right)\Delta\lambda_C\left(t, \tau_0, \cdot\right) \tag{7.3}$$

where $\lambda_C\left(t, \tau_1, \cdot\right)$ represents the rate among current smokers, that is, combining the rates over the distribution of smoking intensities.

Figure 7.1 shows lung cancer mortality rates by age for different smoking history patterns using the Knoke model. Age at initiation has a huge effect on subsequent lung cancer mortality, and the advantage gained by smoking cessation is large, but it can take years to develop. The level of smoking also has a sizeable effect on risk, although the magnitude of that effect is smaller than the effect of age at initiation. To quantify the overall effect of smoking on lung cancer mortality, it is essential that

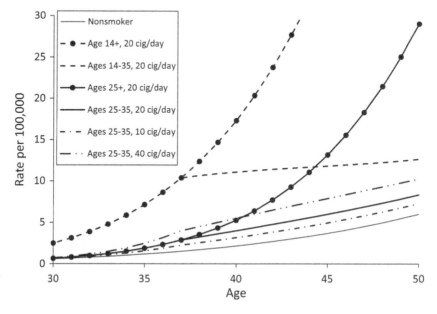

FIGURE 7.1 Lung cancer death rate by age for alternative smoking scenarios using the model described by Knoke, Burns, and Thun (2008)

one has details on dates of initiation and cessation, as well as smoking intensity. For the population, one must have a detailed smoking history summary for individuals. Prevalence of never, current, and former smokers are needed as a function of age, period, and cohort. Initiation and cessation rates are also needed, along with the distribution of smoking intensities.

Exposure trends

The U.S. National Cancer Institute's Cancer Intervention and Surveillance Modeling Network (CISNET) develops population models for cancer that can be used to assess intervention programs that control cancer mortality. The lung group used their models to assess the effect of tobacco control following the Surgeon General's Report (Surgeon General's Advisory Committee on Smoking and Health 1964; Warner 1989; Moolgavkar et al. 2012; Jeon et al. 2018). A variety of different models was used by different groups in the program, but all shared a common set of smoking histories derived from the National Health Interview Survey (NHIS) (Jeon et al. 2012; Holford et al. 2014). Age–period–cohort models were applied to the smoking survey data to obtain estimates of smoking histories, including smoking prevalence, duration and intensity, which were then entered into a carcinogenesis model to obtain estimates of lung cancer mortality.

A compartment model that characterizes a typical smoking history is shown in Figure 7.2, in which a subject begins to smoke after which they may quit. Of course, individuals may be withdrawn or die before these transitions, so the analysis must allow for this. Figure 7.2 oversimplifies what can be a much more complex reality, but it does provide a useful characterization of the experience for most of the population. Smoking cessation can be especially difficult to characterize because it is often not successful on the first attempt. We adopted the rule that subjects who report quitting must have done so at least two years before the interview, otherwise their period of observation is regarded as being truncated at age interviewed.

Let t represent age, b period and c cohort, all three potentially playing a role in smoking history. These temporal indicators are related by $c = b - t$, so we can, without loss of generality, represent them as functions of age and cohort. Data

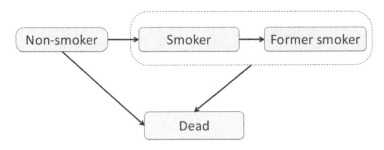

FIGURE 7.2 Compartments considered in developing smoking history

were only obtained for a restricted range of ages, $t \in \left[\underline{t}, \dot{t} \right]$, and periods, $b \in \left[\underline{b}, \dot{b} \right]$, so that the earliest cohort would be $\underline{c} = \underline{b} - \dot{t}$ and the latest $\dot{c} = \dot{b} - \underline{t}$. Available data for a given cohort c would cover an age range that would vary by cohort, that is, $t \in \left[\underline{b} - c, \dot{b} - c \right]$. To fill in smoking history that was not represented in a survey, we represent each temporal effect as a nonparametric function.

In this example, we use mortality data from 1969 to 2010 for ages 35 to 84, which involves birth cohorts 1885 to 1975. Smoking histories were obtained from NHIS conducted from 1965 to 2015. The earliest birth cohort for mortality, 1885, is represented in the 1965 survey by subjects aged 80 and older. Because survey participants must be at least 18, the latest cohort in 2015 was born in 1997, and they would have had a very short smoking history up to that point. Initiation generally occurs around age 20, which is better represented in recent cohorts, but cessation takes place over the lifespan, which is better represented in older ages by earlier cohorts. NHIS surveys have obtained data during different epochs of life, so it was necessary to extrapolate beyond the range of observed data to obtain the lifetime histories for a cohort.

Cross-sectional estimates of ever smokers

For the survey years, 1965–2015, participants provided information to estimate prevalence of ever smokers by age t, for the corresponding cohort. Let Y_i be 1 if the ith individual ever smoked and 0 otherwise, where the probability of the response is a function of age and cohort, $P_E(t,c)$, which is parameterized using a linear logistic model:

$$\text{logit}\left\{ P_E(t,c) \right\} = \beta_0 + \beta_a(t) + \beta_c(c)$$

where β_0 is an intercept and $\beta.(\cdot)$ is a constrained natural spline for age and cohort (Durrleman and Simon 1989). The model was fitted using PROC SURVEYLOGISTIC in SAS® with age knots (40, 50, 60, 70) and cohort knots (1910, 1920, 1930, 1940, 1950, 1960, 1965, 1970, 1980, 1985). This allowed for the inclusion of the survey weights in the analysis. We assumed that the cohort effect remained constant for those born after 1990. Values used for subsequent cohorts were set to be identical to those for the 1990 birth cohort. Figure 7.3 shows estimates for male ever-smoker prevalence by cohort obtained from this cross-sectional analysis along with the estimates from an analysis of the calibrated initiation probabilities described in the following section.

Smoking initiation probability

Smoking initiation probability, $p(t,c)$, is the conditional probability of smoking initiation at age t for cohort c, if not a smoker at $t-1$, that is,

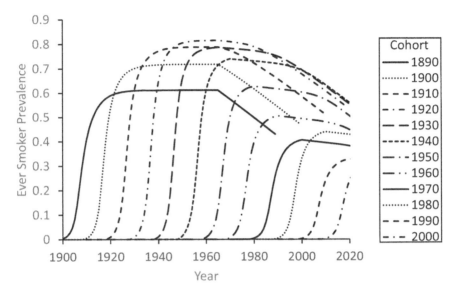

FIGURE 7.3 Ever-smoker prevalence estimates by year and by birth cohort for U.S. males

$$p(t,c) = \Pr\left\{\text{Smoker at } t \,\middle|\, \text{Not smoker at } (t-1), c\right\}.$$

It is related to the cumulative proportion of ever smokers if mortality does not vary by smoking status:

$$
\begin{aligned}
P_{\mathrm{E}}(t,c) &= 1 - \prod_{i=1}^{t}\left[1 - p(i,c)\right] \\
&= 1 - \left[1 - P_{\mathrm{E}}(t-1,c)\right]\left[1 - p(t,c)\right]
\end{aligned}
\tag{7.4}
$$

where $P_{\mathrm{E}}(0,c) = 0$.

Equation 7.4 would apply if probabilities of remaining alive for smokers and nonsmokers were equal. However, smokers have higher mortality so that the observed prevalence of ever smokers is $P_{\mathrm{E}}^{*}(t,c) \leq P_{\mathrm{E}}(t,c)$. Initiation probabilities would be similarly affected, and we represent the estimate from the time an individual is surveyed by $p^{*}(t,c) = p(t,c)/C_{p}$, where $p(t,c)$ is the probability of initiation at the time of occurrence and $C_{p} \geq 1$ is a correction factor. We assume that differential mortality among smoking categories has little effect early in life and that the impact intensifies with age. Cohorts born before 1935 would only have survey data for ages over 30, when one might expect differential mortality to begin to introduce substantial bias in the unadjusted estimate, $\hat{p}^{*}(t,c)$. In recent cohorts, almost all smoking initiation occurred before age 30, but for those born early in the twentieth century it was not uncommon for initiation to occur later in life, especially in women. Later smoking initiation would also tend to postpone the effect of differential mortality in the cohort. We assumed that the differential mortality resulting from cigarette smoking occurred at ages, $t \geq t_0$, and $P_E^*(t,c) = P_E(t,c)$ for $t < t_0$. Initiation probabilities corrected for differential mortality can be found by solving a restructured Equation 7.4:

$$P_E(t_0,c) = 1 - \prod_{i=1}^{t_0}\left[1 - C_p p^*(i,c)\right] \tag{7.5}$$

for C_p, that is, by matching the cumulative initiation rates to the estimated cross-sectional prevalence at age t_0. We assume that t_0 is the age at the first survey in 1965 or 30, whichever was older.

Unadjusted estimates of annual age-specific smoking initiation probabilities for a given cohort, $\hat{p}^*(t,c)$, are derived from NHIS data. For an individual reporting initiation at age t_0, a response is created in which $Y(t) = 0$ for $t < t_0$, and $Y(t_0) = 1$ otherwise. An age–period–cohort model was fitted in which

$$\text{logit}\left\{p^*(t,c)\right\} = \beta_0 + \beta_t(t) + \beta_b(b) + \beta_c(c)$$

where β_0 is an intercept and $\beta.(\cdot)$ are constrained natural splines. We were only interested in fitted values, which are not affected by the identifiability problem. Knots were specified as (10, 13, 16, 19, 22) for age, (1910, 1920, 1930, 1940, 1950, 1960, 1970, 1980, 1990, 2000) for period, and (1910, 1920, 1930, 1940, 1945, 1950, 1955, 1960, 1965, 1970, 1975, 1980, 1990) for cohort.

Age for determining the correction factor was age in 1965 or 30, whichever was older, that is, $t^* = \max\left\{1965 - c, 30\right\}$. The target is the estimate from the cross-sectional estimate of ever-smoker prevalence. The correction factor was found by solving:

$$\hat{P}_E(t^*,c) = 1 - \prod_{i=1}^{t^*}\left[1 - \hat{C}_p \hat{p}^*(t,c)\right]$$

for $\hat{C}_p$, yielding the corrected estimate of initiation probabilities, $\hat{C}_p \hat{p}(t,c)$.

Figure 7.3 shows the corrected male ever-smoker prevalence that made use of the cumulative initiation probabilities that were calibrated before t^* and the cross-sectional estimates after t^*. The highest prevalence occurs at age 30, and the peak increases until the 1920 birth cohort when it is about 0.8. Since then, the peak has declined to about 0.4. Smoking initiation probabilities are shown in Figure 7.4. The

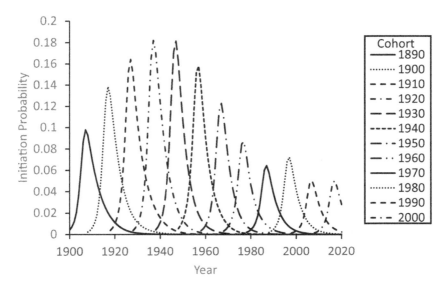

FIGURE 7.4 Yearly smoking initiation probabilities by year and by birth cohort for U.S. males

peak occurs around age 17 and approaches 0.0 by age 30. The highest initiation probabilities occurred for males born around 1920.

Smoking cessation probability

Smoking cessation, assumed to be a function of age for each cohort, is the probability of quitting, conditional on being a smoker:

$$q(t,c) = \Pr\left\{\text{Former smoker at } t \middle| \text{Smoker at } (t-1), c\right\}.$$

We assumed that $q(t,c) = 0$ for $t < 15$ and estimated for $15 \leq t \leq 99$. The cumulative proportion of smokers in cohort c who had not ceased smoking by age t is given by:

$$Q(t,c) = \prod_{i=15}^{t}\left[1 - q(i,c)\right] \tag{7.6}$$

For simplicity, we assumed this quantity did not depend on the age an individual started smoking, the number of cigarettes per day or other factors. Because initiation tends to occur in a narrow age range, variation in age of initiation becomes less of a factor affecting mortality as a cohort gets older. Introducing intensity of smoking into a model for cessation would require detailed lifetime histories of smoking which were not obtained by NHIS. An individual was identified as having quit smoking if they had not smoked for two years. Because of the two-year lag, an individual who reports cessation at age $t-2$ or later could not be classified but only truncated at that age.

If reported age of cessation was younger than 8, it was set to 8. For each year of age following smoking, a binary response was created based on our definition of quitting. Yearly estimates from a linear logistic that included age and cohort effects was used where

$$\text{logit}\left\{q(t,c)\right\} = \beta_0 + t\beta_t + \beta_c(c) + t\beta_c(c)$$

where β_0 is an intercept, β_t the slope for age, and $\beta_c(\cdot)$ a constrained natural spline for cohort. Knots for cohort were (1920, 1930, 1935, 1940, 1943, 1946, 1949). After age 80, the cessation probabilities were constrained to remain constant because they are not reliable. For these ages, the prevalence of current smokers is low, so the constraint has little impact on estimates of current smoker prevalence. Estimates of cessation probabilities are shown in Figure 7.5. Conditional cessation probabilities were used to generate the cumulative probabilities of not quitting, $\hat{Q}(t,c)$, using Equation 7.6.

Current, former and never-smoker prevalence

Current smokers represent ever smokers who have not quit, and given our assumption that this only depends on age for a given cohort, the prevalence is

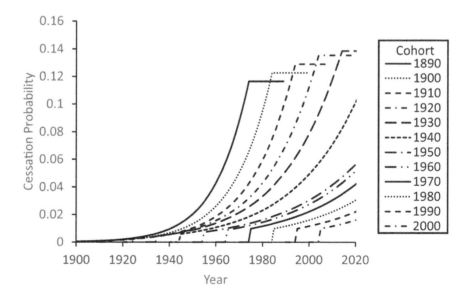

FIGURE 7.5 Yearly smoking cessation probabilities by year and by birth cohort for U.S. males

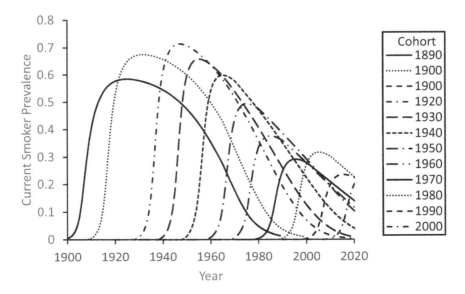

FIGURE 7.6 Current-smoker prevalence estimates by year and by birth cohort for U.S. males

$$P_C(t,c) = P_E(t,c)Q(t,c)$$

as shown in Figure 7.6.

Former smokers are those who have smoked at some point in their lives, but quit before age t:

$$P_F(t,c) = P_E(t,c) - P_C(t,c)$$
$$= P_E(t,c)[1 - Q(t,c)]$$

Finally, the proportion of cohort c who have never smoked is the complement of those who ever smoked:

$$P_N(t,c) = 1 - P_E(t,c)$$

For a given age and cohort, the sets of current, former, and never smokers are exhaustive, that is:

$$P_C(t,c) + P_F(t,c) + P_N(t,c) = 1$$

Cigarettes smoked per day

Reports of the number of cigarettes smoked per day showed extremely high digit preference, especially concentrated at half or whole U.S. packs. Therefore, dose was analyzed as an ordered categorical response with half pack being at the center of the category, which was also usually the mode and close to the mean. Intervals (approximate mean for the interval) employed were: CPD ≤ 5 (3); 5 < CPD ≤ 15 (10); 15 < CPD ≤ 25 (20); 25 < CPD ≤ 35 (30); 35 < CPD ≤ 45 (40); and 45 < CPD (60). A cumulative logistic model was fitted to the data using PROC SURVEYLOGISTIC in SAS® with age, period and cohort represented by additive constrained natural splines with knots (25, 30, 35, 40, 45, 50, 55, 60, 65, 70) for age, (1970, 1975, 1980, 1985, 2000, 2005) for period and (1930, 1940, 1950, 1960, 1970, 1980) for cohort. The fitted estimates of probabilities for each category of smoking dose were used to estimate the distribution in the population. Estimates for cohorts born before 1920 were constrained to be the same as 1920. Similarly, cohorts born after 1985 were constrained to be identical to the 1985 cohort.

Using the approximate mean for each interval, mean number of cigarettes smoked per day was estimated using the distribution for the categories, shown in Figure 7.7. For those born early in the century, the number increases before declining in later ages, but the pattern for recent birth cohorts is quite flat.

Estimating population rates using exposure data

The first step in obtaining model-based estimates of mortality is to use the distribution of relevant exposure history parameters to combine the mix that has been

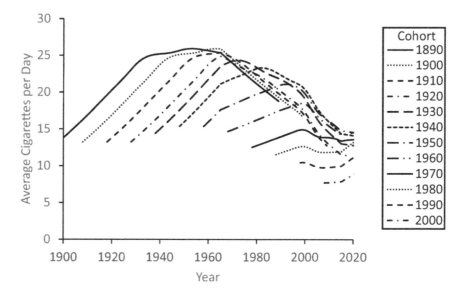

FIGURE 7.7 Estimated average cigarettes smoked per day by year and by birth cohort for U.S. males

estimated using the survey data. These estimates will then need to be calibrated so the values correspond to the observed rates. The adjustment is needed to allow for limitations in the model and exposure estimates, so that the values obtained using the model correspond to what is observed in the population.

Model-based estimate of rates

To determine the probability of lung-cancer death based on this carcinogenesis model, one first considers the probability within each smoking history category. The probability that a never smoker dies of lung cancer at age t is given in Equation 7.1.

For a current smoker, the probability of death from lung cancer depends on the distribution of dose and exposure times. Let $p_d(i|t,c)$ be the probability that an individual age t in cohort c is using category i cigarettes per day. To obtain the distribution of age at initiation, $\tau_0 < t$, use the estimates of the conditional initiation probabilities, giving the cumulative distribution function as

$$F_I(\tau_0|t,c) = 1 - \left[1 - F_I(\tau_0 - 1|t,c)\right]\left[1 - p(\tau_0 - 1|t,c)\right]$$

This yields the probability density function for initiation times:

$$f_I(\tau_0|t,c) = \frac{F_I(\tau_0|t,c) - F_I(\tau_0 - 1|t,c)}{F_I(t|t,c)}$$

Assuming independence of dose and initiation times, and the conditional probability of lung-cancer death from the carcinogenesis model in Equation 7.2, yields the estimated lung-cancer rate for current smokers:

$$\lambda_C(t,c) = \sum_{\tau_0=0}^{t}\sum_{i=1}^{6} p_D(i|t,c) f_I(\tau_0|t,c) \lambda_C(t,\tau_0,i) \tag{7.7}$$

Former-smoker mortality uses the distribution of cessation times among current smokers who began at age τ_0. Using the cumulative cessation probabilities given in Equation 7.6, the probability density of cessation at age τ_1, conditional on when they started, is

$$f_C(\tau_1|t,\tau_0,c) = \frac{F_C(\tau_1|t,\tau_0,c) - F_I(\tau - 1|t,\tau_0,c)}{F_I(t|t,c) - F_I(\tau_0|t,c)} \tag{7.8}$$

Using the distributions of cessation times, initiation times, smoking intensity and the conditional rate of lung cancer deaths yields the lung cancer mortality rate for former smokers:

$$\lambda_F(t,c) = \sum_{\tau_0=0}^{t} \sum_{\tau_1=\tau_0}^{t} \sum_{i=1}^{6} p_D(i|t,c) f_I(\tau_0|t,c) f_C(\tau_1|t,\tau_0,c) \lambda_F(t,\tau_0,\tau_1,i) \qquad (7.9)$$

In the previous section, the approach for estimating the smoking prevalence is described and these are used here to estimate the lung cancer mortality rates for the population based on the carcinogenesis model:

$$\lambda(t,c) = P_N(t,c)\lambda_N(t,c) + P_C(t,c)\lambda_C(t,c) + P_F(t,c)\lambda_F(t,c) \qquad (7.10)$$

Figure 7.8 shows estimates of male age-specific lung cancer mortality rates using the Knoke carcinogenesis model along with the corresponding observed rates for the U.S. While the patterns are somewhat similar, there are clearly large differences between the estimates. The differences cannot be attributed to a scale shift, but they vary with age, period, and cohort. Reasons for these discrepancies may be inadequacies in the carcinogenesis model, which was derived by fitting a model to data from the large American Cancer Society cohort. This was a single cohort which would not capture generational changes in risk that may have occurred. In addition, limitations in the exposure history estimates may result in inaccurate estimates of features that are most relevant for risk. Intensity was only determined at a single interview and, more broadly, the smoking history data from NHIS are not longitudinal.

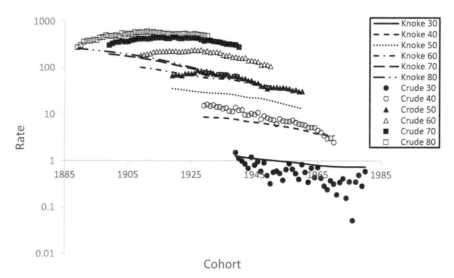

FIGURE 7.8 Lung cancer mortality rates for U.S. males estimated using the Knoke model and observed, 1969–2010

Age–period–cohort calibration of model estimate

When there are apparent limitations to this carcinogenesis model, the age–period–cohort framework offers a way to adjust estimates so that there is better agreement between fitted and observed estimates of lung cancer rates. An age–period–cohort model to accomplish this is:

$$\lambda^{*}\left(t,p,c\right) = \lambda\left(t,c\right)\exp\left\{\mu + \alpha\left(t\right) + \pi\left(b\right) + \gamma\left(c\right)\right\}$$
$$= \exp\left\{\mu + \alpha\left(t\right) + \pi\left(b\right) + \gamma\left(c\right) + \log\lambda\left(t,c\right)\right\} \tag{7.11}$$

where $\lambda^{*}\left(t,b,c\right)$ is the adjusted estimate of the mortality rate and $\lambda\left(t,c\right)$ is the unadjusted rate obtained using Equation 7.10. The adjustment takes the form of an age–period–cohort model, and it includes an overall scale or intercept, μ, an age effect, $\alpha\left(t\right)$, a period effect, $\pi\left(b\right)$, and a cohort effect, $\gamma\left(c\right)$. This model can be expressed in the form of a generalized linear model with an offset, $\log\lambda\left(t,c\right)$.

The observed number of lung cancer deaths is assumed to have a Poisson distribution with mean $N\left(t,b,c\right)\lambda^{*}\left(t,b,c\right)$, where $N\left(t,b,c\right)$ is the population size. As a response, we use the rate, $Y\left(t,b,c\right)/N\left(t,b,c\right)$, which can be fitted using a generalized linear model (McCullagh and Nelder 1989) by specifying the Poisson distribution for the response, a log link and a weight, $N\left(t,b,c\right)$. As can be seen in Equation 7.11, the log of the rate is represented by additive contributions of age, period and cohort with an offset given by the log of the Knoke estimate.

The identifiability problem in age–period–cohort models affects the calibration function parameters (Fienberg and Mason 1978; Holford 1983; Kupper et al. 1983; 1985; Holford 1998). The calibration used here resembles an analysis of variance model, so the usual constraints can be given by

$$\sum_{t}\alpha\left(t\right) = \sum_{b}\pi\left(b\right) = \sum_{c}\gamma\left(c\right) = 0$$

but the linear dependence among age, period and cohort extends to the indices for the three time effects, in that $c = b - t$. Hence, the design matrix for a linear predictor that includes all three factors is not of full rank, and a unique set of parameters for a corresponding generalized linear model does not exist (Fienberg and Mason 1978; Holford 1983). Although not offering a solution to the identifiability problem, it is possible to develop ways of understanding the source of this challenge so that one can express estimable components that are easily interpreted. This can be accomplished by partitioning each temporal effect into overall slope or direction of the trend and curvature or deviation from the linear trend. (Rogers 1982; Holford 1983). For example, age effects can be given by:

$$\alpha\left(t\right) = \left(t - \overline{t}\right)\beta_{\alpha} + \alpha_{C}\left(t\right) \tag{7.12}$$

where $\bar{t}$ is the mean of the ages, β_α is the underlying slope for age, and $\alpha_C(t)$ the curvature or departure from the linear trend. It has been shown, using similar partitions for period and cohort, that all curvature terms ($\alpha_C(t)$, $\pi_C(b)$ and $\gamma_C(c)$) are identifiable, but the slopes (β_α, β_π and β_γ) are not (Rogers 1982; Holford 1983). In effect, the slopes are aliased by an indeterminate constant, v, that is hopelessly entangled with all three effects, so that any particular set of slope estimates (indicated by asterisks) is associated with a true slope by:

$$\beta_a^* = \beta_\alpha + v$$

$$\beta_\pi^* = \beta_\pi - v$$

$$\beta_\gamma^* = \beta_\gamma + v$$

From the data alone, there is no way to estimate v, but some linear combination of the slopes can be estimated, for example, drift ($\beta_\pi + \beta_\gamma$) (Clayton and Schifflers 1987a; 1987b). Fitted values are also an estimable function of the parameters; hence, the identifiability problem only affects individual temporal parameters and not the calibration factor. Calibration requires fitting the age–period–cohort model to a function of the observed rates, thus obtaining optimal estimates of the temporal parameters.

Estimates of the model parameters were obtained using PROC GENMOD in SAS®. A calibrated rate is estimated by the value derived from the estimated exposure and the Knoke model (Knoke et al. 2004) and the corresponding maximum likelihood estimates of the age, period, and cohort effects in the calibration factor. The deviance or Pearson chi-squared goodness-of-fit statistics provide an overall summary of fit. The age–period–cohort model without any smoking contribution is known to provide a good description of temporal trends (Roush, Schymura, Holford et al. 1985; Roush, Holford, Schymura, and White 1987; Holford 1991; Zheng et al. 1994), so it should not be surprising when calibrating for all three temporal factors that one obtains good agreement between fitted and observed rates. Dropping one temporal factor from the calibration demonstrates how well that component of the model is characterized. For example, if one drops age and only calibrates for period, cohort and a constant, comparing observed and fitted rates, then systematic departure would suggest that age is not well characterized by the model. The estimated age, period and cohort calibration parameters provide an indication of how well that aspect of trend has been accounted for in the carcinogenic model. When a plot of these parameter estimates is overlaid onto a similar plot of parameters from the age–period–cohort model that does not include the effects of cigarette smoking one can see how much of the trend has been explained. If the carcinogenesis model is flawless, then the temporal effects estimated in the calibration model should approach zero. Intervals in which the temporal effects are not constant, on the other hand, point to epochs in which the carcinogenesis model is not providing a good characterization of trend.

To obtain a unique set of parameters, the temporal effects are partitioned into a contribution for overall trend, the slope, the deviation about the line that corresponds to the trend line, and the curvature (Holford 1983, 1991, 1992). The slope associated with period was arbitrarily constrained to be 0, so the slope for cohort is the net drift (Holford 1983, 1991, 1992; Clayton and Schifflers 1987a; 1987b). Figure 7.9 shows the calibrated Knoke model estimates and the observed estimates of lung cancer mortality for selected ages. Agreement between observed and fitted values is very close, although the large number of lung cancer deaths in the U.S. results in a statistically significant goodness of fit statistic, $G^2_{2120} = 3168.08$, with p<<.0001. The error distribution is assumed to have an extra-Poisson distribution, and an F-test is used to test effects with Pearson chi-squared giving the estimated error variance in the denominator. Table 7.1 gives as analysis of deviance summary, first for a model without the offset for the Knoke model estimates and then for the offsets included. The fit for the full model is similar in either case, but the deviance for the null model changes from 5,082,658 to 375,982, a reduction of 93%. Both the traditional age–period–cohort model and the calibrated model make a statistically significant temporal contribution to trend, but the contribution of age and period is smaller for the calibrated model, indicating that the Knoke model does account for some of the effects seen in the first model. Figures 7.10 and 7.11 show estimates of the age and period effects for the two models, and in each case the estimates from the calibration model are closer to 0, indicating the magnitude of the contribution explained. The contribution of cohort shown in Table 7.1 is larger for the calibration model and the estimated effects, shown in Figure 7.12, indicating

TABLE 7.1 Analysis of deviance for the APC model and the APC calibration model

	df	G^2	Source	df	ΔG^2	F
APC model						
APC	2,120	3,148.59				
PC	2,174	1,544,901.83	A | PC	54	1,541,753.25	19,187.26
AC	2,160	9,152.11	P | AC	40	6,003.52	100.86
AP	2,215	77,670.51	C | AP	95	74,521.92	527.17
Null	2,309	5,082,758.41	APC	189	5,079,509.82	18,061.42
		X^2				
APC	2,120	3,154.60				
APC calibration of Knoke model						
APC	2,120	3,168.08				
PC	2,174	156,519.21	A | PC	54	153,351.13	1,898.99
AC	2,160	5,089.44	P | AC	40	1,921.36	32.12
AP	2,215	241,173.18	C | AP	95	238,005.10	1,675.30
Null	2,309	375,982.67	APC	189	372,814.59	1,319.05
		X^2				
	2,120	3,170.34				

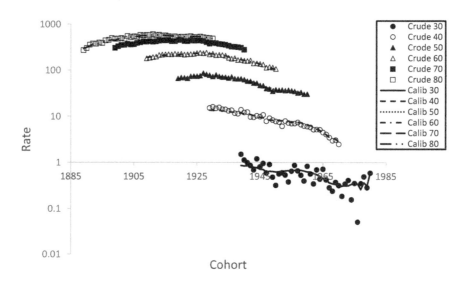

FIGURE 7.9 Lung cancer mortality rates for U.S. males estimated using the APC calibrated Knoke model and observed, 1969–2010

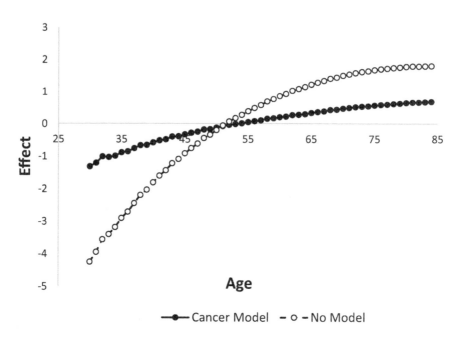

FIGURE 7.10 Age effects for the calibration of the Knoke model and the age–period–cohort model for U.S. lung cancer mortality

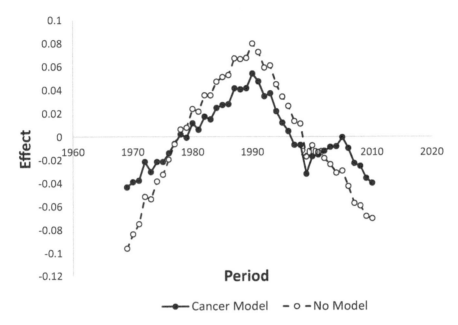

FIGURE 7.11 Period effects for the calibration of the Knoke model and the age–period–cohort model for U.S. lung cancer mortality

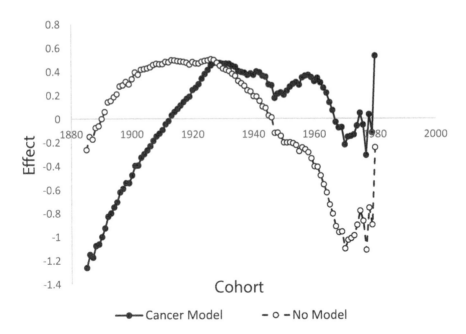

FIGURE 7.12 Cohort effects for the calibration of the Knoke model and the age–period–cohort model for U.S. lung cancer mortality

the increased magnitude of these effects. For the calibration model, the parameters appear to be somewhat linear with a bend occurring near 1930. Before the 1930 birth cohort the trend is increasing but more nearly linear after that. This suggests that the Knoke model appears to provide a better description of trend for the more recent birth cohorts and not so well early in the century.

Discussion and conclusions

This discussion has focused on the analysis of male lung cancer which has a strong causal association with cigarette smoking. The goal is to illustrate the method of analysis that uses the age–period–cohort model framework to calibrate estimates of the effect of smoking derived from analytical studies in epidemiology, and in related work we present similar results for both males and females (Holford et al. 2012; Moolgavkar et al. 2012; Jeon et al. 2018). Smoking is also associated with other diseases and models have been developed to consider all causes of mortality. Using the type of smoking history data described here, we have estimated the impact of tobacco control since publication of the Surgeon General's Report in 1964 (Surgeon General's Advisory Committee on Smoking and Health 1964). Preston and Wang (2006) have also used population measures of smoking exposure in the age–period–cohort modeling framework to describe the role of smoking in mortality differences between the sexes. They used mortality data summarized using five-year age and period intervals, instead of single years, but in other ways there are similarities with what is presented here. A summary index of the level of smoking was obtained from work by Burns et al., which was derived using data from the NHIS using an approach that motivated the methods used to derive the estimates described above (Burns et al. 1998).

The smoking index for each cohort used by Preston and Wang was the average number of years of smoking before age 40. This was included in a regression model that included effects for age and period, along with effects for sex and an interaction between sex and age. Cohort was represented by the smoking index which also included a parameter that allowed for the difference in the effect for males and females. In this approach, the effect of smoking is estimated directly from data for the outcome, all-cause mortality and does not directly use data from analytical studies of individuals that have been followed over time. The single index used to characterize smoking history, average years smoked before age 40, does not allow for other important aspects of exposure that are important to characterize risk, for example, the amount of smoking after age 40, if and when an individual quits, and the intensity of smoking. These are not captured well in a generalized linear model of an outcome that is cross-sectionally available and they have effects that vary by cause of death. The effects of quitting, for example, approach the levels for never smokers much more quickly for cardiovascular disease than lung cancer, so cohort differences in rates of cessation can be important. The dynamics of smoking behavior requires longitudinal data to fully capture the etiology giving rise to the rate trends.

The purpose of a model should direct the choice of the approach to be used. Preston and Wang (2006) focus on describing a set of rates. They also apply a similar approach for the effect of smoking to forecasting mortality trends using a modification of the Lee–Carter model (Lee and Carter 1992) by including this index of smoking exposure for a cohort (Wang and Preston 2009). On the other hand, the model described here is intended as a tool that can be used in the design of strategies for controlling the health effects of specific interventions. For example, changing the legal age for purchase of cigarettes will primarily affect smoking initiation rates, which can then be used directly to estimate smoking histories up to age 40 years and beyond, but the approach would not be as direct using that described by Preston and Wang. Clear air law that would include effects on smoking cessation rates would occur primarily after age 40, so the Preston and Wang approach would not be useful for this application.

Preston and Wang (2006) refer to the parameters in their model as effects of age, period and cohort. However, the 'cohort' parameters represent the contribution of their smoking index and not the usual time measure that is typically used in the age–period–cohort approach. This avoids the identifiability problem that requires an additional constraint, such as the assumption of zero slope for period, used in this chapter. The smoking index is not a linear function of age and period, so the Hessian matrix is of full rank, but their model is no longer the same as the usual age–period–cohort model.

A carcinogenesis model offers a way to quantitatively describe the relationship between trends in risk factor exposure and the effect that that has on disease trends. It provides a way to quantitatively summarize what has been gleaned from carefully designed analytical studies to predict what can be observed in a population with a mixture of individuals behaving in different ways. In the example discussed here, the model accounted for much of the trend, but not all of it. The limitations were temporally complex and could not be addressed by introducing a single corrective constant. The age–period–cohort framework offers a way of introducing a calibration that adjusts for each temporal element, and the result is a model that agrees well with the observed rates.

Examining the temporal parameters from the calibration provides a way of assessing aspects of the modeling exercise that are deficient. In this example, all three of the temporal factors suffer some limitations that remain after the carcinogenesis model has been used. Much of the age effect is accounted for by the Knoke model (Knoke et al. 2004), but some limitations remain. The overall trend has been reduced, but even here some overall trend remains. In addition, the curvature in the age effect indicates that this model is not accounting for some aspects of the age effect. In addition, some of the period and cohort effects remain after introducing the estimates obtained from the carcinogenesis model and the population estimates of exposure trends.

The limitations identified by the parameters estimated in the calibration may be a result of inadequacies in the carcinogenesis model. In our example, the Knoke model (Knoke et al. 2004) was used, which was obtained by fitting a model to data from a large cohort study. Aspects of this model are similar to the multistage model that was initially proposed by Armitage and Doll (1957). A limitation of this model is the lack of a clear correspondence with what is observed by microbiologists studying changes that occur at a cellular level when cancer develops (Moolgavkar and Venson 1979; Knoke, Burns, and Thun 2008).

Another potential set of limitations are the data used in these models. The cohort studies used to estimate parameters in the carcinogenesis model are from an American Cancer Society cohort study which was followed over time. While such studies attempt representation of the population, a commitment of time by the study participant necessarily limits the study to individuals who are in a position that enables them to take the time required to participate. In addition, NHIS surveys are cross-sectional, but what is required are parameters measuring transitions in individuals, for example, initiation and cessation of cigarette smoking. Smoking intensity is only measured at the time an individual is in the survey, which may not be a good representation of their experience over a lifetime. Longitudinal data would be helpful, but data of this kind are not readily available.

While the fit of the calibrated model is good, this does not guarantee that the estimates obtained by considering counterfactual trends in exposure estimates are unbiased because of the limitations in the models and the data. However, good fit should reduce bias in the overall results which helps to improve accuracy of the results. This approach has been useful in quantifying the effects of tobacco control on lung cancer mortality in the U.S. by considering counterfactual trends in cigarette smoking histories (Moolgavkar et al. 2012; Jeon et al. 2018). In addition, it has been used to assess alternative policies affecting the minimum age that one can legally purchase cigarettes by considering counterfactual initiation patterns that would result from such a policy (Institute of Medicine 2015).

An alternative model that has been found to be useful for describing carcinogenesis is the two-stage clonal expansions model (Moolgavkar and Venson 1979; Garfinkel 1985; Moolgavkar, Dewanji, and Venzon 1988; Luebeck and Moolgavkar 2002; Hazelton et al. 2012). The idea here is that the carcinogenesis process in an individual begins with the transformation of a cell, so that it is susceptible to being transformed in one more step to a cancer cell. A susceptible cell divides to become a clone of similar cells, each one of which can be transformed into a cancer cell. It is when this final transformation takes place that the cancerous tumor begins to develop and eventually reaches a point when it is diagnosed. This alternative model has been used in studies of trends for various cancer sites, including lung cancer. It has also been used by CISNET to quantify the effects of cancer control on lung cancer mortality in the U.S. (Moolgavkar et al. 2012; Holford et al. 2012; Jeon et al. 2018).

Population models for diseases like cancer can be important tools for planning public health strategies for controlling disease in that they yield estimates that correspond to what one might expect to see in a region of interest. By introducing counterfactuals, one can analyze alternative scenarios to see what fundamental differences in exposure histories would have had on the health of that population. For cigarette smoking, the Surgeon General's Report of 1964 brought together the science on the effect of smoking on lung cancer, providing a powerful rationale for change. Indeed, change did occur, but quantifying the health effects of that effect is a challenge. Among the models used by CISNET to address this question were calibrated carcinogenesis models that were first estimated using smoking history trends that did occur. These carcinogenesis models included the two-stage clonal expansion model (Moolgavkar and Venson 1979; Hazelton, Clements, and Moolgavkar 2005; Hazelton et al. 2012) and the Knoke model (Knoke, Burns, and Thun 2008). The worst-case counterfactual used history parameters that were unchanged from 1964 on, for those observed at the time that the Report appeared. In the best case, all smokers quit in 1964 and no one took up smoking after that. In this way, the number of lives saved was estimated, along with the additional lives that were lost because the ideal did not occur (Moolgavkar et al. 2012; Jeon et al. 2018).

Counterfactuals can also provide a way to design strategies for assessing the impact of change in factors affecting exposure in the future. A committee of the Institute of Medicine considered a policy change regarding the minimum legal age for access to tobacco products (Institute of Medicine 2015). The status quo assumed that initiation and cessation probabilities, as well as smoking intensity, would remain the same going forward, but the legal age at which one could purchase cigarettes would be 18, 20 or 25. Such a change would primarily affect the initiation probabilities and the smoking prevalence distribution in the future. With a calibrated model for the relationship between exposure and health, the committee was able to quantify the impact that these changes would have on health.

Online supplementary material relating to this book can be found at www.routledge.com/9780367174439.

References

Armitage, P., and R. Doll. 1957. "A two-stage theory of carcinogenesis in relation to the age distribution of human cancer." *British Journal of Cancer* 11: 161–169.

Burns, D.M., L. Lee, L.Z. Shen, E. Gilpin, H.D. Tolley, J. Vaughn, and T.G. Shanks. 1998. "Cigarette smoking behavior in the United States." Chapter 2 In *Smoking and Tobacco Control Monograph No. 8*, edited by D.M. Burns, L. Garfinkel and J. Samet, 13–42. Bethesda, MD: Cancer Control and Population Sciences, National Cancer Institute, U.S. National Institutes of Health. Pp

Clayton, D., and E. Schifflers. 1987a. "Models for temporal variation in cancer rates. I: Age-period and age-cohort models." *Statistics in Medicine* 6 (4): 449–467.

Clayton, D., and E. Schifflers. 1987b. "Models for temporal variation in cancer rates. II: Age-period-cohort models." *Statistics in Medicine* 6 (4): 469–481.

Doll, R., and R. Peto. 1981. "The causes of cancer." *Journal of the National Cancer Institute* 66: 1192–1308.

Durrleman, S., and R. Simon. 1989. "Flexible regression models with cubic splines." *Statistics in Medicine* 8: 551–561.

Fienberg, S.E., and W.M. Mason. 1978. "Identification and estimation of age-period-cohort models in the analysis of discrete archival data." In *Sociological Methodology 1979*, edited by K.F. Schuessler, 1–67. San Francisco: Jossey-Bass.

Garfinkel, L. 1985. "Selection, follow-up, and analysis in the American Cancer Society prospective studies." *National Cancer Institute Monographs* 67: 49–52.

Hazelton, W.D., R.S. Clements, and S.H. Moolgavkar. 2005. "Multistage carcinogenesis and lung cancer mortality in three cohorts." *Cancer Epidemiology Biomarkers and Prevention* 14 (5): 1171–1181.

Hazelton, W.D., J. Jeon, R. Meza, and S.H. Moolgavkar. 2012. "The FHCRC lung cancer model." *Risk Analysis* 32 (S1): s99–s116.

Holford, T.R. 1983. "The estimation of age, period and cohort effects for vital rates." *Biometrics* 39 (2): 311–324.

———. 1991. "Understanding the effects of age, period and cohort on incidence and mortality rates." *Annual Review of Public Health* 12: 425–457.

———. 1992. "Analyzing the temporal effects of age, period and cohort." *Statistical Methods in Medical Research* 1: 317–337.

———. 1998. "Age-period-cohort analysis." In *Encyclopedia of Biostatistics*, edited by P. Armitage and T. Colton, 82–99. Chichester: John Wiley & Sons.

Holford, T.R., D.T. Levy, L.A. McKay, L. Clarke, B. Racine, R. Meza, J. Jeon, and E.J. Feuer. 2014. "Patterns of birth cohort-specific smoking histories, 1965–2009." *American Journal of Preventive Medicine* 46 (2): e31–e37.

Holford, T.R., K. Ebisu, L.A. McKay, C. Oh, and T. Zheng. 2012. "Yale lung cancer model." *Risk Analysis* 32 (S1): S151–S165.

Institute of Medicine. 2015. *Public Health Implications of Raising the Minimum Age of Legal Access to Tobacco Products.* Washington, DC: The National Academies Press.

Jeon, J., R. Meza, M. Krapcho, L.D. Clarke, J. Byrne, and D.T. Levy. 2012. "Actual and counterfactual smoking prevalence rates in the U.S. population via microsimulation." *Risk Analysis* 32 (S1): S51–S68.

Jeon, J., T.R. Holford, D.T. Levy, E.J. Feuer, P. Cao, J. Tam, L. Clarke, J. Clarke, C.Y. Kong, and R. Meza. 2018. "Smoking and lung cancer mortality in the United States from 2015 to 2065." *Annals of Internal Medicine* 169 (10): 684–693.

Knoke, J.D., D.M. Burns, and M.J. Thun. 2008. "The change in excess risk of lung cancer attributable to smoking following smoking cessation: an examination of different analytic approaches using CPS-I data." *Cancer Causes and Control* 19: 207–219.

Knoke, J.D., T.G. Shanks, J.W. Vaughn, M.J. Thun, and D.M. Burns. 2004. "Lung cancer mortality is related to age in addition to duration and intensity of cigarette smoking: an analysis of CPS-I data." *Cancer Epidemiology, Biomarkers and Prevention* 13 (6): 949–957.

Kupper, L.L., J.M. Janis, A. Karmous, and B.G. Greenberg. 1985. "Statistical age-period-cohort analysis: A review and critique." *Journal of Chronic Diseases* 38: 811–830.

Kupper, L.L., J.M. Janis, I.A. Salama, C.N. Yoshizawa, and B.G. Greenberg. 1983. "Age-period-cohort analysis: An illustration of the problems in assessing interaction in one observation per cell data." *Communication in Statistics-Theory and Methods* 12: 2779–2807.

Lee, R., and L. Carter. 1992. "Modeling and forecasting U.S. mortality." *Journal of the American Statistical Association* 87: 659–671.

Luebeck, E.G., and S.H. Moolgavkar. 2002. "Multistage carcinogenesis and the incidence of colorectal cancer." *Proceedings of the National Academy of Sciences, USA* 99: 15095–15100.

McCullagh, P., and J.A. Nelder. 1989. *Generalized Linear Models.* Second ed. London: Chapman and Hall.

Moolgavkar, S.H., A. Dewanji, and D.J. Venzon. 1988. "A stochastic two-stage model for cancer risk assessment. I. The hazard function and the probability of tumor." *Risk Analysis* 8: 383–392.

Moolgavkar, S.H., and D.J. Venson. 1979. "A stochastic two-stage model for cancer risk assessment. I. The hazard function and the probability of tumor." *Mathematical Biosciences* 47: 55–77.

Moolgavkar, S.H., T.R. Holford, D.T. Levy, C.Y. Kong, M. Foy, L. Clarke, J. Jeon, W. Hazelton, R. Meza, F. Schultz, W. McCarthy, R. Boer, O. Gorlova, G.S. Gazelle, M. Kimmel, P.M. McMahon, H.J. de Koning, and E.J. Feuer. 2012. "Impact of the reduction in tobacco smoking on lung cancer mortality in the U.S. during the period 1975–2000." *Journal of the National Cancer Institute* 104: 541–548.

Preston, S.H., and H. Wang. 2006. "Sex mortality differences in the United States: The role of cohort smoking patterns." *Demography* 43 (4): 631–646.

Rogers, W.L. 1982. "Estimable functions of age, period, and cohort effects." *American Sociological Review* 47: 774–796.

Roush, G.C., T.R. Holford, M.J. Schymura, and C. White. 1987. Cancer Risk and Incidence Trends: The Connecticut Perspective. New York: Hemisphere Publishing.

Roush, G.C., M.J. Schymura, T.R. Holford, C. White and, J.T. Flannery . 1985. "Time period compared to birth cohort in Connecticut incidence rates for twenty-five malignant neoplasms." *Journal of the National Cancer Institute* 74 (4): 779–788.

Surgeon General's Advisory Committee on Smoking and Health. 1964. "Smoking and Health: Report of the Advisory Committee to the Surgeon General of the Public Health Service."

US Department of Health and Human Services. 2014. *The Health Consequences of Smoking: 50 Years of Progress. A Report of the Surgeon General*. Atlanta, GA: Department of Health and Human Services, Centers for Disease Control and Prevention, National Center for Chronic Disease Prevention and Health Promotion, Office on Smoking and Health. www.surgeongeneral.gov/library/reports/50-years-of-progress/full-report.pdf.

Wang, H, and S.H. Preston. 2009. "Forecasting United States mortality using cohort smoking histories." *Proceedings of the National Academy of Sciences of the United States of America* 106 (2): 393–398.

Warner, K.E. 1989. "Effects of the antismoking campaign: An update." *American Journal of Public Health* 79 (2): 144–151.

Zheng, T., T.R. Holford, P. Boyle, S.T. Mayne, W. Liu, and J. Flannery. 1994. "Time trend and the age-period-cohort effect on the incidence of histologic types of lung cancer in Connecticut, 1960–1989." *Cancer* 74: 1556–1567.

8

BAYESIAN AGE–PERIOD–COHORT MODELS

Ethan Fosse

Introduction

Researchers in a wide range of fields have long sought to understand social and cultural change by identifying the unique contributions of age, period and cohort (APC) processes on various outcomes (Ryder 1965). The basic idea is that any temporal change can be attributed to three kinds of processes: (1) changes over the life course of individuals, or *age effects*;[1] (2) changes due to the events in particular years, or *period effects*; (3) changes due to the replacement of older cohorts of individuals with younger ones with different characteristics, or *cohort effects*. However, in what has been called the *APC identification problem* (Mason and Fienberg 1985a, 1985b), the linear effects of an APC model cannot be uniquely estimated due to the perfect linear dependency among the age, period and cohort variables. Intuitively, once we know a person's age and the year of measurement (or period), then we also know that person's birth year (or cohort). A variety of approaches have been proposed to deal with the APC identification problem, but the great majority of studies have taken a frequentist rather than Bayesian perspective.

As I discuss in this chapter, the main advantage of the Bayesian framework for APC analysis is that the analyst can, in principle, explicitly incorporate theoretical considerations, qualitative judgments and additional data into the inferential process. In the frequentist tradition, researchers have long noted the importance of integrating what the political scientist Philip Converse (1976) dubbed "side information" into an APC analysis, typically in the form of constraints on the parameters. However, the Bayesian paradigm, which places specification of the prior distribution front and center, underscores that it is more appropriate to talk about the importance of incorporating *primary information* into any APC analysis. The task ahead, then, is to develop a general Bayesian APC model that allows researchers to easily and explicitly incorporate such primary information into their analyses.

Doing so will require specifying what the statistician Paul Gustafson (2015: 15–18) calls a *transparent reparameterization* of an APC model, which renders clear the impact of nonidentifiability on one's conclusions.

The rest of this chapter is organized as follows. First, I introduce the basics of the Bayesian approach to inference. Second, I outline the classical APC (or C-APC) regression model in terms of the Bayesian perspective, comparing it with the classical (or frequentist) approach. Third, I discuss the identification problem from a Bayesian perspective using a transparent reparameterization of the C-APC model. Fourth, I delineate a general framework for Bayesian APC modeling. In doing so, I review previous Bayesian approaches, which have focused primarily on developing reliable forecasts and applying mechanical, one-size-fits-all, prior distributions. In addition, I discuss the specification of prior distributions in APC analysis, outlining a typology of four main kinds of priors. Next, using a transparently reparameterized model, I illustrate a Bayesian approach to APC analysis by examining the temporal effects of political party identification in the United States. Finally, I conclude with suggestions for future research, discussing how a Bayesian approach to the APC identification challenge places theoretical considerations to the fore.

Basics of the Bayesian approach

Before discussing Bayesian APC models, I first outline the basics of the Bayesian approach to inference.[2] Suppose we have an $n \times 1$ column vector of data $\mathbf{y} = (y_1, \ldots, y_n)^T$, where the superscript T denotes the transpose and an unknown parameter θ. For example, $\mathbf{y}$ could represent the values of a socioeconomic index in a sample of n individuals and θ could represent the average socioeconomic index in a population of individuals. Let $p(.)$ denote a probability distribution and $p(. \mid .)$ denote a conditional probability distribution. We can further define a data (or sampling) distribution $p(\mathbf{y} \mid \theta)$, which gives the probability distribution of $\mathbf{y}$ conditional on θ under an assumed parametric model. The typical goal is to obtain a reasonable estimate (or set of estimates) of the unknown parameter.

In the frequentist (or classical) tradition typically adopted by social scientists, the data $\mathbf{y}$ is treated as a random variable while the parameter θ is viewed as a single fixed, unknown quantity. As a result, in the frequentist perspective it makes little sense to talk about a probability distribution for the parameter given the data. Instead, to obtain an estimate of θ, we can define a likelihood function $p(\mathbf{y} \mid \theta) = \mathcal{L}(\theta \mid \mathbf{y})$, where $\mathcal{L}(\theta \mid \mathbf{y})$ produces the likelihood of the parameter given fixed values of the data (Aster et al. 2018).[3] For many of the possible values of θ, the likelihood function will produce output values very close to zero because these values of θ are unlikely to have generated the observed data $\mathbf{y}$. However, for other values of θ the likelihood function will produce considerably larger output values, indicating that the corresponding values of θ are much more likely to have generated the observed data. In fact, by maximizing the likelihood function we obtain the value of θ most likely to have produced the observed data, or what is known as the Maximum Likelihood Estimate (MLE) of θ. The MLE is usually calculated using numerical optimization methods, but in simpler cases it can be derived analytically.[4]

In contrast to the frequentist tradition, in the Bayesian perspective both the data **y** and parameter θ are viewed as random variables (Gill 2008).[5] Accordingly, our goal is to make an informed statement about $p(\theta \mid \mathbf{y})$, or the probability of the parameter given the data under a particular assumed parametric model. To obtain this distribution, we need to make use of Bayes' theorem, which is derived using basic probability theory. Because both **y** and θ are random variables, we can write out the joint probability of **y** and θ, or $p(\theta, \mathbf{y})$. This joint distribution can be factorized as

$$p(\theta, \mathbf{y}) = \sum_{\text{all } \theta} p(\theta) p(\mathbf{y} \mid \theta). \tag{8.1}$$

Moreover, because we can write $p(\theta, \mathbf{y}) = p(\mathbf{y}) p(\theta \mid \mathbf{y})$, after substitution and rearranging terms we obtain Bayes' theorem:

$$p(\theta \mid \mathbf{y}) = \frac{p(\mathbf{y} \mid \theta) p(\theta)}{p(\mathbf{y})}, \tag{8.2}$$

where $p(\mathbf{y} \mid \theta)$ is the likelihood, $p(\theta)$ is the prior distribution and $p(\theta \mid \mathbf{y})$ is the posterior distribution, which is a probability density function if θ is continuous and a probability mass function if θ is discrete. The denominator, $p(\mathbf{y})$, is simply the unconditional (or marginal) probability distribution of the data.[6] If θ is a discrete parameter, then we must sum over all possible values of θ to find the unconditional distribution of the data:

$$p(\mathbf{y}) = \sum_{\text{all } \theta} p(\theta) p(\mathbf{y} \mid \theta). \tag{8.3}$$

Alternatively, as is more commonly the case, if θ is continuous then we must use integration to find the unconditional distribution of the data:

$$p(\mathbf{y}) = \int p(\mathbf{y} \mid \theta) p(\theta) d\theta. \tag{8.4}$$

The quantity $p(\mathbf{y})$ can be viewed as a normalizing constant, the purpose of which is to ensure that the posterior distribution integrates (or sums) to 1 as required by the definition of a probability density (or mass) function. Because $p(\mathbf{y})$, which does not depend on θ, provides no information about which values of θ are more or less likely, the denominator is often omitted when displaying Bayes' theorem, which can be represented compactly as

$$p(\theta \mid \mathbf{y}) \propto p(\mathbf{y} \mid \theta) p(\theta) \tag{8.5}$$

or

$$\text{Posterior} \propto \text{Likelihood} \times \text{Prior}, \tag{8.6}$$

where $\propto$ means "proportional to."[7] Equations 8.5 and 8.6 define the core machinery of Bayesian data analysis, showing how the likelihood $p(\mathbf{y}\,|\,\theta)$ can be "inverted" to produce the posterior $p(\theta\,|\,\mathbf{y})$. The general procedure is as follows.[8] Before we observe the data $\mathbf{y}$, we express our beliefs about the values of the parameter of a particular model using a prior distribution $p(\theta)$. The possible values of θ define what is known as the parameter space of our model. We then use the likelihood $p(\mathbf{y}\,|\,\theta)$ to update our prior beliefs, thereby producing a posterior distribution, or $p(\theta\,|\,\mathbf{y})$.

After obtaining the posterior, we can summarize its distribution to make meaningful conclusions about the probable values of the parameter θ. For example, a researcher can report the expected value, or $E[\theta\,|\,\mathbf{y}]$, and the variance, or $\text{Var}(\theta\,|\,\mathbf{y})$, of the posterior distribution. One can also select various quantiles. Most commonly, for example, researchers cut the posterior distribution at the 2.5% and 97.5% quantiles to construct a Bayesian credible interval (Gill 2008).[9] Alternatively, one might find the interval of minimum length that contains some specified probability level, or what is called the highest posterior density (HPD) interval (Gill 2008: 48–51). Also, because $p(\theta)$ is a distribution, one could present the findings graphically, displaying a range of parameter values and their corresponding probabilities. I now turn to a discussion of the basic APC model in terms of both frequentist and Bayesian perspectives.

The classical APC regression model

It is common in the APC literature to use index notation to keep track of the dimensions of a temporal data structure (Fienberg and Mason 1985: 67–71). We will let $i = 1,\ldots,I$ represent the age groups, $j = 1,\ldots,J$ the period groups, and $k = 1,\ldots,K$ the cohort groups with $k = j - i + I$ and $K = I + J - 1$.[10] Using this index notation, temporal effects in an age–period array can be represented using the classical APC (C-APC) model, also known as the multiple classification model (Mason et al. 1973: 243) or accounting model (Fienberg and Mason 1985: 46–47, 67), which has the following generic form (Fienberg and Mason, 1985: 67–68):[11]

$$Y_{ijk} = \mu + \alpha_i + \pi_j + \gamma_k + \varepsilon_{ijk} \tag{8.7}$$

where Y_{ijk} is the outcome variable to be explained, μ is the intercept, α_i represents the ith age effect, π_j represents the jth period effect, γ_k represents the kth cohort effect, and ε_{ijk} is the error term. The errors are assumed to be additive, independent and identically distributed (iid) according to a normal distribution with a mean zero and variance σ^2, such that $\varepsilon_{ijk} \sim N(0,\sigma^2)$. To avoid overparameterization, we apply the so-called "usual constraints" that the parameters sum to zero,

or $\displaystyle\sum_{i=1}^{I}\alpha_i = \sum_{j=1}^{J}\pi_j = \sum_{k=1}^{K}\gamma_k = 0.$[12]

The parameterization shown in Equation 8.7 is very flexible, allowing the age, period and cohort effects to be highly nonlinear because there is one parameter for each age, period and cohort category (Mason et al. 1973: 246). This can be seen in Table 8.1, which shows how each cell is represented by a unique combination of parameters.

For ease of exposition it is convenient to represent the C-APC compactly using matrix notation:

$$\mathbf{y} = \mathbf{X}\beta + \epsilon, \tag{8.8}$$

where $\mathbf{X}$ is an $(I \times J) \times (I + J + K - 2)$ design matrix with a leading vector of 1s for the constant, β is an $(I \times J) \times 1$ vector of parameters to be estimated, $\mathbf{y}$ is an $(I \times J) \times 1$ vector of outcome values, and ϵ is an $(I \times J) \times 1$ vector of errors. As noted previously, the errors are assumed to be additive, independent and identically distributed (iid) according to a normal distribution with a mean zero and variance σ^2, such that $\epsilon \sim N(0, \sigma^2 \mathbf{I})$, where 0 is an $(I \times J) \times 1$ vector of zeros, and $\mathbf{I}$ is an $(I \times J) \times (I \times J)$ diagonal matrix.

In the frequentist tradition, we can obtain estimates of the parameters by maximizing the likelihood function. For Equation 8.8, the likelihood function, or the probability of the data given the parameter vector β and scalar σ^2 as well as the input variables $\mathbf{X}$, is given by:

$$p(\mathbf{y} \mid \beta, \sigma^2, \mathbf{X}) = \mathcal{L}(\beta, \sigma^2 \mid \mathbf{y}, \mathbf{X}) = (\frac{1}{\sqrt{2\pi}\sigma})^{(I \times J)} \times e^{\left[-\frac{1}{2\sigma^2} (\mathbf{y} - \mathbf{X}\beta)^T (\mathbf{y} - \mathbf{X}\beta) \right]}, \tag{8.9}$$

where e and π are the conventional constants. Under the standard assumptions of the normal linear model, maximizing the likelihood function in Equation 8.9 results in estimates that coincide with those of ordinary least squares (OLS), such

TABLE 8.1 Classical APC model on an age–period array

Age groups	Period groups		
	j=1	j=2	j=3=J
i=1	$\mu + \alpha_1 + \pi_1 + \gamma_5 + \epsilon_{1,1,5}$	$\mu + \alpha_1 + \pi_2 + \gamma_6 + \epsilon_{1,2,6}$	$\mu + \alpha_1 + \pi_3 + \gamma_7 + \epsilon_{1,3,7}$
i=2	$\mu + \alpha_2 + \pi_1 + \gamma_4 + \epsilon_{2,1,4}$	$\mu + \alpha_2 + \pi_2 + \gamma_5 + \epsilon_{2,2,5}$	$\mu + \alpha_2 + \pi_3 + \gamma_6 + \epsilon_{2,3,6}$
i=3	$\mu + \alpha_3 + \pi_1 + \gamma_3 + \epsilon_{3,1,3}$	$\mu + \alpha_3 + \pi_2 + \gamma_4 + \epsilon_{3,2,4}$	$\mu + \alpha_3 + \pi_3 + \gamma_5 + \epsilon_{3,3,5}$
i=4	$\mu + \alpha_4 + \pi_1 + \gamma_2 + \epsilon_{4,1,2}$	$\mu + \alpha_4 + \pi_2 + \gamma_3 + \epsilon_{4,2,3}$	$\mu + \alpha_4 + \pi_3 + \gamma_4 + \epsilon_{4,3,4}$
i=5=I	$\mu + \alpha_5 + \pi_1 + \gamma_1 + \epsilon_{5,1,1}$	$\mu + \alpha_5 + \pi_2 + \gamma_2 + \epsilon_{5,2,2}$	$\mu + \alpha_5 + \pi_3 + \gamma_3 + \epsilon_{5,3,3}$

that $\hat{\beta}_{MLE} = \hat{\beta}_{OLS} = (\mathbf{X}^T\mathbf{X})^{-1}\mathbf{X}^T\mathbf{y}$, where the superscript -1 denotes a regular inverse.[13]

The Bayesian C-APC model

From the Bayesian perspective our goal is to make a statement about the probability of the parameters given the data. In other words, we want to summarize the posterior distribution $p(\beta, \sigma^2 \mid \mathbf{y}, \mathbf{X})$. However, the design matrix $\mathbf{X}$ and outcome vector $\mathbf{y}$ are both commonly considered "the data". This implies a full Bayesian model includes not only the parameters β and σ^2 linked to the conditional distribution of $\mathbf{y}$ given $\mathbf{X}$, but also another set of parameters ψ linked to the unconditional distribution of $\mathbf{X}$ (Gelman et al. 2014: 354). Using Bayes' theorem, this in turn suggests the following set-up (see Jackman 2009: 99–103; Trader 2014: 2):

$$p(\beta, \sigma^2, \psi \mid \mathbf{y}, \mathbf{X}) = \frac{p(\mathbf{y}, \mathbf{X} \mid \beta, \sigma^2, \psi)p(\beta, \sigma^2, \psi)}{p(\mathbf{y}, \mathbf{X})}, \tag{8.10}$$

where $p(\beta, \sigma^2, \psi \mid \mathbf{y}, \mathbf{X})$ is the posterior distribution, $p(\mathbf{y}, \mathbf{X} \mid \beta, \sigma^2, \psi)$ is the joint likelihood, $p(\beta, \sigma^2, \psi)$ is the prior distribution, and $p(\mathbf{y}, \mathbf{X})$ is a normalizing constant.

However, Equation 8.10 does not encode the typical model of interest among social scientists. Specifically, the Bayesian version of the C-APC model does not entail estimating a set of parameters for the joint distribution of $\mathbf{y}$ and $\mathbf{X}$; rather, as a regression model, it involves estimating parameters for the distribution of the outcome $\mathbf{y}$ conditional on the variables in $\mathbf{X}$. However, under standard regression assumptions, ψ provides no additional information about the parameters β and σ^2 after conditioning on $\mathbf{X}$. Accordingly, we can factorize Equation 8.10 into two distinct, independent parts:

$$p(\beta, \sigma^2, \psi \mid \mathbf{y}, \mathbf{X}) = p(\beta, \sigma^2 \mid \mathbf{y}, \mathbf{X})p(\psi \mid \mathbf{X})$$

$$= \frac{p(\mathbf{y} \mid \mathbf{X}, \beta, \sigma^2)p(\beta, \sigma^2)}{p(\mathbf{y} \mid \mathbf{X})} \times \frac{p(\mathbf{X} \mid \nu)p(\psi)}{p(\mathbf{X})}. \tag{8.11}$$

Equation 8.11 tells us that we can independently focus on one of two analyses. Either we can make inferences about β and σ^2 based on the conditional distribution of $\mathbf{y}$ given $\mathbf{X}$ or we can make inferences regarding ψ using the unconditional distribution of $\mathbf{X}$. Our interest lies in the former. Noting that $p(\psi \mid \mathbf{X}) = [p(\mathbf{X} \mid \psi)p(\psi)] / p(\mathbf{X})$, we can write Bayes' formula for the C-APC as:

$$p(\beta,\sigma^2 \mid \mathbf{y}, \mathbf{X}) = \frac{p(\mathbf{y} \mid \mathbf{X}, \beta, \sigma^2) p(\beta, \sigma^2)}{p(\mathbf{y} \mid \mathbf{X})}, \tag{8.12}$$

where $p(\beta, \sigma^2 \mid \mathbf{y}, \mathbf{X})$ is the posterior distribution, $p(\mathbf{y} \mid \mathbf{X}, \beta, \sigma^2)$ is the likelihood, $p(\beta, \sigma^2)$ is the prior distribution and $p(\mathbf{y} \mid \mathbf{X})$ is a normalizing constant. Because conditioning on the design matrix $\mathbf{X}$ is implicit in our model and the denominator is just a normalizing constant, Equation 8.12 is often simplified as:

$$p(\beta, \sigma^2 \mid \mathbf{y}) \propto p(\mathbf{y} \mid \beta, \sigma^2) p(\beta, \sigma^2), \tag{8.13}$$

where as before $\propto$ means "proportional to" (cf. Equations 8.5 and 8.6). This is just another way of stating that our prior beliefs about the parameters, encoded in terms of a prior distribution, can be updated by the likelihood function, which arises from the statistical model and the data. The result of this updating is a posterior distribution, which represents our "post-data" beliefs about the parameters (Gustafson 2015: 6).

To obtain Bayesian estimates we must specify our beliefs about the parameters in the form of a prior distribution. Because there are many types of distributions, each of which can take any number of forms, there are many ways to set up our model. Using "stacked" notation (e.g., see McElreath 2018: 124), which explicitly reveals our distributional assumptions, one way to set up the Bayesian version of the C-APC model is as follows:

$$Y_{ijk} \sim N\left(\hat{Y}_{ijk}, \sigma\right) \tag{8.14}$$

$$\hat{Y}_{ijk} = \mu + \sum_i^{I-1} \alpha_i A_i + \sum_j^{J-1} \pi_j P_j + \sum_k^{K-1} \gamma_k C_k \tag{8.15}$$

$$\mu \sim N\left(\mu_\mu, \sigma_\mu^2\right) \tag{8.16}$$

$$\alpha_i \sim N\left(\mu_{\alpha_i}, \sigma_{\alpha_i}^2\right) \quad \text{for} \quad i = 1, \ldots, I-1$$

$$\pi_j \sim N\left(\mu_{\pi_j}, \sigma_{\pi_j}^2\right) \quad \text{for} \quad j = 1, \ldots, J-1 \tag{8.17}$$

$$\gamma_k \sim N\left(\mu_{\gamma_k}, \sigma_{\gamma_k}^2\right) \quad \text{for} \quad k = 1, \ldots, K-1$$

$$\sigma \sim \text{Uniform}\left(a_\sigma, b_\sigma\right), \tag{8.18}$$

where A_i, P_j and C_k are sum-to-zero effect (or deviation) contrasts, with the last of each age, period and cohort category dropped. The corresponding parameters $\alpha_i, \ldots, \alpha_{I-1}, \pi_j, \ldots, \pi_{J-1}$ and $\gamma_k, \ldots, \gamma_{K-1}$ give the age, period and cohort deviations, respectively, from the overall (or grand) mean, captured by the intercept μ. Equation 8.14 represents the likelihood and Equation 8.15 represents the model, while Equations 8.16–8.17 outline the prior distributions for the model parameters. In this specification of the C-APC model I use normal priors for the intercept and deviation parameters while I use a uniform prior for the variance.[14] The Bayesian version of the C-APC model outlined above is general, requiring the researcher to input center and spread values for the normal priors as well as lower and upper values for the uniform prior. Any number of input values are possible, reflecting the wide range of possible prior beliefs about the parameters. An initial approach might be to use what are known, somewhat incorrectly, as "noninformative" (i.e., diffuse or flat)[15] priors for the parameters, which would typically produce Bayesian estimates comparable to those from MLE or OLS in the frequentist tradition. However, the Bayesian estimates generated by the C-APC model are highly sensitive to the choice of priors, even those deemed to be "noninformative." As a consequence, researchers naively estimating the model outlined in Equations 8.14–8.18 may fail to realize that their findings are driven, in no small part, by their prior beliefs rather than the data and model. It is for this reason that I do not recommend that researchers use the C-APC model to estimate temporal effects, even in the context of a Bayesian analysis. To better understand why I advise against using the C-APC model, I now turn to the issue of model identification from a Bayesian perspective.

The identification problem

A model is unidentified[16] when multiple values of one or more of the parameters correspond to the same distribution of observed data (Gustafson 2015: 1–2). When a model is identified, there is a one-to-one mapping between the distribution of the observed data and the parameter space, or the set of possible values of the parameters of a model. Accordingly, altering the values of the parameters will in general change the distribution of the data. In contrast, when a model is unidentified, there is a one-to-many mapping between the data and the parameter space. As such, it is possible to alter the values of at least one of the parameters and yet keep the distribution of the data unchanged. Furthermore, in the absence of identification, this one-to-many mapping between the data and the parameter space remains even as the sample size goes to infinity.

As is well known, the C-APC model in Equation 8.7 suffers from a fundamental identification problem due to linear dependence in the columns of the design matrix (Fosse and Winship 2018; 2019a). Algebraically, at least one of the columns of $\mathbf{X}$ can be rewritten as a function of the other columns, such that the design matrix $\mathbf{X}$ is rank deficient one (i.e., singular).[17] Accordingly, a regular inverse $(\mathbf{X}^T\mathbf{X})^{-1}$ does not exist and the model lacks a unique set of parameter estimates. In other words, there is a one-to-many mapping between the data and the parameter space. More formally, the set of parameters of the C-APC model can be altered without affecting the likelihood. Viewing the likelihood as a "hill," the identification problem corresponds to a "ridge" in the likelihood. This is a direction in the parameter space in which the likelihood is flat, extending from negative to positive infinity, no matter how large the sample (Gelman 2014: 89). In the frequentist tradition, researchers have typically dealt with the lack of identification by applying a constraint, such as setting two adjacent age groups equal to each other or dropping one of the temporal dimensions altogether. However, as a number of scholars have pointed out (e.g., Fosse and Winship 2019a; O'Brien 2015; Yang and Land 2013), such constraints can rely on quite strong, often untenable, theoretical assumptions.

In the Bayesian approach, it has been suggested that nonidentification is not inherently a problem because a prior must be specified (see Gelfand and Sahu 1999; Neath and Samaniego 1997; Poirier 1998). As the statistician Dennis Lindley (1972: 46) has noted, "unidentifiability causes no real difficulties in the Bayesian approach." That is, as long as the researcher specifies a legitimate probability distribution as the prior, then Bayes' theorem will produce the posterior in terms of a legitimate probability distribution. For example, using the Bayesian version of the C-APC model outlined in Equations 8.14–8.18, one can choose some set of values for the priors, "turn the Bayesian crank" and generate a set of Bayesian estimates, which can then be summarized in the conventional way (Gustafson 2015: 5–6). This is true even though the C-APC model is not identified. However, an unidentified Bayesian model is not without the potential for misuse, especially if the parameterization obscures the flow of information, as is the case with the C-APC model. As Gustafson (2015) has forcefully argued, although the choice of parameterization in an unidentified model is mathematically arbitrary, some parameterizations are more useful than others for clarifying the influence of the prior distribution on the posterior distribution (see also Gustafson 2005, 2009). In particular, he makes the case that nonidentified models should be expressed in terms of a transparent parameterization, which clearly separates those parameters directly informed by the observed data from those that are, so far as possible, indirectly informed by the data.

Transparent reparameterization of the classical APC model

In this section I outline a transparent reparameterization of the C-APC model that will clarify the underlying assumptions of the model. Let α, π and γ denote the true, unknown linear effects. Similarly, let α^*, π^* and γ^* denote some other set of values of the linear effects. We can write the identification problem algebraically as (Fosse and Winship 2018: 316):

$$\alpha^* = \alpha + v, \quad \pi^* = \pi - v, \quad \text{and} \quad \gamma^* = \gamma + v, \tag{8.19}$$

where v is some unknown scalar. Setting a range of values for v traces out what is known as the *canonical solution line*, which is the set of possible values of the linear effects consistent with the data (Fosse and Winship 2018: 313–319). This line corresponds with the maximum likelihood (or OLS) estimates in the frequentist tradition. The canonical solution line lies in a three-dimensional parameter space, where the dimensions are the values of the age, period and cohort linear effects ranging from negative to positive infinity.[18]

The linearized APC model

Researchers typically fit some version of the C-APC model, which, under sum-to-zero constraints, is expressed in terms of deviations (or "effects") relative to a grand (or overall) mean. However, an equivalent representation entails decomposing each "effect" in the C-APC into their respective linear and nonlinear effects. Fosse and Winship (2019b) call this reparameterized model the linearized APC (or L-APC) model (see also Chapter 6).

The ith age effect in the C-APC can be represented in the L-APC model in terms of an overall linear age effect along with a unique parameter for the ith age nonlinearity: $\alpha_i = \left(i - i^*\right)\alpha + \tilde{\alpha}_i$, where α is the age linear effect, $\tilde{\alpha}_i$ is the ith age nonlinear effect, and the asterisk denotes a midpoint or referent index $i^* = (I+1)/2$ (which ensures that the sum-to-zero constraints are satisfied). In other words, each age effect α_i is split into the sum of a common parameter α representing the age slope for the entire array, with a value shifting across rows (or age categories) as a function of the age index i, and a unique parameter $\tilde{\alpha}_i$, which is a nonlinearity specific to each age category. One can similarly decompose each period effect as $\pi_j = \left(j - j^*\right)\pi + \tilde{\pi}_j$ with $j^* = (J+1)/2$ and each cohort effect as $\gamma_k = \left(k - k^*\right)\gamma + \tilde{\gamma}_k$ with $k^* = (K+1)/2$. The L-APC model thus has the following general form:

$$Y_{ijk} = \mu + \alpha\left(i - i^*\right) + \pi\left(j - j^*\right) + \gamma\left(k - k^*\right) + \tilde{\alpha}_i + \tilde{\pi}_j + \tilde{\gamma}_k + \epsilon_{ijk}. \qquad (8.20)$$

The L-APC model is based on a design matrix in which the linear and nonlinear components are in some way orthogonal to each other. There is a variety of ways to set up this design matrix, but orthogonal polynomial contrasts give parameter results that are easiest to interpret (for details, see Fosse and Winship 2018).

It is important to underscore that, because each of the "effects" in the C-APC can be decomposed into their respective linear and nonlinear parts, the parameters from the L-APC and C-APC are fundamentally equivalent. That is, the L-APC parameter vector is simply a decomposed version of the C-APC, such that

$$\beta = (\mu, \alpha^*, \pi^*, \gamma^*, \tilde{\alpha}_1, \ldots, \tilde{\alpha}_{I-1}, \tilde{\pi}_j, \ldots, \tilde{\pi}_{J-1}, \tilde{\gamma}_k, \ldots, \tilde{\gamma}_{K-1})^T$$

$$= (\mu, \alpha + v, \pi - v, \gamma + v, \tilde{\alpha}_1, \ldots, \tilde{\alpha}_{I-1}, \tilde{\pi}_j, \ldots, \tilde{\pi}_{J-1}, \tilde{\gamma}_k, \ldots, \tilde{\gamma}_{K-1})^T. \qquad (8.21)$$

I will make use of this identity in the next section when I separate the C-APC model into identified and unidentified components. Note that the presence of the scalar ν indicates some of the parameters are not identified. In particular, some set of slopes α^*, π^* and γ^* will correspond to the true parameter slopes α, π and γ only if ν is exactly specified. This is equivalent to stating that the analyst needs to apply an exactly correct just-identifying constraint to recover the true, unknown values of the temporal effects. However, because the intercept and nonlinear effects do not include the scalar ν, they are identified.

Transparent reparameterization of the classical model

To construct a transparent reparameterization of the C-APC, it is necessary to split the parameter vector into identified and unidentified components. To do so, I will take advantage of the L-APC parameterization discussed in the previous section. Formally let $\beta = (\xi, \lambda) = h(\beta)$, where β is the original C-APC parameterization (see Equation 8.7), ξ is some set of identified parameters, λ is an unidentified parameter, and $h(\beta)$ is the transparent reparameterization. There are several ways to define ξ and λ – and thus, by definition, $h(\beta)$. One approach is to drop the period linear component from the design matrix of the L-APC model, which results in the corresponding identified parameter vector:[19]

$$\xi = (\mu, \alpha^*, \gamma^*, \tilde{\alpha}_i, \dots, \tilde{\alpha}_{I-1}, \tilde{\pi}_j, \dots, \tilde{\pi}_{J-1}, \tilde{\gamma}_k, \dots, \tilde{\gamma}_{K-1})^T. \tag{8.22}$$

Simple algebra can be used to show that ξ is, in fact, identified. To demonstrate this, note that dropping the period linear component from the design matrix is equivalent to stating that $\pi^* = 0$ or, equivalently, $\pi - \nu = 0$. Accordingly, we know that, in the identified parameter vector above, $\nu = \pi$. Using the fact that $\alpha^* = \alpha + \nu$ and $\gamma^* = \gamma + \nu$, after plugging in $\nu = \pi$ we can thus express the identified parameter vector as

$$\xi = (\mu, \theta_1, \theta_2, \tilde{\alpha}_i, \dots, \tilde{\alpha}_{I-1}, \tilde{\pi}_j, \dots, \tilde{\pi}_{J-1}, \tilde{\gamma}_k, \dots, \tilde{\gamma}_{K-1})^T, \tag{8.23}$$

where, in the terminology of Fosse and Winship (2019b), $\theta_1 = \alpha + \pi$ and $\theta_2 = \gamma + \pi$. Because dropping the linear component is equivalent to constraining $\pi^* = 0$, we can express the unidentified parameter as $\lambda = \pi = \nu$, where ν is an unknown scalar.

To summarize the foregoing, we can write the transparent reparameterization of the C-APC model as $h(\beta) = (\xi, \lambda)$, where ξ is defined in Equation 8.23 and $\lambda = \nu$. This transparent reparameterization of the C-APC model has two fundamental properties (Gustafson 2015). First, the distribution of the outcome given the design matrix depends only on the identified parameter vector ξ, not on the unidentified parameter λ. In other words, the likelihood with and without the unidentified parameter is the same, such that $p(\mathbf{y} \mid \mathbf{X}, \xi, \lambda, \sigma^2) = p(\mathbf{y} \mid \mathbf{X}, \xi, \sigma^2)$. Second, regular parametric asymptotic theory applies to the model represented by $p(\mathbf{y} \mid \mathbf{X}, \xi, \sigma^2)$. In other words, the estimate of ξ converges in probability to its true value as the sample size increases to infinity. With these two insights, we are now ready to examine the identification problem within a Bayesian framework.

Bayesian interpretation of the APC identification problem

Using the transparent reparameterization outlined previously, we can write out the identification problem in Bayesian terms. Recall that we can write the posterior distribution of the Bayesian version of the C-APC model as follows:

$$p(\beta, \sigma^2 \mid \mathbf{y}, \mathbf{X}) = \frac{p(\mathbf{y} \mid \mathbf{X}, \beta, \sigma^2) p(\beta, \sigma^2)}{p(\mathbf{y} \mid \mathbf{X})}. \tag{8.24}$$

To make sense of the identification problem from a Bayesian perspective, it is useful to re-express the parameter vector β into identified and unidentified parts. The transparent reparameterization discussed previously informs us that we can substitute (ξ, λ) for β, where λ is an unidentified parameter and ξ is a vector of identified parameters. Two important relationships follow from this reparameterization. First, we can write the likelihood as:

$$p(\mathbf{y} \mid \mathbf{X}, \xi, \lambda, \sigma^2) = p(\mathbf{y} \mid \mathbf{X}, \xi, \sigma^2), \tag{8.25}$$

which is another way of stating that the unidentified parameter λ is not itself informative about the likelihood. Second, we can decompose the prior distribution as:

$$p(\xi, \lambda, \sigma^2) = p(\xi, \sigma^2) p(\lambda \mid \xi, \sigma^2), \tag{8.26}$$

where $p(\xi, \sigma^2)$ is the prior for the identifiable parameters and $p(\lambda \mid \xi, \sigma^2)$ is the prior for the unidentified parameter, conditional on the identified parameters. Using these identity relationships, we can thus split the model into two separate parts, one of which is identified and the other which is not (see Gustafson 2015; Nielsen and Nielsen 2014; Poirier 1998):

$$p(\xi, \sigma^2 \mid \mathbf{y}, \mathbf{X}) = \frac{p(\mathbf{y} \mid \mathbf{X}, \xi, \sigma^2) p(\xi, \sigma^2)}{p(\mathbf{y} \mid \mathbf{X})} \tag{8.27}$$

and

$$p(\lambda \mid \mathbf{y}, \mathbf{X}, \xi, \sigma^2) = p(\lambda \mid \xi, \sigma^2), \tag{8.28}$$

where $p(\xi, \sigma^2 \mid \mathbf{y}, \mathbf{X})$ is the posterior of the identified parameters and $p(\lambda \mid \mathbf{y}, \mathbf{X}, \xi, \sigma^2)$ is the posterior of the unidentified parameter, conditional on the identified parameters. Equation 8.27 tells us that the identified part acts as a standard Bayesian model, such that the prior $p(\xi, \sigma^2)$ is updated by the likelihood $p(\mathbf{y} \mid \mathbf{X}, \xi, \sigma^2)$ to produce the posterior $p(\xi, \sigma^2 \mid \mathbf{y}, \mathbf{X})$. In contrast, Equation 8.28 reveals that the conditional prior of the unidentified parameter, or $p(\lambda \mid \xi, \sigma^2)$, is not updated by a likelihood function. In fact, regardless of the sample size, the conditional posterior distribution of the unidentified parameter equals its conditional prior distribution. It also follows that the predictive distribution does not depend on the conditional prior for λ (see Nielsen and Nielsen 2014: 8).

The implications of the Bayesian interpretation of the APC identification problem can be further clarified by restricting our attention to the linear effects (e.g., see Fosse and Winship 2018). Focusing just on the linear effects of the C-APC, this means that $\beta = (\xi, \lambda) = (\alpha^*, \pi^*, \gamma^*) = (\theta_1, \theta_2, v)$. The parameters θ_1 and θ_2, along with some value for v, are sufficient to derive a set of values for α^*, π^* and γ^*. Crucially, the likelihood is equal to $p(\mathbf{y} \mid \mathbf{X}, \beta) = p(\mathbf{y} \mid \mathbf{X}, \xi)$ or $p(\mathbf{y} \mid \mathbf{X}, \alpha^*, \pi^*, \gamma^*) = p(\mathbf{y} \mid \mathbf{X}, \theta_1, \theta_2)$. In other words, the likelihood is a function of θ_1 and θ_2, not the unidentified parameter v. The prior distribution can be written as $p(\beta) = p(\xi, \lambda) = p(\xi) p(\lambda \mid \xi)$ or $p(\alpha^*, \pi^*, \gamma^*) = p(\theta_1, \theta_2, v) = p(\theta_1, \theta_2) p(v \mid \theta_1, \theta_2)$. That is, we have a prior for the identifiable parameters, denoted by $p(\theta_1, \theta_2)$, and a prior for the unidentified parameter, conditional on the identified parameters, given by $p(v \mid \theta_1, \theta_2)$. Using Bayes' theorem, we can accordingly write the posterior distribution for the identified parameters as:

$$p(\xi \mid \mathbf{y}, \mathbf{X}) = \frac{p(\mathbf{y} \mid \mathbf{X}, \xi) p(\xi)}{p(\mathbf{y} \mid \mathbf{X})} \quad \text{or}$$

$$p(\theta_1, \theta_2 \mid \mathbf{y}, \mathbf{X}) = \frac{p(\mathbf{y} \mid \mathbf{X}, \theta_1, \theta_2) p(\theta_1, \theta_2)}{p(\mathbf{y} \mid \mathbf{X})}, \tag{8.29}$$

which shows that the posterior distribution for θ_1 and θ_2 is a function of the likelihood $p(\mathbf{y} \mid \mathbf{X}, \theta_1, \theta_2)$ as well as the prior distribution $p(\theta_1, \theta_2)$. In other words, our prior beliefs about θ_1 and θ_2 are, in fact, updated by the data. In contrast, focusing on the unidentified parameter, we can write:

$$p(\lambda \mid \mathbf{y}, \mathbf{X}, \xi) = p(\lambda \mid \xi) \quad \text{or} \quad p(v \mid \mathbf{y}, \mathbf{X}, \theta_1, \theta_2) = p(v \mid \theta_1, \theta_2), \tag{8.30}$$

which indicates that the conditional prior for the unidentified parameter v is not updated by the likelihood. That is, given values of θ_1 and θ_2, the data do not modify our prior beliefs about the possible values of v. As a consequence, the choice of the prior is absolutely critical in determining the estimates of the linear APC effects. To avoid arbitrary results, APC analysts should, whenever possible, use a transparent reparameterization of the underlying model, basing their priors on careful, theoretically informed decisions.

Even though one's prior beliefs are crucial in determining the results of the C-APC model, the data are still informative about the parameters, even those that are unidentified (Gustafson 2015: 18–22). Specifically, the transparent reparameterization of the C-APC model reveals that the nonlinear effects are directly informed by the observed data, while the linear effects are indirectly informed by the data via the values of θ_1 and θ_2. Given a set of estimated values for θ_1 and θ_2, we will have a restricted set of possible estimates of the linear effects (Fosse and Winship 2018). That is, only a subset of possible values of the slopes are actually consistent with the observable data. Furthermore, in the limit of an infinite amount of data, the posterior distribution can be described as a *limiting posterior distribution*, with a point mass at some value of θ_1 and θ_2 combined with a conditional prior distribution for the unidentified parameter ν (Gustafson 2015: 16–39). In other words, as the sample size goes to infinity, the estimates of θ_1 and θ_2, which are directly informed by the data, become concentrated at a single point, providing maximal information on the set of possible combinations of the slopes. Thus, even if the only parameters of interest are the linear effects, in general a larger sample size will be preferable to a smaller sample size.

The transparent reparameterization outlined above clarifies the APC identification problem from a Bayesian perspective. Placing prior distributions over the parameters of the C-APC model has the potential to mislead researchers. The reason is that, in both the frequentist and Bayesian versions of the C-APC model, virtually the entire parameter vector is unidentified, because each estimated effect (i.e., each deviation from the grand mean) is composed of both linear and nonlinear effects. An unfortunate consequence is that the influence of the prior on the parameter estimates is unclear, because the prior is only partly updated by the likelihood.[20] In contrast, the reparameterized model splits the parameter vector into a set of identifiable parameters and an unidentified parameter, elucidating the central role of the prior in Bayesian APC models.

Introducing the linearized Bayesian APC model

The previous sections discussed how one can reparameterize the C-APC model into the L-APC model, which can then be used to illuminate the identification problem from a Bayesian perspective. Besides clarifying the identification problem, we can also use the L-APC model's parameterization to set up a linearized Bayesian APC (L-BAPC) model. As with the conventional (i.e., non-Bayesian) L-APC model, the design matrix is one that simply separates the linear from the nonlinear components. Prior distributions are then placed over the parameters, with particular attention to priors placed over the linear effects in light of their particular sensitivity to the specified priors. There are a wide range of possibilities for setting up the L-APC model. For example, one way to specify the L-BAPC model is as follows (again using "stacked" notation):

$$Y_{ijk} \sim \mathrm{N}\left(\hat{Y}_{ijk}, \sigma\right) \tag{8.31}$$

$$\hat{Y}_{ijk} = \mu + \alpha A_L + \pi P_L + \gamma C_L + \sum_{2}^{I-1} \tilde{\alpha}_i A_i + \sum_{2}^{J-1} \tilde{\pi}_j P_j + \sum_{2}^{K-1} \tilde{\gamma}_k C_k \tag{8.32}$$

$$\mu \sim \mathrm{N}\left(\mu_\mu, \sigma_\mu^2\right) \tag{8.33}$$

$$\alpha \sim \mathrm{Uniform}\left(a_\alpha, b_\alpha\right)$$

$$\pi \sim \mathrm{Uniform}\left(a_\pi, b_\pi\right) \tag{8.34}$$

$$\gamma \sim \mathrm{Uniform}\left(a_\gamma, b_\gamma\right)$$

$$\tilde{\alpha}_i \sim \mathrm{N}\left(\mu_{\tilde{\alpha}_i}, \sigma_{\tilde{\alpha}_i}^2\right) \quad \text{if} \quad i = 2,\dots,l-1$$

$$\tilde{\pi}_j \sim \mathrm{N}\left(\mu_{\tilde{\pi}_j}, \sigma_{\tilde{\pi}_j}^2\right) \quad \text{if} \quad j = 2,\dots,m-1 \tag{8.35}$$

$$\tilde{\gamma}_k \sim \mathrm{N}\left(\mu_{\tilde{\gamma}_k}, \sigma_{\tilde{\gamma}_k}^2\right) \quad \text{if} \quad k = 2,\dots,n-1$$

$$\tilde{\alpha}_i \sim \mathrm{Laplace}\left(\mu_{\tilde{\alpha}_i}, \sigma_{\tilde{\alpha}_i}^2\right) \quad \text{if} \quad i = l,\dots,I-1$$

$$\tilde{\pi}_j \sim \mathrm{Laplace}\left(\mu_{\tilde{\pi}_j}, \sigma_{\tilde{\pi}_j}^2\right) \quad \text{if} \quad j = m,\dots,J-1 \tag{8.36}$$

$$\tilde{\gamma}_k \sim \mathrm{Laplace}\left(\mu_{\tilde{\gamma}_k}, \sigma_{\tilde{\gamma}_k}^2\right) \quad \text{if} \quad k = n,\dots,K-1$$

$$\sigma \sim \mathrm{Uniform}\left(a_\sigma, b_\sigma\right), \tag{8.37}$$

where A_L, P_L and C_L represent the linear components and A_i, P_i and C_i represent the nonlinear components. The linear and nonlinear components are represented in terms of sum-to-zero orthogonal polynomial contrasts. For example, A_2 denotes a quadratic orthogonal polynomial age contrast, A_3 a cubic orthogonal polynomial age contrast, A_4 a quartic orthogonal polynomial age contrast, and so on. As with the C-APC model, the overall (or grand) mean is captured by the intercept μ. Equation 8.31 denotes the likelihood and Equation 8.32 denotes the model, while Equations 8.33–8.37 outline the prior distributions for the model parameters. In this particular version of the L-BAPC model I use uniform priors for the linear effects and variance. However, as I discuss below, many other options are available, which is an especially important consideration for the linear effects. When using orthogonal polynomials it is desirable to set more restrictive priors for the higher-order polynomials, which arguably just capture noise (or relatively minor fluctuations in the data). I define higher-order (versus lower-order) polynomials by some cut-off levels l, m and n for age, period and cohort, respectively. For the lower-order polynomials I use normal priors, while for the higher-order polynomials

I use Laplace distributions, also known as double-exponential distributions. The Laplace distribution can be specified so that there is a spiked concentration near zero, acting to "shrink" the coefficients.

Typology of priors

The priors outlined in the L-BAPC model above are just one set of distributions that could be placed over the parameters. Depending on the choice of prior distributions the L-BAPC model can be used to encode a wide range of explicit theoretical assumptions. In general, there are four main kinds of priors one can place over the linear and nonlinear effects: (1) proxy variables; (2) variable selection; (3) smoothing; and (4) bounding. This typology not only can help guide APC model-building, but also elucidates how a flexible Bayesian framework maps onto existing APC models coming out of the frequentist tradition. The distinctions between these priors are not hard-and-fast, however, and in practice multiple kinds of priors can be used in the same L-BAPC model.[21] For example, one could easily incorporate all four main kinds of priors by simply altering the input values of the priors in the L-BAPC model outlined in Equations 8.31–8.37. I review each of these types of priors in turn.

First, there are priors that represent information about proxy variables (or mechanisms). The conventional proxy variables approach involves replacing age, period or cohort with another variable thought to represent an underlying mechanism, such as relative cohort size in lieu of cohort (O'Brien, 1989). A more sophisticated version of the proxy variables technique is the mechanism-based approach advocated by Fosse and Winship (2019a), which entails specifying multiple mechanisms between one or more of the temporal variables and the outcome (see also Winship and Harding 2008). Using the L-BAPC model, the proxy variables approach implies placing informative priors on the linear and nonlinear parameters based on knowledge of specific mechanisms, possibly using estimates from previous studies or other datasets.

Second, variable selection priors can be used to encode beliefs that the parameter of interest is at or near zero. This is not an uncommon assumption. In fact, as noted by Fosse and Winship (2019a: 475), the great majority of studies examining social change simply drop one of the temporal variables altogether without explicitly specifying a full APC model. The variable selection approach using the L-BAPC would entail setting extremely strong priors towards zero on the linear and nonlinear effects of age, period or cohort. For example, instead of dropping the period variable, one could specify highly concentrated Laplace distributions at or near zero for the period linear effect and nonlinear effects.

Third, some priors can be used to smooth the temporal effects. In the frequentist tradition, a number of researchers have used age and age-squared instead of a full set of age parameters in an APC model, effectively smoothing the age nonlinearities. In terms of the L-BAPC, a comparable approach would entail, for instance, using highly concentrated Laplace distributions centered around zero for the higher-order age polynomials. Another way of applying a smoothing restriction in the frequentist tradition is the equality constraints approach, which typically involves grouping some pair of adjacent categories in the C–APC model. This constraint can be interpreted as a kind of smoothing technique in that the overall effects for the two adjacent categories are forced to be the same. An equivalent approach using the L–BAPC would involve, for example, specifying a prior for one of the linear effects with a distribution concentrated at that particular slope value implied by the desired equality constraint (see Fosse and Winship 2019a: 475–476).

Finally, there are priors that reflect bounding analyses. Using theoretically informed sign, size and shape constraints, Fosse and Winship (2019b) demonstrate how researchers can "zero out" parts of the parameter space to set upper and lower limits on one or more of the temporal effects. An equivalent approach using the L–BAPC would be the specification of uniform priors based on various beliefs about the sign, size or shape of the temporal effects. However, a wide range of other distributions are possible and in some cases slightly more exotic distributions might more closely represent existing theoretical knowledge on a topic. For example, instead of using a uniform prior for the age linear effect to encode the belief that the slope ranges from zero to positive infinity with equal probability, one could use a gamma distribution, reflecting the belief that the slope ranges from zero to positive infinity with some decreasing probability (Fosse and Winship 2019b: 2001).

Previous Bayesian APC models

The L–BAPC model presents a transparent parameterization, clarifying which parts of the model are identified and which parts are not, with the goal of using theoretical considerations to place informative prior distributions over some of the parameters. Previous Bayesian APC models have taken a different approach, focusing on either developing a more-or-less general estimator or using Bayesian models for forecasting. By and large, Bayesian APC models have not been widely used in sociology and related fields. Nonetheless, two Bayesian approaches have received significant attention in the APC literature: the Nakamura model and RW-1/RW-2 models (for discussions, see Glenn 2005; Smith and Wakefield 2016).[22] Both of these approaches begin with the C–APC model as the baseline parameterization.

The Bayesian model proposed by the statistician Takashi Nakamura (1986) has been touted as a "mechanical solution" that is applicable in a wide range of applied contexts (Sasaki and Suzuki 1989: 761). As Sasaki and Suzuki (1987: 1063) have claimed: "The Bayesian procedure in Nakamura's new method can provide a satisfactory explanation for the data almost automatically, without the identification specification that has occurred in previous cohort analysis and resulted in misleading findings". The basic idea of Nakamura's approach is that the temporal effects (i.e., deviations from the overall mean) of the C–APC model change relatively gradually, such that first-order differences in the successive effects are "close to zero" (Fukuda 2006; Nakamura 1986).

Specifically, let us define first-order differences $\alpha_i - \alpha_{i+1}$ for age groups $i = 1,\dots,I-1$, $\pi_j - \pi_{j+1}$ for period groups $j = 1,\dots,J-1$, and $\gamma_k - \gamma_{k+1}$ for cohort groups $k = 1,\dots,K-1$. Nakamura's method entails minimizing a weighted sum of squares of the first-order differences of the effects, or the following:

$$\frac{1}{\sigma_\alpha^2}\sum_{i=1}^{I-1}(\alpha_i - \alpha_{i+1})^2 + \frac{1}{\sigma_\pi^2}\sum_{j=1}^{J-1}(\pi_j - \pi_{j+1})^2 + \frac{1}{\sigma_\gamma^2}\sum_{k=1}^{K-1}(\gamma_k - \gamma_{k+1})^2, \tag{8.38}$$

where σ_α^2, σ_π^2 and σ_γ^2 are hyperparameters (Fukuda 2006, 2007, Miller and Nakamura 1996, 1997). Given values for these hyperparameters, the parameter vector β of the C-APC model can be estimated by the mode of the posterior distribution proportional to

$$p(\mathbf{y} \mid \mathbf{X},\beta,\sigma^2)p(\beta^\star \mid \sigma_\alpha^2,\sigma_\pi^2,\sigma_\gamma^2,\sigma^2), \tag{8.39}$$

where $\beta^\star$ is the parameter vector β excluding the intercept. To select values of the hyperparameters σ_α^2, σ_π^2 and σ_γ^2, Nakamura uses a fit statistic known as the Akaike Bayesian Information Criterion (ABIC), which in this case is defined as

$$\text{ABIC} = -2\ln\int p(\mathbf{y} \mid \mathbf{X},\beta,\sigma^2)p(\beta^\star \mid \sigma_\alpha^2,\sigma_\pi^2,\sigma_\gamma^2,\sigma^2)d\beta^\star + 2h, \tag{8.40}$$

where h is the number of hyperparameters and again $\beta^\star$ is the parameter vector β excluding the intercept (see Akaike 1998).

As with any APC approach that attempts to separate out all three time effects, Nakamura's technique is only as valid as its theoretical assumptions. There are two caveats regarding the Nakamura method (see also the criticisms by Glenn 1989, 2005). First, it is assumed to be a one-size-fits-all, mechanical estimator by at least some of its proponents (e.g., Sasaki and Suzuki 1987). However, only theoretical knowledge or additional data can justify the assumptions implied by the model. In particular, the claim that the parameters change gradually might be valid for some aging processes, but wholly contrary to basic assumptions for period and cohort-related processes, where abrupt discontinuities may be expected. Second, the technique is based on the C-APC parameterization and, as such, the flow of information is obscured. In light of the fact that only the intercept and nonlinear effects are identified, the prior distribution is imposing potentially strong assumptions on the linear effects.

A related set of Bayesian models has been developed based on random walk smoothing priors (Besag et al. 1995; Berzuini and Clayton 1993; Havulinna 2014; Knorr-Held and Rainer 2001; Schmid and Held 2004; Smith and Wakefield 2016). Typically these models have been used for extracting more reliable forecasts from APC models, essentially sidestepping the identification issue (e.g., see Bray et al.

2001; Havulinna 2014; Riebler and Held 2017; Schmid and Held 2007). The first-order random walk (RW1) prior penalizes deviations from a constant, stochastically shrinking the first-order differences towards zero, while the second-order random walk (RW2) prior penalizes deviations from a linear effect, stochastically restricting the second-order differences towards zero (Havulinna 2014: 847). The RW1 prior corresponds to the following for, say, the age effects:

$$\alpha_i \mid \alpha_i,...,\alpha_1 \sim N\left(\alpha_{i-1}, \sigma_\alpha^2\right), \quad \text{for} \quad i = 2,...,I, \tag{8.41}$$

with a uniform prior for the first age effect, α_1. In contrast, the RW2 prior corresponds to:

$$\alpha_i \mid \alpha_i,...,\alpha_1 \sim N\left(2\alpha_{i-1} - \alpha_{i-2}, \sigma_\alpha^2\right), \quad \text{for} \quad i = 3,...,I, \tag{8.42}$$

with independent uniform priors for the first and second age effects, α_1 and α_2. More generally, the random walk smoothing prior has the following form:

$$p(\alpha \mid \kappa_\alpha) \propto \kappa_\alpha^{\left(\frac{I-1}{2}\right)} e^{\left(-\frac{1}{2}\alpha^T \kappa_\alpha R\alpha\right)}, \tag{8.43}$$

where $\alpha = (\alpha_i,...,\alpha_I)^T$ is a column vector of age effects; κ_α is the precision, or inverse of the variance for age (i.e., $1/\sigma_\alpha^2$); e is the well-known constant; and **R** is a so-called "structure matrix" of dimension $I \times I$ that reflects some specified neighborhood structure depending on whether a RW1 or RW2 prior is desired (for examples, see Rue and Held 2005).[23] The precision κ_α is an estimated parameter that determines the degree of smoothing: the higher the precision (i.e., the lower the variance), the smoother the corresponding set of estimated temporal effects.

There are two main advantages to using models with random walk smoothing priors. First, smoothing the temporal effects is desirable because the extreme categories of age and cohort tend to have relatively few observations. As a result, in absence of smoothing, the estimated effects can fluctuate wildly. Second, smoothing is desirable for the purposes of social forecasting. In general, researchers have found that a model with RW2 priors gives more reliable forecasts than one with RW1 priors (e.g., see Smith and Wakefield 2016). The reason is that the estimated effects from the RW2 model tend to be smoother than those from the RW1 model, thereby generating projections that are less dependent on local variation in the data. The primary limitation of the APC literature on RW1 and RW2 models is that there have been few attempts to directly incorporate informative priors for the linear effects, which constitute the crux of the identification problem. Moreover, most APC studies using random walk smoothing priors have focused on the C-APC model rather than a reparameterized version that clearly differentiates those parameters that are identified from those that are not (for an exception, see Smith and Wakefield 2016: 603–608).

Example: political party strength

For the purposes of illustrating the utility of the L-BAPC with informative priors, I now turn to an examination of APC effects on political party strength (Converse 1976). The data consists of $n = 51,956$ respondents from the U.S. General Social Survey (GSS). Age and period are grouped into five-year intervals. The outcome variable captures political party strength, with higher values indicating greater strength, and lower values less strength.[24] Specifically, the variable is calculated by assigning a numerical value to one of four groups: $0 =$ independent , $1 =$ lean independent, $2 =$ weak party affiliation, $3 =$ strong party affiliation. This is identical to the coding used by the political scientist Philip Converse (1976: 166). For simplicity of exposition, and to parallel Converse's analysis, I assume the outcome is continuous.[25]

The joint estimated effects of age, period and cohort on party strength are shown in Figures 8.1 and 8.2. The number in each cell of Figure 8.1 and the surface height of Figure 8.2 indicate the predicted average party strength from a C-APC model with an arbitrary equality constraint. Note that the predicted means are identified, such that the C-APC model will generate the same set of predicted values regardless of the just-identifying constraint. The pattern of averages in Figures 8.1 and 8.2 suggests that all three temporal effects are operating, with age playing a particularly dominant role. However, these conclusions are tentative at best. Extreme care should be taken when interpreting the pattern of effects in Figures 8.1 and 8.2. Due to the linear dependency of the three time scales one cannot, from these visualizations alone, determine the unique contributions of age, period and cohort on party strength.

I next estimated the L-BAPC in Equations 8.31–8.37 using Markov Chain Monte Carlo (MCMC) techniques (for a detailed discussion, see Gelman et al. 2014: 275–292). For all models I used three chains, which is conventional in Bayesian modeling (McElreath 2018: 356–357). For all results reported here, standard diagnostic measures and visual output indicated convergence was achieved across chains. For instance, Gelman and Rubin's potential scale reduction factor, or $\hat{R}$, was near 1 for all parameters (Gelman et al. 2014: 285). Similarly, traceplots showed random scatter around an average value, indicating that the chains were "mixing" well. I placed noninformative prior distributions over the intercept and variance. For the quadratic, cubic, quartic and quintic polynomial parameters I used noninformative normal priors, while for the remaining higher-order polynomials I used Laplace priors concentrated around zero. As discussed previously, this set-up for the polynomials helps to reduce noise in the tails of age and cohort, which tend to be quite sparse. To derive informative priors for the linear effects, I considered three main sources of information: previously published results, theoretical claims

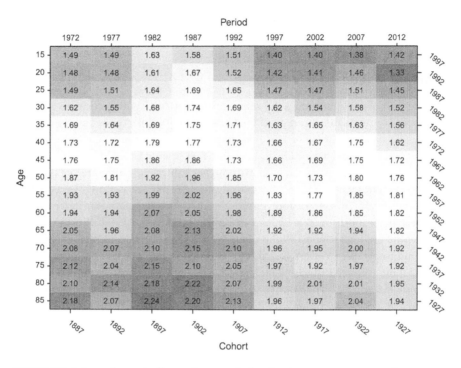

FIGURE 8.1 Joint estimated effects of age, period and cohort on party strength

in the literature on party strength, and qualitative judgments elicited from one or more subject matter experts.

First, regarding previously published results, Dassonneville (2017) examines the relationship between aging and party strength. The author fits a hierarchical age–period–cohort (HAPC) model, which tends to fix the cohort linear effect near zero (Fosse and Winship 2019a: 477–479).[26] An equivalent approach using the L-BAPC model entails placing a strong prior near zero for the cohort slope and noninformative priors for the age and period slopes. Accordingly, I used a highly concentrated Laplace distribution centered on zero for the cohort slope and diffuse normal priors for the age and period slopes. The results are shown in Figures 8.3 and 8.4. Figure 8.3 displays the posterior distributions for the linear and quadratic effects, while Figure 8.4 shows the overall estimated APC effects. For each distribution in Figure 8.3, a thick vertical line denotes the mean, and the shaded area the 95% credible interval. These results, mirroring the assumptions embedded in Dassonneville's model, reveal that party strength increases dramatically across the life course. However, these findings rely on the extremely strong assumption that the cohort effects exhibit trendless fluctuation, which may be called into question on a priori grounds.

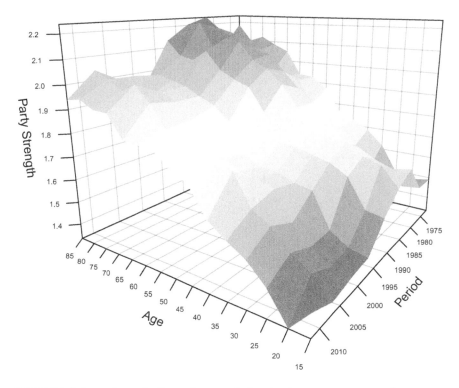

FIGURE 8.2 Joint estimated effects of age, period and cohort on party strength

A second source for constructing informative priors is sociological or political theory. Converse (1976) outlines a cognitive-behavioral argument for why partisanship is likely to increase with age (see also Converse 1969). In essence, he argues that partisan strength increases monotonically with age because people accumulate particular patterns of voting. The act of voting for one party more than another, even if initially by chance, will develop over time into a sustained preference for one party over another. Based on Converse's theory, the aging effect is approximated by a minimum monotonically increasing quadratic curve (see Figure 8.2 in Converse 1976: 44). To derive a prior for the age slope, I first ran the L-BAPC model with arbitrary priors on the slopes and noninformative priors on the remaining parameters. I estimated the age nonlinear effects using only the quadratic term, reflecting the smoothness of Converse's hypothetical age curve. Next, I used a monotonicity constraint to find the age slope corresponding to the minimum monotonically increasing set of age effects, where the effects are based only on the linear and quadratic terms (for details, see Fosse and Winship 2019b: 1989–1994). I then used the resultant age slope (0.234) as the mean in a normal prior for age in the full L-BAPC model, with the variance set to an arbitrarily small value.[27] The findings are shown

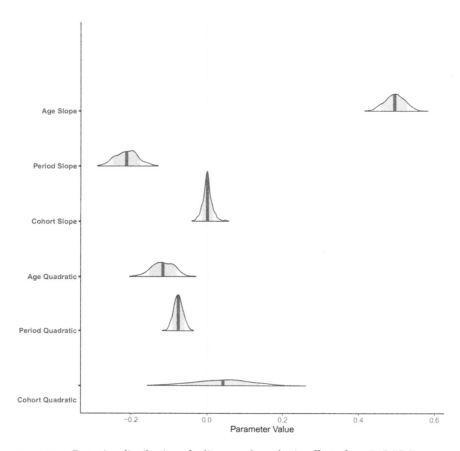

FIGURE 8.3 Posterior distributions for linear and quadratic effects, from L–BAPC model with a strong zero prior for the cohort slope

in Figures 8.5 and 8.6. As with the previous example, Figure 8.5 displays the posterior distributions for the linear and quadratic effects, while Figure 8.6 shows the corresponding overall estimated APC effects. Most strikingly, these findings reveal that, given Converse's cognitive-behavioral theory, there has been a steep decline in partisan affiliation across cohorts.

Finally, I elicited expert knowledge to extract a range of values for the age linear effect (Gill and Walker 2005; Kadane and Wolfson 1998; Meyer and Booker 2001). I used a graphical approach to elicit the requisite information, which has been shown to be superior to numerical-based methods of elicitation (Casement and Kahle 2018; Jones and Johnson 2014). Specifically, I recruited a subject matter expert who was knowledgeable on the aging process and life course theory. Next, I showed this expert a set of estimated age effects with the age slope fixed to zero. I then varied the slope parameter, asking the expert to report the most likely age

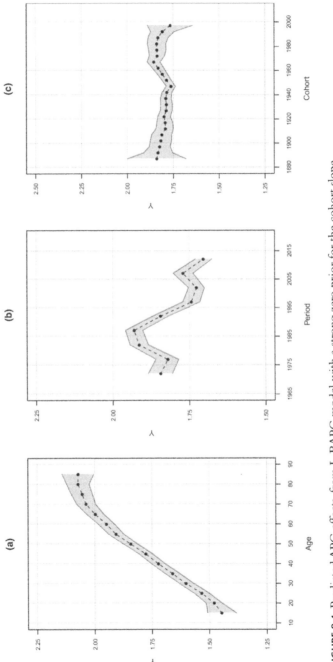

FIGURE 8.4 Predicted APC effects, from L–BAPC model with a strong zero prior for the cohort slope

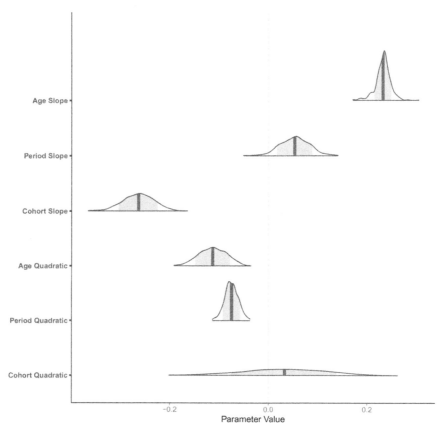

FIGURE 8.5 Posterior distributions for linear and quadratic effects of APC, from L-BAPC model with age assumed to monotonically increase

curve. For example, Figure 8.7 shows a set of different age curves, where the only difference is that the age slope is fixed to a different value. The expert was not shown graphs of the period or cohort effects during elicitation. Once the expert selected a particular curve as the most likely one, I set upper and lower limits of increasing size around it. For each set of limits I asked whether or not the interval contained 95% of the theoretically possible age slopes. From this graphical elicitation I obtained an implied prior on the linear age effect. The estimated APC effects are shown in Figure 8.8. These findings reveal that party strength has declined primarily due to cohort replacement, although there is a somewhat smaller negative period effect as well. Analyses also indicate that as people age they become more partisan, consistent with Converse's claim that younger people in general have not yet formed strong partisan attachments.

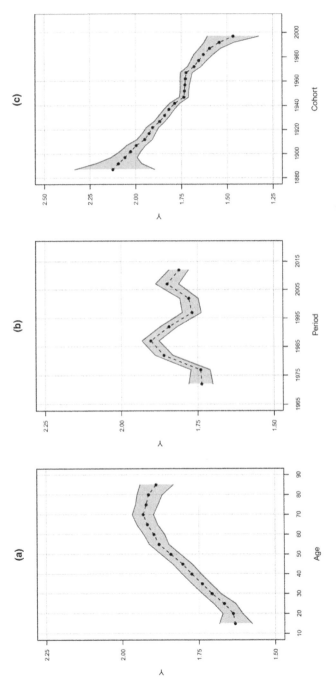

FIGURE 8.6 Predicted APC effects, from L–BAPC model with age constrained to monotonically increase

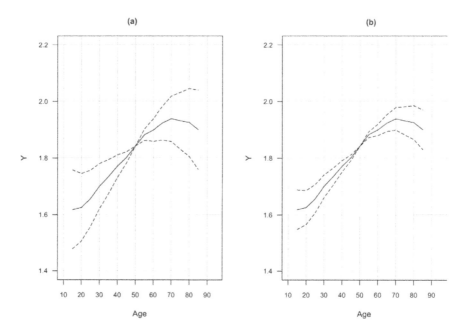

FIGURE 8.7 Age curves under different slope constraints, as shown to a subject matter expert

Conclusion

This chapter outlined a Bayesian perspective on APC modeling, illustrating how a transparent reparameterization can clarify the underlying, sometimes implicit, assumptions of many temporal models. The Bayesian framework can be viewed as a generalization of the constraint-based approach commonly used by APC analysts coming out of the frequentist tradition. In many cases, a Bayesian model using concentrated prior distributions will provide virtually the same point and interval estimates as constraint-based methods. Notwithstanding this, the advantage of the Bayesian framework is that one can arguably use a much more diverse set of prior distributions than those implied by the frequentist approach.

From a modeling perspective, a Bayesian analysis is often not that different from a frequentist approach, but there are some important issues that have prevented Bayesian methods from gaining wider use. For example, to estimate the normalized posterior distribution one needs the unconditional distribution of the data, which typically requires evaluating a high-dimensional integral. In all but the simplest cases, the unconditional distribution of the data has no tractable closed-form solution.[28] As a result, Bayesian inference focuses extensively on the appropriate use of computational procedures, most commonly MCMC methods. This can entail a fairly high upfront cost for the researcher in terms of time and effort. Besides computational issues, additional

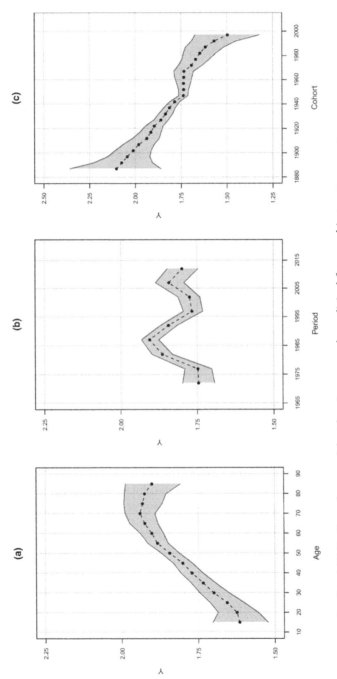

FIGURE 8.8 Predicted APC effects, from model with prior on age slope elicited from a subject matter expert

considerations in the Bayesian framework include, for example, eliciting relevant information for the prior distribution from subject matter experts, choosing an appropriate likelihood function, and succinctly summarizing the posterior distribution.

However, in the case of APC data, additional care is required because of the underlying identification problem. As I have demonstrated, the choice of the prior distribution in APC models typically has a very strong influence over the posterior distribution, because only one part of the data, in fact, induces variation in the likelihood function. Moreover, the influence of the prior on the unidentified parameters does not diminish as the sample size increases. This issue is complicated by the fact that the influence of the prior is often "hidden" due to the way in which APC models are conventionally parameterized, which fails to separate the identified from the unidentified components. Consequently, there is a real danger of researchers using a Bayesian APC model mechanically without fully understanding the extent to which the results rely critically on potentially strong assumptions encoded in the prior distribution.

The recovery of the true, unknown APC effects is only as reliable as the social, biological or cultural theories on which one's assumptions are based. Theories of underlying processes may be fundamentally flawed, thereby leading to mistaken conclusions about APC effects. There is, in this sense, no ultimate resolution of the APC identification problem. Yet, the Bayesian framework is a powerful engine for incorporating additional information, or what I have called *primary information*, into an APC analysis. Future work should consider more carefully the various ways in which such primary information, encoded as prior distributions, can be more effectively elicited and incorporated into APC models.

Online supplementary material relating to this book can be found at www.routledge.com/9780367174439.

Notes

1 Following the convention in the APC literature, I use the shorthand of "effects" when referring to age, period and cohort processes (e.g., Fienberg et al. 1979; Glenn 1981; Mason et al. 1973;). These "effects" need not refer to causal effects in the sense of parameters with well-defined potential outcomes or (counterfactuals) (see Morgan and Winship 2014).

2 For excellent technical overviews, see Gelman et al. (2014: 3–28); Gill (2008: 1–71); Jackman (2009: 3–48); Lynch (2007: 47–76); and Wang et al. (2018: 3–18).

3 It is important to remember that $\mathcal{L}(\theta \mid \mathbf{y})$ is *not* a probability distribution for the parameter θ given the data $\mathbf{y}$. Rather, it is a function that expresses how probable a given set of observations is for different values of the parameter, with the uncertainty deriving not from the fixed (albeit unknown) quantity θ but from the random variable $\mathbf{y}$.

4 For mathematical convenience, instead of a likelihood function, researchers will often use a log-likelihood function, denoted by $\ell(\theta \mid \mathbf{y}) = \log(\mathcal{L}(\theta \mid \mathbf{y}))$. However, conceptually the log-likelihood function presents no additional complications.

5 Even though the parameters are treated as random variables in the Bayesian approach, by convention they are still denoted using Greek letters because they are unknown quantities.

6 Sometimes the denominator is also referred to as the *marginal likelihood* or the *prior predictive distribution* (Gill, 2008: 44).

7 The product $p(\mathbf{y} \mid \theta)p(\theta)$ can be interpreted as the unnormalized posterior distribution. Often a researcher can focus on estimating an unnormalized posterior distribution because, in many but not all cases, the posterior can be renormalized in the final step of the analysis (Gill 2008: 43–44).

8 So far I have focused on inference for a single parameter, but the discussion extends easily to a vector of parameters. Define $\theta = (\theta_1, \ldots, \theta_k)^T$, where k is the number of parameters. With multiple parameters, we can simply refer to a joint prior distribution $p(\theta)$, joint likelihood $p(\mathbf{y} \mid \theta)$ and joint posterior distribution $p(\theta \mid \mathbf{y})$, with $p(\theta \mid \mathbf{y}) \propto p(\theta)p(\mathbf{y} \mid \theta)$.

9 With diffuse or flat priors, the Bayesian credible interval is similar to a 95% confidence interval in the frequentist perspective.

10 Note that I is added to $j - i$ so that the cohort index begins at $k = 1$. This ensures that, for example, $i = j = k = 1$ refers to the first group for all three temporal measures. One could just as easily index the cohorts using $k = j - i$, but this identity would be lost.

11 This model assumes we have aggregated data in a Lexis table. If we have individual-level data, we may also want to index the individuals in the data using $n = 1, \ldots, q$, where q is the sample size. This would lead to a model specified as $Y_{ijkn} = \mu + \alpha_i + \pi_j + \gamma_k + \epsilon_{ijkn}$. For simplicity in the rest of this chapter I assume we are using aggregated data, such that the data has $I \times J$ rows.

12 For the rest of this chapter, I will assume that sum-to-zero constraints are specified, with the last category of each temporal variable dropped. However, a number of other constraints are possible. For example, one could fix the parameters at one of the levels to zero (e.g., $\hat{\alpha}_{i=1} = \hat{\pi}_{j=1} = \hat{\gamma}_{k=1} = 0$ or $\hat{\alpha}_{i=I} = \hat{\pi}_{j=J} = \hat{\gamma}_{k=K} = 0$).

13 Both $\hat{\beta}_{\mathrm{MLE}}$ and $\hat{\beta}_{\mathrm{OLS}}$ give unbiased estimates of the true parameter vector β. However, unlike OLS, maximum likelihood estimation will generate a biased estimate of σ^2, thus requiring a bias correction (Wang et al. 2018: 40).

14 Before the widespread availability of powerful computing, it was especially important to specify what is called a *conjugate* prior (Gill 2008: 54, 111–116). A conjugate prior refers to a prior in which the posterior has the same probability distribution family. Accordingly, there is an analytical solution – an explicit formula – for the posterior distribution expressed in terms of the prior parameters and the data. The main limitation of using conjugate priors is that analytical solutions are typically only feasible for quite simple models (Gelman et al. 2014: 35–36). However, with modern computing techniques there is considerably greater flexibility in modeling choices.

15 All priors are informative in the sense that the analyst is introducing some kind of information into the model.

16 I use the terms "unidentified" and "nonidentified" interchangeably. Gustafson (2015: 4) prefers the phrase "partially identified" to underscore that even when a model is not identified there is often some information to be gleaned from the unidentified parameters.

17 The linear dependence is reflected in the null vector (i.e., the eigenvector with a zero eigenvalue) of the design matrix, which has non-zero elements (e.g., Kupper 1985: 829).

18 Fosse and Winship (2019b) show how the canonical solution line can be visualized using what they call a *2D-APC graph* (1984–1987).

19 Note that the identified parameter vector length is one less than that of the full parameter vector, reflecting the fact that the full design matrix of $\mathbf{X}$ is rank deficient one after applying sum-to-zero constraints.

20 It is common in the APC literature to use a non-transparent parameterization, which can easily lead analysts astray. Two researchers analyzing the same APC data may inadvertently

impose different conditional prior distributions on the unidentified parameter, thereby generating divergent findings.

21 For an excellent overview of the three main kinds of priors used in Bayesian analysis (conjugate, noninformative and informative), see Gill (2008: 135–189).
22 Due to space limitations I do not cover here the hierarchical age–period–cohort (HAPC) model, which has an implicit Bayesian interpretation due to the hierarchical structure of the model. For an explicitly Bayesian implementation of the HAPC, see Yang (2006). For an overview of the assumptions of the HAPC, see Fosse and Winship (2019a: 477–479).
23 Note that the structure matrix is of rank $I-1$ for the RW1 prior and rank $I-2$ for the RW2 prior. The RW1 and RW2 priors are both prominent examples of intrinsic Gaussian Markov random fields (GMRF) (for details, see Rue and Held 2005).
24 Converse (1976: 10–11) distinguishes between the direction of party choice (e.g., Democratic vs. Republican) and strength of party identification regardless of party choice (e.g., "strong" vs. "weak").
25 I obtain similar results treating the outcome as an ordered categorical variable.
26 See Table 7.2 and Figure 7.4 in Dassonneville (2017: 153–154), which indicate a near-zero linear effect for cohort.
27 Unfortunately, Converse's theory does not suggest a spread for the age slope prior distribution.
28 A special case occurs when the prior distribution is a conjugate prior, which enables a relatively simple analytical solution. With a conjugate prior, the prior distribution is chosen so that the likelihood and prior combine to generate a posterior distribution in the same family as the prior distribution.

References

Akaike, Hirotugu (1998). "Likelihood and the Bayes Procedure". In *Selected Papers of Hirotugu Akaike*. Edited by Emanuel Parzen, Kunio Tanabe, and Genshiro Kitagawa. New York, NY: Springer, pp. 309–332.

Aster, Richard C., Brian Borchers, and Clifford H. Thurber (2018). *Parameter Estimation and Inverse Problems*. Cambridge, MA: Elsevier.

Berzuini, Carlo (1993). "Bayesian Inference on the Lexis Diagram". *Bulletin of the International Statistical Institute* 50, pp. 149–164.

Besag, Julian et al. (1995). "Bayesian Computation and Stochastic Systems". *Statistical Science* 10.1, pp. 3–41.

Bray, Isabelle, Paul Brennan, and Paolo Bo (2001). "Recent Trends and Future Projections of Lymphoid Neoplasms: A Bayesian Age–Period–Cohort Analysis". Cancer Causes & Control, 12, 813–820.

Casement, Christopher J. and David J. Kahle (2018). "Graphical Prior Elicitation in Univariate Models". *Communications in Statistics – Simulation and Computation* 47.10, pp. 2906–2924.

Converse, Philip E. (1969). "Of Time and Partisan Stability". *Comparative Political Studies* 2.2, pp. 139–171.

——— (1976). *The Dynamics of Party Support: Cohort-Analyzing Party Identification*. Beverly Hills: Sage.

Dassonneville, Ruth (2017). "Age and Voting". In Arzheimer, Kai, Jocelyn Evans, and Michael S. Lewis-Beck, eds. *The SAGE Handbook of Electoral Behaviour*. London: Sage, pp. 137–158.

Fienberg, Stephen E. (1979). "Identification and Estimation of Age–Period–Cohort Models in the Analysis of Discrete Archival Data". *Sociological Methodology* 10, pp. 1–67.

Fienberg, Stephen E. and William M. Mason (1985) "Specification and implementation of age, period and cohort models". In Mason, William M. and Stephen E. Fienberg, eds. *Cohort Analysis in Social Research*. New York: Springer, pp. 45–88.

Fosse, Ethan and Christopher Winship (2018). "Moore–Penrose Estimators of Age–Period–Cohort Effects: Their Interrelationship and Properties". *Sociological Science* 5.14, pp. 304–334.

———— (2019a). "Analyzing Age–Period–Cohort Data: A Review and Critique". *Annual Review of Sociology* 45, pp. 467–492.

———— (2019b). "Bounding Analyses of Age–Period–Cohort Effects". *Demography* 56.5, pp. 1975–2004.

Fukuda, Kosei (2006). "A Cohort Analysis of Female Labor Participation Rates in the U.S. and Japan". *Review of Economics of the Household* 4.4, pp. 379–393.

———— (2007). "An Empirical Analysis of US and Japanese Health Insurance Using Age–Period–Cohort Decomposition". *Health Economics* 16.5, pp. 475–489.

Gelfand, Alan E. and Sujit K. Sahu (1999). "Identifiability, Improper Priors, and Gibbs Sampling for Generalized Linear Models". *Journal of the American Statistical Association* 94.445, pp. 247–253.

Gelman, Andrew et al. (2014). *Bayesian Data Analysis*. 3rd ed. Boca Raton: CRC Press.

Gill, Jeff (2008). *Bayesian Methods: A Social and Behavioral Sciences Approach*. 3rd ed. Boca Raton: CRC Press.

Gill, Jeff and Lee D. Walker (2005). "Elicited Priors for Bayesian Model Specifications in Political Science Research". *The Journal of Politics* 67.3, pp. 841–872.

Glenn, Norval D. (1981). "The Utility and Logic of Cohort Analysis". *The Journal of Applied Behavioral Science* 17.2, pp. 247–257.

———— (1989). "A Caution About Mechanical Solutions to the Identification Problem in Cohort Analysis: Comment on Sasaki and Suzuki". *American Journal of Sociology* 95.3, pp. 754–761.

———— (2005). *Cohort Analysis*. 2nd ed. Thousand Oaks, CA: Sage Publications.

Gustafson, Paul (2005). "On Model Expansion, Model Contraction, Identifiability and Prior Information: Two Illustrative Scenarios Involving Mismeasured Variables". *Statistical Science* 20.2, pp. 111–140.

———— (2009). "What Are the Limits of Posterior Distributions Arising From Nonidentified Models, and Why Should We Care?" *Journal of the American Statistical Association* 104.488, pp. 1682–1695.

———— (2015). *Bayesian Inference for Partially Identified Models: Exploring the Limits of Limited Data*. Boca Raton: CRC Press.

Havulinna, Aki S. (2014). "Bayesian Age–Period–Cohort Models with Versatile Interactions and Long-Term Predictions: Mortality and Population in Finland 1878–2050". *Statistics in Medicine* 33.5, pp. 845–856.

Jackman, Simon (2009). *Bayesian Data Analysis for the Social Sciences*. Chichester: Wiley.

Jones, Geoffrey and Wesley O. Johnson (2014). "Prior Elicitation: Interactive Spreadsheet Graphics With Sliders Can Be Fun, and Informative". *The American Statistician* 68.1, pp. 42–51.

Kadane, Joseph B. and Lara J. Wolfson (1998). "Experiences in Elicitation". *Journal of the Royal Statistical Society. Series D (The Statistician)* 47.1, pp. 3–19.

Knorr-Held, Leonhard and Evi Rainer (2001). "Projections of Lung Cancer Mortality in West Germany: A Case Study in Bayesian Prediction". *Biostatistics* 2.1, pp. 109–129.

Kupper, Lawrence L. et al. (1985). "Statistical Age–Period–Cohort Analysis: A Review and Critique". *Journal of Chronic Diseases* 38.10, pp. 811–830.

Lindley, D. V. (1972). *Bayesian Statistics: A Review*. Philadelphia: Society for Industrial and Applied Mathematics.

Lynch, Scott M. (2007). *Introduction to Applied Bayesian Statistics and Estimation for Social Scientists*. New York: Springer.

Mason, Karen Oppenheim, William M. Mason, et al. (1973). "Some Methodological Issues in Cohort Analysis of Archival Data". *American Sociological Review* 38.2, p. 242.

Mason, William M. and Stephen E. Fienberg, eds. (1985a). *Cohort Analysis in Social Research: Beyond the Identification Problem*. New York, NY: Springer.

——— (1985b). "Introduction: Beyond the Identification Problem". In Mason, William M. and Stephen E. Fienberg, eds. *Cohort Analysis in Social Research*. New York: Springer, pp. 1–8.

McElreath, Richard (2018). *Statistical Rethinking: A Bayesian Course with Examples in R and Stan*. 1st ed. Boca Raton: Chapman and Hall/CRC.

Meyer, Mary A. and Jane M. Booker (2001). *Eliciting and Analyzing Expert Judgment: A Practical Guide*. Philadelphia, PA: Society for Industrial and Applied Mathematics and American Statistical Association.

Miller, Alan S. and Takashi Nakamura (1996). "On the Stability of Church Attendance Patterns during a Time of Demographic Change: 1965–1988". *Journal for the Scientific Study of Religion* 35.3, p. 275.

——— (1997). "Trends in American Public Opinion: A Cohort Analysis of Shifting Attitudes from 1972–1990". *Behaviormetrika* 24.2, pp. 179–191.

Morgan, Stephen L. and Christopher Winship (2014). *Counterfactuals and Causal Inference: Methods and Principles for Social Research*. 2nd ed. New York: Cambridge University Press.

Nakamura, Takashi (1986). "Bayesian Cohort Models for General Cohort Table Analyses". *Annals of the Institute of Statistical Mathematics* 38.1, pp. 353–370.

Neath, Andrew A. and Francisco J. Samaniego (1997). "On the Efficacy of Bayesian Inference for Nonidentifiable Models". *The American Statistician* 51.3, pp. 225–232.

Nielsen, Bent and Jens P. Nielsen (2014). "Identification and Forecasting in Mortality Models". *The Scientific World Journal* 2014, pp. 1–24.

O'Brien, Robert (1989). "Relative Cohort Size and Age-Specific Crime Rates: An Age-Period-Relative-Cohort-Size Model". *Criminology* 27, pp. 57–78.

O'Brien, Robert (2015). *Age–Period–Cohort Models: Approaches and Analyses with Aggregate Data*. Boca Raton: CRC Press.

Poirier, Dale J. (1998). "Revising Beliefs in Nonidentified Models". *Econometric Theory* 14.4, pp. 483–509.

Riebler, Andrea and Leonhard Held (2017). "Projecting the Future Burden of Cancer: Bayesian Age–Period–Cohort Analysis with Integrated Nested Laplace Approximations: Projecting the Future Burden of Cancer". *Biometrical Journal* 59.3, pp. 531–549.

Rue, Håvard and Leonhard Held (2005). *Gaussian Markov Random Fields: Theory and Applications*. Boca Raton: Chapman & Hall/CRC.

Ryder, Norman B. (1965). "The Cohort as a Concept in the Study of Social Change". *American Sociological Review* 30.6, pp. 843–861.

Sasaki, Masamichi and Tatsuzo Suzuki (1987). "Changes in Religious Commitment in the United States, Holland, and Japan". *American Journal of Sociology* 92.5, pp. 1055–1076.

——— (1989). "A Caution About the Data to Be Used for Cohort Analysis: Reply to Glenn". *American Journal of Sociology* 95.3, pp. 761–765.

Schmid, Volker and Leonhard Held (2004). "Bayesian Extrapolation of Space-Time Trends in Cancer Registry Data". *Biometrics* 60.4, pp. 1034–1042.

——— (2007). "Bayesian Age–Period–Cohort Modeling and Prediction – BAMP". *Journal of Statistical Software* 21.8, pp. 1–15.

Smith, Theresa R. and Jon Wakefield (2016). "A Review and Comparison of Age–Period–Cohort Models for Cancer Incidence". *Statistical Science* 31.4, pp. 591–610.

Trader, Ramona L. (2014). "Regression, Bayesian". *Wiley StatsRef: Statistics Reference Online*. eprint: https://onlinelibrary.wiley.com/doi/pdf/10.1002/9781118445112.stat00246.

Wang, Xiaofeng, Yuryan Yue, and Julian J. Faraway (2018). *Bayesian Regression Modeling with Inla*. 1st ed. Boca Raton: Chapman and Hall/CRC.

Winship, Christopher and David J. Harding (2008). "A Mechanism-Based Approach to the Identification of Age–Period–Cohort Models". *Sociological Methods & Research* 36.3, pp. 362–401.

Yang, Yang. (2006). "Bayesian Inference for Hierarchical Age–Period–Cohort Models of Repeated Cross-Section Survey Data". *Sociological Methodology* 36, pp. 39–74.

Yang, Yang and Kenneth C. Land (2013). *Age–Period–Cohort Analysis: New Models, Methods, and Empirical Applications*. Boca Raton: Chapman and Hall/CRC.

9

AGE–PERIOD–COHORT ANALYSIS

What is it good for?

Herbert L. Smith

If you know when someone was born, and you know what time it is, you know how old he or she is. If you know how old someone is and when he or she were born, you know the date on which he or she are being observed. If you know someone's age as of a given time, you know when he or she were born. These are ineluctable features of algebra (age ≡ period − cohort) and geometry, as reflected in the Lexis diagram (Chauvel 2014, 384–389). There are many ways that one can turn the problem (*e.g.*, cohort ≡ period − age) and thus many alternative forms of observation, classification and depiction. However, there is a strong statistical sense in which there are only two pieces of information, not three.

This chafes, because in sociology and other social and population sciences, it is not hard to conjure for each temporal dimension "a distinct causal interpretation" (Mason *et al*. 1973, 243). A primordial example is political party identification (Oppenheim 1970):

> [T]he political environment in which a particular birth cohort first enters the electorate may help determine the extent to which individuals in that cohort identify with a political party for the remainder of their lives. As that party experiences normal fluctuations in political fortunes, however, some members of the cohort may temporarily shift their loyalties. Both cohort and short-term period effects can thus contribute to party identification. Since the aging process might also independently affect party identification (as persons become more "conservative" with age, for example, they may find the Republicans increasingly attractive), we have here another example in which age, period and cohort conceptually have distinct causal impacts on the dependent variable.
>
> (Mason *et al*. 1973, 244–245)

Persons reaching their majority in the New Deal era may have been more likely to be Democrats than those in preceding or subsequent cohorts. Net of this, aging into mid-life may have pushed them more toward the Republicans. With a bit more precision, you can know that we are looking at party identification circa 1964, when the Republicans nominated a candidate viewed as too conservative to win, and the Democrats benefited from the holdover popularity of a recently assassinated young president. The period under observation is knowable from the age and the birth cohort of a set of respondents. However, there is nothing about the events of the period shaping party identification that follow necessarily from the experience of this cohort in early adult life or the leavening effects of prosperity and responsibility on youthful idealism. The temporal markers are linear functions of one another. Their manifestations are not.

On cohort analysis

"Any quantitative *cohort* analysis is a form of time-series analysis" (Fienberg and Mason 1985, 85 [emphasis added]). A corollary is that the concept of a cohort is what is distinct about age-graded data analyzed over historical time. Keeping this in mind helps in specifying models and analyses that convey meaning in the presence of a linear identity that is algebraically tautological and sociologically meaningless.

In sociology, the foundational paper on cohort analysis is Ryder (1965). At the time of the publication of Mason *et al.* (1973), it hit a steady pace of citations (Figure 9.1). This pace persisted through its republication in the volume on *Cohort Analysis in Social Research: Beyond the Identification Problem* (Mason and Fienberg 1985), and onward to 2005, when it was recognized as being among the "greatest hits" of the *American Sociological Review* (Jacobs 2005). This was also the time when it was becoming clear that the field had not yet moved beyond the identification problem. Citations to Ryder (1965) accelerated, coincident with a new wave of papers on issues of identification in age–period–cohort analysis – in particular, the Intrinsic Estimator (Yang *et al.* 2004). This is notwithstanding that Ryder (1965) is not a technical paper and does not mention the identification problem. The paper concludes with a summary statement that does sound like a call for the estimation of something like cohort effects: "The purpose of this essay is to direct the attention of sociologists toward the study of time series of parameters for successive cohorts of various types, in contradistinction to conventional period-by-period analyses" (861).

However, the methodological concerns that are touched on concern the onerous demands for data collection and the difficulty of making comparisons across cohorts under conditions of differential selectivity. They are, in the event, essentially second-order: "Yet such difficulties are not so much those of the method itself as meaningful reflections of the research investment necessary to study a long-lived species experiencing structural transformation" (861). People live a long time, but they do not live forever. Experiences at early ages can have profound effects. Events at a given time can have differential effects on individuals at different ages.

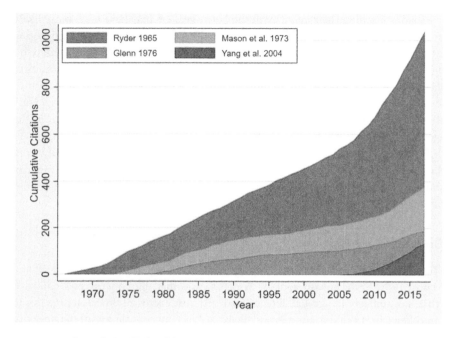

FIGURE 9.1 Cumulative Web of Science citations to Ryder (1965) and to selected subsequent papers in sociology on cohort analysis

Social change via the succession of differentiated cohorts implicates: the distinction between changes in an individual and changes in a population; socialization and social control across the life course; the adaptiveness of a society versus the "limited intellectual flexibility" (844) of an individual; and the role of a cohort as the embodiment and historical representation of an admix of social events and individual experiences. Ryder's (1965) synthesis of ideas from the sociology of generations (Mannheim 1952), demography, history, developmental psychology and what is now known as life course analysis has become such a touchstone for the concept of cohort analysis that it is easy to miss something that he does not talk about: *linear trends*. Nor are they present in analyses that are faithful to this conceptual perspective.

ConsiderYang's (2016) cohort biography of the Red Guard generation, the Chinese who were teens and young adults at the time of the 1966–68 Cultural Revolution. They were the first cohort raised under Communism. They were mobilized to fight against functionaries in the Cultural Revolution, were subsequently exiled to the countryside, and were variously rehabilitated, deradicalized and reintegrated in a fraught journey that shaped and reshaped Chinese history – and their cohort.

> I use terms such as *trajectories, journey*, and *life course* to talk about the history of the Red Guard generation. These words may convey a sense of linear progress, as if, from the time of birth, members of the Red Guard generation

were destined to march toward a clear, fixed, and grand goal … By analyzing the longer history of the Red Guard generation, which will highlight the many ups and downs of the generation, I … will show the futility of grand teleological perspectives for understanding history. There is neither linearity nor teleology to the trajectory of the Red Guard generation, or perhaps other political generations in other times and places … For the protagonists of my story, the history of a generation was nothing less than a history of perpetual disruption of personal lives.

(Yang 2016, 5)

Yang's (2016) study, which pertains to a single cohort and is non-quantitative at that, is an example of the kind of "composite cohort biograph[y]" whose comparison with other cohorts "would yield the most direct and efficient measurement of the consequences of social change" (Ryder 1965, 847). Which can also be done quantitatively. The radicalizing political and social events in China circa 1968 had contemporaneous parallels globally, including in France. Thus it is not surprising that *les soixante-huitards* – the generation that came of political age, at least emblematically, among the civil unrest of May 1968 – figures often, via comparison of cohort "destinies," in Chauvel's (2014) analysis of changes in French social structure across the 20th century (and into the current one). This was a generation that turned from street protest to electoral participation: In the legislative elections of 1981 they displaced a prior generation of politicians whose youth in the aftermath of the Second World War had provided *them* with opportunities given the number of *their* elders tarnished by the war and the Occupation. The *soixante-huitards* thereupon encrusted themselves in the French body politic in a manner that left scant room for subsequent generations (Chauvel 2014, 36–43).

This is a form of "generational domination" (Chauvel 2014, 10) that highlights not just the social, historical and political biographies of generations, but their interplay. In France, a cohort's experience at a given point in time reflects not just its past and its development, but the opportunity structure of a period as conditioned by the experience of *other* cohorts at other times. Policy decisions made at one time for one reason – on the expansion of education, for example – can be a boon for one generation, to the detriment of those that follow (Chauvel 2014, 232–239).

Generational dominance, or the hoarding of opportunities, is only one manner in which cohorts are useful for understanding how historical events reshape social structure. "To some extent all cohorts respond to any given period-specific stimulus. Rarely are changes so localized in either age or time that their burden falls exclusively on the shoulders of one cohort" (Ryder 1965, 847).

So which cohorts shoulder the burden – or reap the rewards? The Nineteenth Amendment to the United States Constitution, enacted in 1920, extended to women the right to vote. The degree to which women took up the franchise depended on how long they had been living in a polity in which voting was forbidden to them. The longer they had lived under the old regime, the more they seem to have been inculcated with the idea that voting is not for women, and the less likely they were to vote during the remainder of their lives. We know this because voting among women, *relative to voting among same-generation men*, picked up in inverse correlation to their age (cohort membership) in 1920. Eventually, women who were either too young in 1920 to have been aware of their disenfranchisement, or who were born after 1920, could no longer be distinguished from men in their propensity to vote (Firebaugh and Chen 1995). Another feature of this study reinforces the power of the cohort as a tool for understanding social change: The voting data are from national elections between 1952 and 1988, long after the historical event whose effects are being inferred. The concept of a cohort thus provides both a window on the past, and a glimpse into the future.

I once wrote that sociologists and demographers are "mad for cohorts" (Smith 2008, 289), which is infelicitous insofar as it implies that there is something either frivolous or romantic in the frequency with which the concept figures in our research. There can be a real power to cohort analysis. At the same time, we should not unduly reify the construct. Ryder (1965) was simultaneously of two minds about this:

> As a minimum, the cohort is a structural category with the same kind of analytic utility as a variable like social class. Such structural categories have explanatory power because they are surrogate indices for the common experiences of many persons in each category. Conceptually the cohort resembles most closely the ethnic group: membership is determined at birth, and often has considerable capacity to explain variance, but need not imply that the category is an organized group.
>
> (847)

So is a cohort like a social class, or isn't it? An occupation indexes a class in the same sense that a birthdate indexes a cohort, but in the former instance the analytic category entails interests as well, if not self-consciousness (Wright 1997). There may indeed be historical cohorts that are like social classes in that sense — the Red Guard generation being an obvious example, perhaps the *soixante-huitards* as well — but the women who were sentient at the time of the Nineteenth Amendment probably did not constitute cohorts in the same fashion. Their birthdates are just a way of keeping track of them.

> From this view comes an operating conception of a cohort, conceived not as a concrete group, but as a possible key to understanding social change. As a result it is very different from the concept of social class: It is based above all on its technical construction and constitutes an instrument of objectification. The cohort is thus a tool and not necessarily a strong element of the theoretical apparatus of sociology: Its characterization as a relevant group can only be a result—true, false, or somewhere in between—according to the purpose [of the exercise], and not an a priori hypothesis.
>
> (Chauvel 2014, 383 [my translation])

"'Cohort analysis,' after all, is a means and not an end in itself" (Duncan 1985, 300). The proof of the pudding is inevitably in the tasting (Smith, Mason, and Fienberg 1982, 792). Many of the perceived analytic problems associated with so-called age–period–cohort analysis recede if we keep the cohorts in the fore, not for any special statistical reason, but because of the conceptual utility for reading the data. In the sections that follow, I revisit from this perspective several of the key issues in the identification of these models, and conclude with some orienting suggestions. There is no panacea, but this has less to do with the remorselessness of algebra and geometry than it does with the absence of an ailment. Once one stops thinking about events (or is it their causes?) flowing simultaneously (and, implicitly, infinitely) through historical time in two non-concomitant directions, things improve considerably.

Identification entails a constraint on linear terms

The *mésalliance* between an algebraic identity and theoretical aspirations put a bad curse on *statistical* treatments of "age–period–cohort analysis." This is unfortunate. From the beginning, it was recognized that the algebraic identity that reduces three dimensions to two obtains only with respect to the *linear* terms in age, period and cohort. Thus whereas

$$Y = \alpha + \beta_1 A + \beta_2 P + \beta_3 C + \varepsilon \tag{9.1}$$

is not estimable,

$$Y = \alpha + \beta_1 A^2 + \beta_2 P + \beta_3 C + \varepsilon \tag{9.2}$$

is estimable, and under certain circumstances it might be appropriate to think about models in which at least one of the three temporal dimensions is not linearly related to the response:

> For example, if we were studying age-period-specific fertility rates as a cohort problem, we clearly would not want to specify a linear relationship between fertility rates and age … Women do not, we know, have a higher probability of a birth with each additional year that they age.
>
> (Mason *et al.* 1972, 7)

This led to a consideration of "relatively functional free" (Mason *et al.* 1973, 246) specifications linking age, period and cohort to outcomes of interest based on multiple classification analysis (sets of categorical variables representing each temporal dimension). Parsing the temporal dimensions into categorical indicators does not in and of itself "solve" the estimation issue posed by the linear identity $A \equiv P - C$. Rather, the linear identity means that not even differences between category coefficients are uniquely estimable (Mason *et al.* 1973, 246–247). The algebra and geometry of this point have been made many times since, and there is nothing that I will or can say that will change them. Nonetheless, since a theme of this chapter is that it is rarely useful to *think* of the *linear* effects of period and cohort as coexisting independent of one another, it is useful to have a perspective and notation that explicitly distinguishes linear from non-linear effects. These I borrow liberally from Holford (1983), and adapt slightly.

Consider the classic data array in which there are I age groups observed across J periods.[1] The general representation of the multiple classification analysis framework is

$$g\left(\gamma_{ijk}\right) = \mu + \alpha_i + \beta_j + \gamma_k \tag{9.3}$$

where γ_{ijk} is some measure (count, rate, etc.) at age i in period j hence cohort $k = j - i + J$.[2] A standard method for identifying the sets of effects $\left\{\alpha_i, \beta_j, \gamma_k\right\}$ is via effect coding:

$$\sum_{i=1}^{I} \alpha_i = \sum_{j=1}^{J} \beta_j = \sum_{k=1}^{K} \gamma_k = 0 \tag{9.4}$$

This is, however, insufficient for resolving the identification issue in the situation in which we are seeking to maintain representations of all three temporal dimensions (Fienberg and Mason 1985, 67–68). To see this, create linear rescalings of the dimensional indexes

$$A_i = i - \frac{I+1}{2} \left(\Rightarrow \sum_{i=1}^{I} A_i = 0 \right) \tag{9.5a}$$

$$P_j = j - \frac{J+1}{2} \left(\Rightarrow \sum_{j=1}^{J} P_j = 0 \right) \tag{9.5b}$$

$$C_k = k - \frac{K+1}{2} \left(\Rightarrow \sum_{k=1}^{K} C_k = 0 \right) \tag{9.5c}$$

and use them to redefine the $\left\{\alpha_i, \beta_j, \gamma_k\right\}$ terms as

$$\alpha_i = \alpha^L A_i + \alpha_i^d \tag{9.6a}$$

$$\beta_j = \beta^L P_j + \beta_j^d \tag{9.6b}$$

$$\gamma_k = \gamma^L C_k + \gamma_k^d. \tag{9.6c}$$

Each term $\{\alpha_i, \beta_j, \gamma_k\}$ is thus a function of a constant rate of change in, respectively, age (α^L), period (β^L) and cohort (γ^L); plus a corresponding deviation $\{\alpha_i^d, \beta_j^d, \gamma_k^d\}$ from the linear trend. These new terms are what would be estimated were we somehow to have known (or estimated) the sets of category-specific coefficients $\{\alpha_i, \beta_j, \gamma_k\}$ and regressed them on their respective linear locations $\{A_i, P_j, C_k\}$.

A corresponding implication is that

$$\sum_{i=1}^{I} A_i \alpha_i^d = \sum_{j=1}^{J} P_j \beta_j^d = \sum_{k=1}^{K} C_k \gamma_k^d = 0 \tag{9.7}$$

i.e., no covariance (correlation) between deviations (residuals) and trend (predictors).[3]

"[S]pecifying a model with linear and nonlinear effects does not solve the identification problem" (Fienberg and Mason 1978, 15), but it can keep clear what is at issue. Substitute Equations 9.6a–c into Equation 9.3, to yield

$$g\left(y_{ijk}\right) = \mu + \alpha^L A_i + \beta^L P_j + \gamma^L C_k + \alpha_i^d + \beta_j^d + \gamma_k^d \tag{9.8}$$

There are three new terms in this functionally equivalent expression, but also, as per Equation 9.7, three new restrictions — restrictions that render the category effects independent of their corresponding linear indexes. The model is still not identified, but any further single restriction on these parameters will make the model just-identified, with equivalent predicted values $\hat{y}_{ijk}$. Estimates of the category-specific (de-trended) deviations $\{\alpha_i^d, \beta_j^d, \gamma_k^d\}$ are unique and invariant regardless of the (single) identifying restriction that is chosen (Holford 1991, 432–433).

Since $P_j \equiv A_i + C_k$, Equation 9.8 is equivalently

$$g\left(y_{ijk}\right) = \mu + \left(\alpha^L + \beta^L\right) A_i + \left(\gamma^L + \beta^L\right) C_k + \alpha_i^d + \beta_j^d + \gamma_k^d \tag{9.9}$$

Although all just-identified models will yield unique and invariant estimates of these additive combinations of coefficients on linear trend $\alpha^L + \beta^L$ and $\gamma^L + \beta^L$, the particular values of this set of coefficients $\{\alpha^L, \beta^L, \gamma^L\}$ will vary according to the identifying restriction that is employed.

Holford (1983) suggested identification by a constraint on a linear parameter itself, in particular period, as per

$$\beta^L = 0, \tag{9.10}$$

or zero linear trend (ZLT) in the period coefficients (O'Brien 2015, 51). This reduces Equations 9.8 and 9.9 to

$$g\left(y_{ijk}\right) = \mu + \alpha^L A_i + \gamma^L C_k + \alpha_i^d + \beta_j^d + \gamma_k^d \tag{9.11}$$

The assumption underlying this identifying restriction may or may not be accurate. If it is at all inaccurate, we can see from Equation 9.9 that estimates for α^L and γ^L will be too high (low) to the extent that the assumption of no linear trend in period (Equation 9.10) is too low (high) relative to "whatever the true value of $[\beta^L]$ happens to be" (Holford 1983, 316). Even though the deviations $\{\alpha_i^d, \beta_j^d, \gamma_k^d\}$ are not affected by this assumption, the category effects $\{\alpha_i, \beta_j, \gamma_k\}$ from the multiple classification schema (Equations 9.3 and 9.4) will be, via Equations 9.6a–c.[4]

All assumptions underlying just-identified age–period–cohort models are constraints on the linear coefficients $\{\alpha^L, \beta^L, \gamma^L\}$, if only implicitly. Thus identification by equating two adjacent terms in the multiple classification specification (Mason *et al.* 1973) — the constrained generalized linear model (CGLIM) (Yang and Land 2013a, 66) — is equivalent to a constraint on the corresponding linear term as a function of the deviation terms. In general, for adjacent categories w and $w+1$, $\theta \in \{\alpha, \beta, \gamma\}$, and $V_w \in \{A_i, P_j, C_k\}$; and from Equations 9.6a–c we see that

$$\theta_w = \theta_{w+1} \Rightarrow \theta^L V_w + \theta_w^d = \theta^L V_{w+1} + \theta_{w+1}^d \Rightarrow \theta^L = \theta_{w+1}^d - \theta_w^d. \qquad (9.12)$$

This is *not* what any researcher to date has been arguing for *explicitly* in estimating a CGLIM model, and yet there it is. The corollary is that any model identified by a constraint on one of the linear coefficients implies a CGLIM model. O'Brien (2019, 218) distinguishes identification via constraints on a pair of effect coefficients ("simple constraints") from "more complicated just identifying constraints such as setting the linear trend of the period effects to some value such as zero." Equation 9.12 shows that these are two sides of the same coin.

Recall from Equation 9.9 that two additive combinations of linear terms $\{\alpha^L, \beta^L, \gamma^L\}$ are estimable (*e.g.*, $\alpha^L + \beta^L$ and $\gamma^L + \beta^L$), so that "[i]f any one of the slopes is fixed at a particular value, then the other two are immediately determined, as well" (Holford 1991, 434). Any slope determined in one dimension must find some "compensation" in the other dimensions, subject to the two estimable (hence observable) sums of linear coefficients. This is why the literature is replete with demonstrations that different just-identified CGLIM models yield wildly varying estimates of $\{\alpha_i, \beta_j, \gamma_k\}$ (*e.g.*, Mason *et al.* 1973, Table 4; Kupper *et al.* 1985, Tables 3a–c; Holford 1991, Table 2; Yang, Fu, and Land 2004, Table 3).[5]

When William Mason and I (1985) reconstructed and extended Frost's (1939, Table 1) data on tuberculosis (TB) mortality in Massachusetts, we noted that classification of the non-pulmonary forms of TB had been changing over time (169–170), and that these non-respiratory tuberculoses were concentrated prior to adulthood (177). In focusing on pulmonary TB alone — a disease classically associated with young adulthood — we were struck that mortality in both of the first two decades of life was comparatively low and virtually indistinguishable in level, whether viewed from a period or a cohort perspective (Mason and Smith 1985, 175–178; cf. Smith 2004, 114). In adopting the identifying restriction

$$\alpha_{0-9} = \alpha_{10-19} \qquad (9.13)$$

in our age–period–cohort analysis of pulmonary tuberculosis mortality, we ignored the implications of this restriction for the *linear* effects of age (hence period and cohort). Implicitly, however, we were fixing the linear effect of age as (from Equation 9.12)

$$\alpha^L = \alpha^d_{0-9} - \alpha^d_{10-19} \tag{9.14}$$

It is hard to think about what (if anything) the perspective afforded by Equation 9.14 means a priori since, by construction (Equation 9.7), these category-specific deviation coefficients $(\alpha^d_{0-9}, \alpha^d_{10-19}, \ldots)$ are uncorrelated with the linear term for age (α^L). As it turns out, this was one instance where the implicit constraint on the linear term does not seem to have done any violence to the analysis, at least in terms of estimated parameters (*pace* Rodgers 1982, 785). Estimation of the parameters in Equation 9.8, as a log-rate model fitted to the Massachusetts TB mortality data (Mason and Smith 1985, Tables A1 and A2),[6] with identifying restrictions as per Equations 9.4, 9.7 and 9.14, yields $\widehat{\alpha^L} = -0.0148\left(\widehat{SE}_{\alpha^L} = 0.0051\right)$, $\widehat{\beta^L} = 0.0022\left(\widehat{SE}_{\beta^L} = 0.0053\right)$ and $\widehat{\gamma^L} = -0.0545\left(\widehat{SE}_{\gamma^L} = 0.0053\right)$. Thus we had concomitantly and implicitly set mortality as declining by age at approximately 1.5% a year, a result that, in and of itself, is neither here nor there: Mortality rates for respiratory tuberculosis should decline with age after early adulthood. But before adulthood, rates of pulmonary TB are low, too; so that there is no substantive sense to a linear trend in age, even if it must exist algebraically. The more important consequence of the identification of the linear term for age (α^L) is that it simultaneously identifies linear terms for period (β^L) and cohort (γ^L). In the case of the latter, the decline is precipitous, at over 5% per annum, or a >40% decline in mortality at all ages across every ten years of births (*i.e.*, cohorts). This is a reasonable parameterization of something long known: that TB moves in waves, and that when mortality drops, it drops in a wave across cohorts (Andvord [1930] 2002; Frost 1939).

In contrast, under this model, identified even if only implicitly by $\widehat{\alpha^L} = -0.0148$ (Equation 9.14 as implied by Equation 9.13), there is essentially no *linear* trend in period, as the estimated 0.2% increase per annum $(\widehat{\beta^L} = 0.0022$ or +2.2% per decade) is less than half of its estimated standard error $(\widehat{SE}_{\beta^L} = 0.0053)$. The implication is that had the model been identified under the assumption of zero linear trend in period (Equation 9.10 in lieu of Equation 9.14), the estimated parameters would have been the same. This is confirmed in Figure 9.2, where the coefficients for these two models — the circles and diamonds — are indistinguishable. The coefficients plotted in this figure sum the estimated linear trends and deviations as per Equations 9.6a–c and thus a linear regression of time on the coefficients in any dimension has as slope the estimated effects discussed above, at least for the identifying assumption that the terms for the first two age categories are equivalent (Equation 9.13).[7]

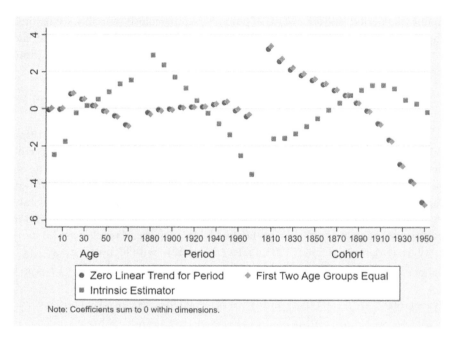

FIGURE 9.2 Estimated effect coefficients (including linear trend) for three just-identified age–period–cohort models fit to the Massachusetts TB data from Mason and Smith (1985)

It is by happenstance, then, that the CGLIM model proposed by Mason and Smith (1985) corresponds to a ZLT for a *period* model: It *just happens* that $\alpha^L + \beta^L \approx \alpha^L$, where $\alpha^L + \beta^L$ is an estimable term that does not depend on the identifying restriction (as per Equation 9.9) and α^L is the constraint on the linear trend in *age* as per Equation 9.14, which is implied by the CGLIM constraint in Equation 9.13. Under this specification, we observe that $\beta^L \approx 0$ and infer that the ZLT for period specification would fit the data equivalently, as confirmed in Figure 9.2. Not all CGLIM models will imply such "clean" constraints (*e.g.*, a ZLT specification) on the linear terms $\left\{\alpha^L, \beta^L, \gamma^L\right\}$, but recognizing the correspondence between constraints on effect coefficients (such as CGLIM models) and constraints on linear terms is useful when thinking about identifying specifications (Fienberg and Mason 1985, 70). The plausibility of a set of estimated parameters is enhanced when they can be reproduced empirically from alternative constraints that do not necessarily imply one another.

In contrast, there is a large class of just-identified specifications, including the Intrinsic Estimator (IE) (Yang, Fu, and Land 2004) that have some desirable *statistical* properties, but obscure constraints on the linear terms (O'Brien 2011). These constraints turn out to be non-intuitive functions of the *design* of the data array, that is, the values of I and J, hence K (Fosse and Winship 2018). Figure 9.2 also shows (square points) the estimated coefficients from the canonical IE model as applied to the Massachusetts respiratory TB data, from whence it can be seen that linear trends contrary to those involved in either the Mason–Smith CGLIM constraint (Equations 9.13 or 9.14) or period ZLT specification (Equation 9.10) give a different picture of the temporal structure of the disease as it disappeared in the commonwealth. The slopes under the IE constraint are, respectively, $\widehat{\alpha^L} = 0.0565$, $\widehat{\beta^L} = -0.0692$ and $\widehat{\gamma^L} = -0.0364$. The idea that TB mortality would rise monotonically with age, not to mention at such a high rate, is precisely what Frost (1939) was pushing back against 80 years ago.

From bounding to over-identification: further perspectives on linear trends

One could say that there is a lot of spurious precision in the various estimates presented above. Or if not in these estimates specifically — since we do generate the same estimates under two quite different identifying restrictions — in just-identified age–period–cohort models in general. How can we be so confident in a particular restriction on the linear parameters?

In brief: We can't. Confidence in the precise if occult IE identification for the Massachusetts TB data, for example, would have been misplaced. Cohort analysis thus shares with the more general social scientific literature (Manski 1995) an appreciation for the modesty (acknowledged ignorance) associated with identification through bounding the acceptable range of estimates of a parameter or set of parameters. The idea of identifying age–period–cohort models with reference to a restricted range of plausible values — e.g., that linear trends in one or more dimensions are non-decreasing with time — dates to at least Wickramaratne et al. (1989). O'Brien (2019) proposes similar restrictions for a restricted range of one dimension, and Fosse and Winship (2019) give a generalized treatment of the underlying idea. The thread that I pull on in the remainder of this section has a particular orientation. Models with a linear bound in one dimension are equivalent to CGLIM models. Perhaps because no one seems to think about them as CGLIM models, no one seems to be as bothered by the identifying restriction as they are when an identifying restriction *starts* as a restriction on two adjacent terms in an ANOVA model. Nor am I bothered by this lack of visceral antipathy. It allows us to glide easily to interesting tests of models that are over-identified. At which point I draw the (precise algebraic) analogy with the problem of testing an age–period–cohort model against a model in which one of the three dimensions is excluded in its entirety – or in its linearity.

For any monotonic increasing constraint on effect coefficients $\{\theta_w : \theta_1 \le \theta_2 \le \ldots \le \theta_{W-1} \le \theta_W\}$, there is a corresponding minimal value to the linear trend θ^L. Call this θ_M^L. This value can be obtained with reference to a corresponding CGLIM model $\theta_w = \theta_{w+1}$ where w is determined by observing where $\theta_w^d - \theta_{w+1}^d$ is greatest across the $w = 1,\ldots,W-1$ first differences among deviation coefficients $\{\theta_w^d\}$. The set of deviations $\{\theta_w^d\}$ for any temporal dimension

θ is estimable and invariant across all just-identified models. Thus the initial model consulted (fitted) to establish the maximal $\theta^d_w - \theta^d_{w+1}$ does not affect the linear term θ^L_M obtained, or the other two linear terms, which are determined once θ^L_M is specified for one of the three dimensions. This does not mean that any CGLIM (or other just-identified) model will by itself generate sets of coefficients that maintain monotonicity in a given dimension. However, the estimates from any such model, *combined with the identifying assumption regarding monotonicity*, will identify a CGLIM that defines a slope restriction (by reversing the derivation in Equation 9.12) that creates a boundary. All values $\theta^L > \theta^L_M$ are part of a region that maintains $\{\theta_w : \theta_1 \le \theta_2 \le \dots \le \theta_{W-1} \le \theta_W\}$, albeit at the "cost" of inducing compensating change in the linear trends for the other two dimensions. With the boundary specifications of $\{\alpha^L, \beta^L, \gamma^L\}$ and the fitted $\{\alpha^d_i, \beta^d_j, \gamma^d_k\}$ in hand, Equations 9.6a–c define the coefficients $\{\alpha_i, \beta_j, \gamma_k\}$ that maintain monotonicity in one dimension with the minimal linear slope.[8]

For example, if one wishes to stipulate that period coefficients $\{\beta_i\}$ be non-decreasing with time, then the minimal linear slope β^L_M that will sustain this stipulation is equal to the maximal first difference $\beta^d_w - \beta^d_{w+1}$, where the model is equivalently identified by setting $\beta_w = \beta_{w+1}$. In this sense, the bounding is weak. Consider, for example, a lower bound β^L_M conforming to the specification of mono-tonically increasing period effects. Then

$$\left(\alpha^L + \beta^L\right) - \beta^L_M \ge \alpha^L \tag{9.15a}$$

$$\beta^L \ge \beta^L_M \tag{9.15b}$$

$$\left(\beta^L + \gamma^L\right) - \beta^L_M \ge \gamma^L, \tag{9.15c}$$

where both $\alpha^L + \beta^L$ and $\beta^L + \gamma^L$ are estimable and invariant (Equation 9.9) and thus can be determined from whatever just-identified model was estimated to determine β^L_M. Only for Equation 9.15b does bounding identify the sign of a linear term (in this case, β^L) — by definition, since increasing monotonicity in period implies $\beta^L_M \ge 0$. Linear terms in age (α^L) and cohort (γ^L) can still take on both positive and negative values, at least until $\alpha^L + \beta^L$ and $\beta^L + \gamma^L$, respectively, are observed (estimated).[9]

We can advance matters by asking how putting further inequality restrictions on slope coefficients might plausibly tighten bounds. If in addition to monotonically increasing effects in period we further stipulate that the linear trend in cohort is also increasing — a less specific additional constraint, since it does *not* imply that cohort coefficients are necessarily monotonically increasing — then we are asserting that

$$\gamma^L \ge 0 \tag{9.16}$$

and thus defining tighter bounds:

$$\left(\alpha^L + \beta^L\right) - \beta^L_M \ge \alpha^L \ge \left(\alpha^L + \beta^L\right) - \left(\beta^L + \gamma^L\right) \tag{9.17a}$$

$$\beta^L + \gamma^L \geq \beta^L \geq \beta_M^L \tag{9.17b}$$

$$\left(\beta^L + \gamma^L\right) - \beta_M^L \geq \gamma^L \geq 0. \tag{9.17c}$$

These are elaborations of inequalities found in Holford (1991, 447), "for using knowledge about the underlying biology of a disease to understand something about the trends involv[ing] a restriction on one or more time factors." They differ from Holford's (1991) inequalities primarily in having sharpened the specification of the linear trend in period to include not just non-negativity in the linear trend, but also monotonicity in effect coefficients.

All of the bounds in Equations 9.17a–c only hold conditional on

$$\beta^L + \gamma^L \geq \beta_M^L \tag{9.18}$$

which can be viewed as an alternative hypothesis to the null hypothesis

$$\beta^L + \gamma^L < \beta_M^L. \tag{9.19}$$

In this sense a test of Equation 9.19 is a test of the over-identifying restriction provided by Equation 9.16. (Compare Equations 9.15b and 9.17b.)

Why "[i]n this sense"? Because Equations 9.17–9.19 lean on β_M^L, a quantity that is itself based on an assumption or identifying restriction. Were it to turn out that $\beta^L \not\geq \beta_M^L$ — i.e., that Equation 9.15b, the inequality conforming to the original identifying assumption, that period effects increase monotonically, were false — then the apparent tightness of the bounding on linear effects provided by Equations 9.17a–c would be illusory. Estimation of linear trends continues to rely on an identifying restriction, even under an empirically maintained over-identifying restriction. This said, *conditional on* the stipulation provided by Equation 9.15b, the test of Equation 9.19 and its potential sequelae — rejection in favor of Equation 9.18 and adoption of the bounds in Equations 9.17a–c — could be quite informative. The fact that we do not *know* that period effects should increase monotonically does not mean that we cannot or should not *assume* (posit) that period effects increase monotonically, and to reason and observe from there.

Tests of over-identifying restrictions relative to the fit of a just-identified model have long been a feature of the cohort analysis literature (*e.g.*, Mason *et al.* 1973; Fienberg and Mason 1978, 42–61).

> If the full logistic response model with age, period, and cohort effects, whether under-identified, just-identified, or over-identified, provides an acceptable fit to the data, then it will usually be of interest to explore whether we can set the effects of one or two dimensions to zero. Fitting age-period, age-cohort, cohort-period models, and even further reduced models, is a straightforward task with any computer program designed to fit standard log linear models to multidimensional arrays. Such reduced models pose no special identification

> problems because there is no way for the linear component of one dimension to become confounded with the linear components of the other two.
>
> (Fienberg and Mason 1978, 29)

Yang and Land (2013a, 109, Ch. 5) outline a method for age–period–cohort analysis that may culminate in the application of a just-identified model (including the IE), but only if more parsimonious two-dimensional models (*e.g.*, age-cohort) do not provide a satisfactory fit to the data. They attribute criticism of the IE by Luo (2013) to an instance where preference for a more restricted model should have ruled out the application of the IE (or any just-identified ["full-blown"] APC model) in the first place (Yang and Land 2013b).[10]

Except that, as Holford (1991, 436–437) pointed out, two-factor models (over-identified models featuring only two of the three conceptual temporal dimensions) may not be what we think they are, at least with reference to a just-identified model.[11] Whereas in estimating a simplified multiple classification model of the form of (e.g.)

$$g\left(y_{ijk}\right) = \mu + \alpha_i + \gamma_k \tag{9.20}$$

and comparing it with Equation 9.3 we might imagine that we have tested as null the full set of omitted coefficients

$$\beta_j = 0 \tag{9.21}$$

for all j, hence linearity in period as well (Equation 9.10), we may have done no such thing. In particular, what we have tested is "only"

$$\beta_j^l = 0 \tag{9.22}$$

for all j, as in

$$g\left(y_{ijk}\right) = \mu + \left(\alpha^L + \beta^L\right)A_i + \left(\gamma^L + \beta^L\right)C_k + \alpha_i + \gamma_k \tag{9.23}$$

versus Equation 9.9, on $J - 2$, not $J - 1$, degrees of freedom (Fienberg and Mason 1985, 71–72). Uh-oh: There, in Equation 9.23, is β^L again, free to be more or less anything, absent a further restriction on the linear terms!

This state of affairs — if state of affairs it is — discomfited Holford (1991, 437). Having noted that "[i]t is impossible to test the null hypothesis that the slope is zero [$\beta^L = 0$] when both age and cohort also are included in the model" he ventured, tentatively, that "[i]t would be surprising if a causal agent that changed over time did so in a strictly linear fashion. Typically, you also would expect to see a certain amount of curvature." Which is to say that if Equation 9.22 holds, something — experience? theory? common sense? — would suggest that Equation 9.21 should hold as well. This is notwithstanding the fact that there is no algebraic or statistical reason to rule out the existence of a linear trend in period (rejection of Equation 9.10). Holford (1991, 437) thus yields to the dictates of algebra and statistics and concludes that "an analysis that is limited to the consideration of just two factors is not really a solution to the problem, because the possibility for bias has not been eliminated." Fosse and Winship (2018, 322) reprise this perspective:

> Unfortunately, it is impossible to determine from the data alone whether or not all three temporal variables are operating. Believing otherwise can seriously mislead researchers … [B]y fitting the two-factor model … one is imposing the identification assumption that the [omitted] linear effect is zero … The zero-linear trend constraint on the cohort variable is external to the data, imposed by the researcher. Depending on the substantive application, it may or may not be reasonable to assume that because the nonlinear effects of [one temporal dimension] are observed to be zero, its linear effect is also zero … [T]his is an assumption that can only be justified by appealing to theory or the inclusion of additional data.

O'Brien (2016, 366 [emphasis in original]) is even more admonitory:

> When the model contains just two factors, those two factors take credit for their own linear trend effects, their effects that involve deviations from their linear trends, *and they take credit for the linear trend effects of the third (left-out) factor* … Leaving the third factor out of the model based on its incremental fit not being statistically significant will too often eliminate a substantively important factor. This elimination affects the coefficient estimates of the two factors in the model.

It is one thing to realize that all just-identified models featuring effects for all three temporal dimensions necessitate restrictions on the linear terms. It is quite another to see that even if one is willing to forego consideration of one of the temporal dimensions, one is (perhaps) still prey to the indeterminacy deriving from the fact that any of age, period or cohort is a linear combination of the other two. What is going on here? In the case of two-factor models, "[t]he left-out factor's effects are constrained to be zero, both its linear trend effects and the effects of its deviations from the linear trend" (O'Brien 2016, 365). We can parse this further to specify that the constraint on the deviations (*e.g.*, Equation 9.22) is estimable, hence testable, while the constraint on the linear term (*e.g.*, Equation 9.10) is an assumption. The situation is completely analogous to that discussed just above, in conjunction with an over-identifying restriction to tighten the bounds on effects (Equations 9.17–9.19). Holford (1991, 437) hazarded that if deviations from trend in one dimension are not statistically detectable, then one might plausibly infer that there is no linear trend in the same dimension, either. I would turn it around to ask, why not just acknowledge that the test of an over-identified two-factor model against a just-identified age–period–cohort model is, specifically, a test against the just-identified model in which the linear term in the soon-to-be-absent dimension is assumed to be zero? Conditional on this assumption, the test that there are also no non-linear effects in this dimension is a perfectly useful one.

How can we — or why might we — wish to entertain such an assumption? Theory or additional data specific to the analysis at hand (O'Brien 2016, 369; Fosse and Winship 2018, 322) are always welcome, but there may also be some general ways of thinking about the analysis of data in terms of age, period and cohort that help to structure the models and methods in common use. The ones I discuss in the remainder of this chapter mostly abjure imagining that there *are* linear effects operating simultaneously in period and cohort. The problem is less that age, period and cohort are definitively bound (age ≡ period − cohort) than that we have come to substitute the algebra of the situation for the logic of social science. When O'Brien (2016, 322) writes that "[l]eaving the third factor out of the model based on its incremental fit not being statistically significant will too often eliminate a substantively important factor," I look for evidence of a social world, theoretical and/or empirical, in which it makes sense to think of all of these time dimensions as indexing factors that move both simultaneously and linearly in their effects on some phenomenon of interest. What I find instead are references to "the data-generating processes" (O'Brien 2016, 365) or "the true data generating parameters" (Fosse and Winship 2018, 324) or even "the true A, P, and C trends" (Luo and Hodges 2016, 710). Far be it from me to gainsay the utility of a received specification in adjudicating arguments in the statistical realm (Smith, Mason, and Fienberg 1982, Tables 1 and 2). But do such entities — data generating processes or parameters, "true" trends — really exist? I am mindful that all of our models are mental constructs; also, that it is hard to refute on the one hand or prove on the other a Platonic concept. Nonetheless, the indeterminacies intrinsic to the statistical perspective may be distracting us from some fundamentals that could make the ground feel less shaky underfoot.

Against concomitant linear trends in cohort and period

Fosse and Winship (2018) conclude their survey of statistical approaches for identifying simultaneous age, period and cohort effects with a set of practical guidelines:

> [T]he full set of linear and nonlinear effects should be reported. This will allow the researcher to evaluate the legitimacy of the constraint imposed on the true, unknown linear APC effects ... Ultimately, any linear constraint should be grounded in an underlying social, cultural, or biological theory.
>
> (328)

If categorical terms for each dimension of time are normalized as per Equation 9.4, then Equations 9.5 and 9.6 make it straightforward to deduce linear and nonlinear effects, in fitting a regression line to the observed coefficients in at least two of the dimensions (Holford 1983). It has long been known that all just-identified age–period–cohort models maintain and/or require a restriction on a linear term in time (Fienberg and Mason 1978, 6), even if the nature of those restrictions is sometimes obscure. Earlier in this chapter I treated some comparatively simple cases (ZLT, CGLIM, bounding) compared to those unearthed by Fosse and Winship (2018).

Given all the time that has passed since cohort analysis veered into the identification problem, and all of the work that has been done within the age–period–cohort frame as well as at the edges, it would be (a) hard to dispute the generic advice that any and all identifying restrictions be motivated with reference to the specific problem at hand, and the theory and state of knowledge that surround it; and (b) fatuous to suggest a general solution. Nevertheless, might not some reorientation be in order, to keep us focused on the point of the enterprise, hence to avoid algebraic distractions? The association of the data structure with a set of challenges and strictures from statistics and mathematics has had the unfortunate consequences of (a) turning attention from substantive issues, first assuming that we are less knowledgeable than we are, then making it appear that this is true; and (b) causing us to overlook what the basic identity $A \equiv P - C$ is telling us about how we should be thinking about age, period and cohort as explanatory concepts. The nub of the problem is an epistemological one — what it is we think we are thinking about — and not a mathematical one. Age, period and cohort might be exchangeable algebraically and geometrically, but conceptually they are distinct. For the two constructs associated with historical time, period and cohort, it is hard to think of when and why we would want to imagine *linear* trends in both.

We are often faced with the following: social and/or demographic data arrayed over time by age, and a desire to know "what is going on" with respect to these age-graded rates and counts, including what has transpired in the past and what we have reason to think might transpire in the future. In such instances, which are ubiquitous, statistical accounts in terms of age (and aging) and cohorts (including trends) should come to the fore. What about period effects — don't *they* exist? Well, of course they exist; or might exist; or we might think that they exist; or thinking that they exist might help with our thoughts more generally. But, in the first instance, our preference should be for age–cohort models with specific interactions, and/or age–period–cohort models with identification residing in the presumption that the linear trend in period is zero. In many respects — as a *technical* treatment of the issue — this is not only not new, it is *old*: Adepts of the literature may recognize that these are the procession of models used by Holford (1983, 314–318) to illustrate estimation of age, period and cohort effects. What I want to offer in addition, in the set of interconnected remarks that follow, is a *rationale* for thinking this way, as opposed to worrying, for example, that an implied cohort linear trend is somehow taking credit for something that in some sense belongs to period (cf. O'Brien 2016, 366). The orientation I proffer here is situational and not categorical. I am suggesting that cohort is in general the more logical "carrier" of historical or temporal trends.

One reason is that age effects usually are best interpreted with reference to cohorts. The theory of *age* effects is primarily developmental and longitudinal, hence within cohorts, not cross-sectional. This is true whether the primary emphasis is on understanding how some phenomenon unfolds across the life course (Baltes 1968), or whether the question is historical change across some phenomenon known to vary systematically with age (*e.g.*, Dorius, Alwin, and Pacheco 2016). Sometimes the structure connecting rates with age — the linear increase in log-mortality with age over most of adulthood, for example (see *e.g.*, Cohen, Bohk, and Rau 2018) — can have the same shape whether viewed from a cohort or period perspective (Lenert and Missov 2010). In other circumstances, the proponents of theories regarding age patterns of behavior and events have not noticed the distinction between age patterns hypothesized longitudinally but viewed cross-sectionally. In criminology, Hirschi and Gottfredson (1983) posited an age effect on crime that "is invariant across social and cultural conditions" (560), motivated it with respect to developmental factors, but illustrated it primarily with reference to cross-sectional patterns. This made matters ripe for misunderstanding as overall crime rates changed over time (Porter *et al.* 2016, 34–35).

What are the implications for identification? There are at least three. First, age–cohort models are in some sense primordial. This is unless we happen to be in a theoretical plane where age–period models are primordial. It is not impossible to give a scientifically coherent reading to an age pattern that applies in the cross-section: Social and economic punishments and rewards may be age-graded, and their relative application conditional on age might be a function of period-specific circumstances and resources alone. In this event, the cohort biographies found in the data could well be of historical interest, but the patterns within the cohorts of punishments and rewards would give an inaccurate rendering of how age figures in their allocation, absent adjustment for period. The distinction between the two is a theoretical one, as it has always been (*e.g.*, Fienberg and Mason 1978, 50, 58–59) — not a matter of comparative goodness-of-fit. The crucial point is that the mental baseline should not be an age–period–cohort model with no identification restriction in sight, because therein lies the madness of Equation 9.23, a twisting whirligig we would not even have imagined unless our view of the world *began* with Equations 9.8 and 9.9.

Second, to the extent that we have an understanding of what age patterns should look like, for example, within a cohort, then extended models — A–P–C models, with all three temporal dimensions represented — can be identified with reference to age effects. Fienberg and Mason (1978, 42–61) worked from the beginning with an over-identifying restriction on age effects: In an era with little adult education, the level of schooling in a cohort should be relatively fixed after young adulthood, at least through the middle ages, until mortality and poor recall kick in. Mason and Smith (1985) have provided a just-identified example. The fact that the restriction on age (Equation 9.13) proved isomorphic with a zero linear trend restriction on period (Equation 9.10) increases confidence that the estimated coefficients convey a reasonable partition of the various time dimensions, including the restriction of all trend in historical time to the coefficients indexing cohort.

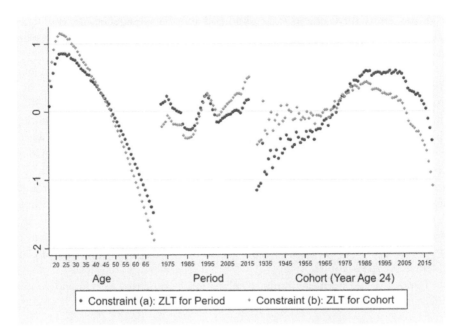

FIGURE 9.3 Estimated age, period and cohort efficients for two zero linear trend restrictions on a model for prison sentence spells in North Carolina, 1972–2016

The third implication is the converse of the second: If we are restricting trend in historical time to one dimension alone (period), one test of the plausibility of this restriction is whether or not it generates a pattern of age coefficients that comports with expectations regarding the age pattern of the phenomenon under study. Figure 9.3 shows age, period and cohort coefficients (darker points) under a ZLT constraint on period (Equation 9.10) for a just-identified model fit to data on correctional supervision and prison spells for North Carolina males, by age, between 1972 and 2016 (Shen *et al.* 2019). The coefficients for age show the anticipated pattern, with judicial sanction being highest in the mid- to late-20s, and dropping off at an accelerating pace thereafter. (The response variable is a *log*-rate.) Such an "eye test" can (and should!) be made for *any* identifying restriction. But it may be more helpful and reassuring in the context of a decision to restrict the *trend* in effect coefficients to two dimensions alone: developmental and historical time. Figure 9.3 also presents an alternative version of this partition, in which period is allowed to assume all historical trend (lighter points), and the general age pattern is not terribly different. One could not (nor should not) choose between the two specifications on this basis alone; but given the general reasonableness of the age pattern under two alternative apportionments of the linear component of historical trend, it is easier to turn to the substantive component of the exercise. This involved assessing the effects of a 1994 sentencing reform (clearly visible in the plot of period effect coefficients) against the backdrop of secular change in crime and punishment which, given the high propensity for crime in early adulthood and the subsequent effects of early incarceration on the chances of later involvement with the criminal justice system, can be best represented as so-called cohort effects (Porter *et al.* 2016).

Many other choices of identifying restriction, otherwise untethered and indifferently specified, could reorient the age pattern(s) in a manner that is un-credible. See again the IE estimates in Figure 9.2. One of the lessons of stipulating monotonicity in any set of effects $\{\theta_W\}$ is the "hands on" experience of finding that there is always an extreme value of θ_M^L that will functionally annihilate what-ever information is (was) contained in the unique estimates of the deviation coefficients $\{\theta_w^l\}$. The arithmetic of the situation notwithstanding, this is not a desirable state of affairs. From an analytic standpoint, there really is a sense in which these coefficients need be privileged against the super-abundance (three versus two) of the linear terms, even if the elimination of a linear term in the potential presence of deviations from linearity in the same dimension does appear to stand on its head the common understanding of marginality in linear models (Nelder 1977, 49–50).

Trends that are purportedly the combination of offsetting period and cohort effects are difficult to understand:

> For any dataset, there is a space of possible estimates, all equally consistent with the data, but with different linear trends in age, period, and cohort, and no way from the data alone to choose among these ... On the other hand, some of the estimates seem to make more sense than others. For example, consider a model which adds the following three trends: (i) since 1948, an increase of 1% per year in the overall probability of Democratic identifica-tion, (ii) starting at age 18, an increase of 1% per year in the probability of an individual being a Republican as he or she gets older, and (iii) for each cohort, an increase of 1% in the probability of being Republican, compared to the cohort that was born one year earlier. Add these three trends together and you get zero—the combination has no effect on any observable data— but they do not make much political sense. What does it really mean to talk about a linear time trend toward the Democrats if it is exactly canceled by each cohort being more Republican than the last? To put it another way, some methods of constraining the possible space of solutions seem more rea-sonable than others.
>
> (Gelman 2008, 2–3)

A similar argument can be made against taking too seriously the idea that there are conceptually separable period and cohort trends that are moving in the same dir-ection. What exactly would that mean, given that we would be talking about *linear* trends? That the march of history is progressing or regressing in some continuous reapportionment of its effects, from universal with respect to age to transmitted via early socialization — or vice versa? The impossibility — and inutility — of attempting to distinguish these trends as between cohort and period is exemplified in the comparative study of income, where an historical trend is assumed, and the question of substantive interest is how different cohorts fare relative to this trend:

> As we explain how cohorts diverge from overall income trends, substantive reasons also exist for focusing on fluctuations around a linear trend, instead of focusing on the linear trend itself. Namely, the linear trend that one generation gets born into a society that is richer than the same society at an earlier point in time would generally not be considered unfair, but inevitable. Immanuel Kant (1784) most prominently argued that we are accustomed to one generation profiting from the efforts of the preceding one, so that overall, a long-run cohort (or period-based; *one can never know*) progression of living standards is the baseline to expect.
>
> (Chauvel and Schröder 2014, 1285 [emphasis added])

Into the future

None of which is to imply that there is no reason to distinguish period from cohort effects, either conceptually or in age–period–cohort models. The enduring charm of these models is that there is age-graded variability in proportions, rates, counts and the like that derives from the irruption of historical events against the backdrop of the secular change embedded in cohorts. I close with a brief foray into how the allocation of historical linear trend to the dimension indexed by cohort may be of value when it comes to projecting or forecasting the future.

Demography is the only social science that routinely makes projections or forecasts over long horizons (Granger 2007, 6). The reason is the cohort conception that attaches to data arrayed by time and indexed by age (Smith 2009, 145–151). This and the long-livedness of the species (Ryder 1965). Many of the men and women surveyed in the National Election Studies of the second half of the 20th century had been alive, and at varying ages, when women were given the right to vote in 1920. This — coupled with observation of the age pattern of voting over the life course — was leveraged by Firebaugh and Chen (1995) to make inferences on the impact of this period-specific political reform on the political involvement of different generations. Conversely, the cohort differentiation that can be observed in the past opens up the possibility of using the characteristic age pattern to project phenomena forward, as when differences in the early life-course uptake of smoking foreshadow mortality many years into the future (Wang and Preston 2009).

Which is not to say that the variation that exists historically in rates will primarily be due to factors associated with cohort membership. To the contrary, there are many phenomena for which, from the standpoint of observed variation, "*short-term* period effects" (Mason *et al.* 1973, 245; emphasis added), such as those adduced with respect to political party identification, will dominate the partition of variance as between period and cohort. Consider Figure 9.4 and Figure 9.5, which update figures that first appeared in Sobotka (2003, Figures 1a and 1b). Figure 9.4 presents

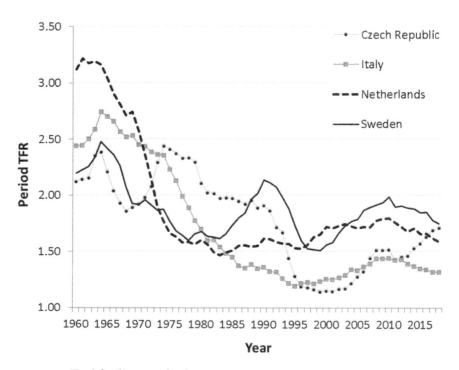

FIGURE 9.4 Total fertility rates for four European countries

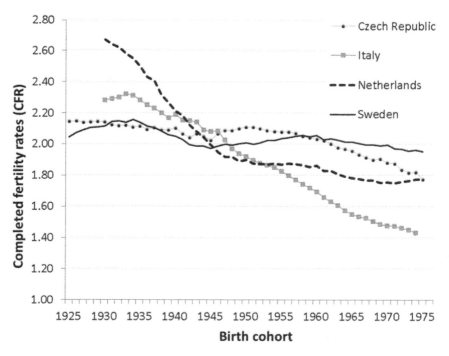

FIGURE 9.5 Completed cohort fertility for four European countries[12]

total fertility rates (TFR), which are period-specific summations of age-specific fertility rates and, as such, are a strong first-approximation to the period effects in the age × period data array. Figure 9.5 displays completed fertility rates (CFR) that are within cohort summations of age-specific rates for the corresponding age × cohort array of age-specific fertility rates. As such, they are a strong first-approximation to the cohort effects for this historical period. Period variation is paramount (Ní Bhrolcháin 1992). Moreover, this period variation is decidedly non-random. Focus, for example, on the dots and thin connecting line in Figure 9.4, for the Czech Republic: There was a substantial decline in fertility in the run-up to the Prague Spring (1968), with a substantial recovery thereafter, before fertility dropped precipitously again in the early 1990s, coincident with the end of the Soviet Union and its control over Czechoslovakia, and the subsequent separation of the Czech Republic from the union with Slovakia.

The issue, however, is that these consequential period-specific shocks are, from a forecasting standpoint, all but unknowable. Things happen; we react. We can give knowledgeable accounts of the effects of past happenings, but we are not so good at predicting them, much less their timing (Smith 1987). The argument in favor of approaching fertility change from a cohort perspective (*e.g.*, Ryder 1960) always had two aspects to it: "first, the description or analysis of fertility patterns, and second, the formation of inferences about the course of fertility" (Hutchinson 1960, 117). It is with respect to the future course of events that a projection structure based on an underlying age–cohort model, with all historical trend allocated to cohort, has a crude but basic utility. It is possible to forecast from age–period–cohort models with linear trend in both cohort and period (Riebler, Held, and Rue 2012, 315–322; Yang and Land 2013a, 171–188); however, in all events, there is some added clarity to the exercise when the partition of trend is clear. In Figure 9.2 and again in Figure 9.3, I have been at pains to present estimated coefficients on a common graph, hence on a common scale, which I claim immodestly only makes sense, given that age, period and cohort have a common metric. I do not know why this practice is not more common. It has the great advantage of making clear not just the trend in estimated effects under alternative models, but the comparative variation in outcomes attributable to each temporal dimension conditional on constraints on linear trends.

The variation visible in these figures in, respectively, age, period and cohort effects, and the dependence of this variation on our treatment of linear components, is evident in the following equations, which re-express the set of effect coefficients $\{\alpha_i, \beta_j, \gamma_k\}$ as variances, expanded with reference to Equations 9.6a–c:

$$\sigma_{\alpha_i}^2 = \left(\alpha^L\right)^2 \left(\frac{I^2 - 1}{12}\right) + \sigma_{\alpha_i^d}^2 \tag{9.24a}$$

$$\sigma_{\beta_j}^2 = \left(\beta^L\right)^2 \left(\frac{J^2 - 1}{12}\right) + \sigma_{\beta_j^d}^2 \tag{9.24b}$$

$$\sigma^2_{\gamma_k} = \left(\gamma^L\right)^2 \left(\frac{K^2-1}{12}\right) + \sigma^2_{\gamma^d_k} \tag{9.24c}$$

As previously, the components corresponding to deviations from trend $\left\{\sigma^2_{\alpha^d_i}, \sigma^2_{\beta^d_j}, \sigma^2_{\gamma^d_k}\right\}$ are unique — they do not depend on the choice of identifying restriction. Nor do the dimension-specific scalars denominated by 12, which vary across age, period and cohort in function of the span of the data array (*i.e.*, in a standard age × period design, I and J, hence K). Because $K > J$, *ceteris paribus* $\left(\left|\beta^L\right| = \left|\gamma^L\right| \text{ and } \sigma^2_{\beta^d_j} = \sigma^2_{\gamma^d_k}\right)$

$$\sigma^2_{\gamma_k} > \sigma^2_{\beta_j} \tag{9.25}$$

implying some normalization may be in order when comparing the extent of period and cohort effects (cf. Vaisey and Lizardo 2016, 9–13).

When there are linear trends in both period (β^L) and cohort (γ^L), the corresponding variances $\sigma^2_{\beta_j}$ and $\sigma^2_{\gamma_k}$ can become quite expansive. In contrast, under the assumption of zero linear trend in period (Equation 9.10)

$$\sigma^2_{\beta_j} = \sigma^2_{\beta^d_j} \tag{9.26}$$

and the proportion of historical variability attributable to differences between cohorts is

$$\frac{\sigma^2_{\gamma_k}}{\sigma^2_{\beta_j} + \sigma^2_{\gamma_k}} = \frac{\left(\gamma^L\right)^2\left(\frac{K^2-1}{12}\right) + \sigma^2_{\gamma^d_k}}{\sigma^2_{\beta^d_j} + \left(\gamma^L\right)^2\left(\frac{K^2-1}{12}\right) + \sigma^2_{\gamma^d_k}}. \tag{9.27}$$

This quantity can be either reassuring or sobering with respect to forecasts based on the set of age and cohort coefficients $\left\{\alpha_i, \gamma_k\right\}$, since under this baseline parameterization, $\sigma^2_{\beta^d_j}$ is a minimum estimate of the secular variability that is historical but not embedded in cohort effects. In this sense, it is a non-stochastic measure of error — in the form of ignorance — in our quest to see into the future based on what we have learned in the past. Further decomposition of $\sigma^2_{\gamma_k}$ in terms of trend and deviance from trend (via Equation 9.24c) can be similarly instructive.

What is it good for?

Alas, there is not too much that is intrinsic in social life. Even if our biology and our physical environment circumscribe our range of behavior, what we make of it seems to be quite varied. Small wonder that our methods for making sense of the human world rarely have the fixity that our scientific minds crave. For roughly half a century, thinking about age–period–cohort models has tended to drift away from their specific utility for specific problems to absolutism, both for and against. This chapter represents an umpteenth effort — my fifth, personally (Fienberg 2013, p. 1982) — to explore how the age–period–cohort accounting model framework (Smith, Mason and Fienberg 1982; Mason and Smith 1985) can be used to illuminate the world around us, with reference to specific and general ideas in sociology, demography and epidemiology. If I have perseverated a bit on the algebra of the situation, the homeliness of the effort is a reminder that this is not akin to splitting the atom on the one hand, or handling poisonous serpents on the other. It is just another way of getting temporary purchase on the social world around us. When it illuminates, it is good.

Online supplementary material relating to this book can be found at www. routledge.com/9780367174439.

Notes

1 I assume that age groups conform to intervals between periods — *i.e.*, if periods are observed every five years, then age categories span five years — although all the points here generalize to more complicated data arrays and observation schemes (Fienberg and Mason 1978, 37–42).

2 The function $\mathscr{g}\left(\gamma_{ijk}\right)$ implies the generalized linear model (McCullagh and Nelder 1989). The indexing of cohort (k) assumes that ages are indexed from youngest to oldest, and periods from most distant to most recent.

3 Estimation of linear effects $\alpha^L, \beta^L, \gamma^L$ via regression is as per, *e.g.*, Holford (1991, 433). The normalization to 0 of both categorical effects (Equation 9.4) and linear trends (Equations 9.5a–c) eliminates the intercept term. Thus in the regression interpretation of Equations 9.6a–c, the deviations $\left\{\alpha_i^d, \beta_j^d, \gamma_k^d\right\}$ are akin to the respective error terms, not to intercepts.

4 The exceptions, as can be derived from Equations 9.6a–c and Equations 9.5a–c, are the

terms $\alpha^{\frac{I+1}{2}} \beta^{\frac{J+1}{2}} \gamma^{\frac{K+1}{2}}$, which will exist when I, J and/or K are odd, and which will

not vary under alternative identification assumptions. In one sense this is a trivial artifact of normalization assumptions (Equations 9.4 and 9.5a–c). On the other hand, it does explain why plots of effects for given dimensions under alternative identifying restrictions rotate around a central value (*e.g.*, Holford 1991, Figure 1; O'Brien 2019, Figures 5–7).

5 But not estimates of $\left\{\alpha_i^d, \beta_j^d, \gamma_k^d\right\}$; these are unique (*e.g.*, Holford 1991, Table 2).

6 *I.e.*, $\mathscr{g}\left(\gamma_{ijk}\right) = \ln \dfrac{\gamma_{ijk}}{N_{ijk}}$, with N_{ijk} as corresponding population counts (as proxies for

person-years of exposure at age[s] i in year j), fixed by design; and $Y_{ijk} \sim Poisson$ a random variate.

7 The pattern of coefficients is thus that depicted as "net effects Model VII" in Mason and Smith (1985, Figures 4–6), with three minor differences. First, the earlier analysis used a logistic response (rather than log-rate) model, although at such low rates, the difference in specifications is minuscule (*e.g.*, Clogg and Eliason 1987, 28–29). Second, in the original analysis, identification of the set of category coefficients was done by omitting dummy variables, *i.e.*, setting one or more to zero, rather than norming the set to sum to

zero, as per Equation 9.4. This affects the constant of the equation, hence the location of the coefficients — but not their difference from one another. Third, in Mason and Smith (1985), the absence of deaths in the three cells associated with the cohorts of 1960 and 1970 led to constraining the cohort effect for the cohorts of 1950, 1960 and 1970 to be identical. Here, no effects were estimated for these last two cohorts. Results are not sensitive to the treatment of these small cohorts and the corresponding cells.

8 In the case where the identifying restriction is that coefficients in a given dimension be monotonically *decreasing*, then all of the above obtains with reversals of inequalities and the corresponding language, *i.e.*, "maximal" for "minimal," "least" or "lowest" for "greatest," and so on. In the case where monotonicity is only expected to obtain after a given time — *e.g.*, a peak in homicide rates at ages 20–24, with rates decreasing monotonically thereafter (O'Brien 2019) — then the definition of the lowest (most negative) value $\theta_w^d - \theta_{w+1}^d$ can be restricted to values of w that index categories over which monotonicity is assumed to obtain.

9 Wikramaratne *et al.* (1989) posit $\beta_M^L = 0$, observe $\beta^L + \gamma^L > 0$, and note (338) that this implies (as per Equation 9.15c) that γ^L could be either positive or negative, absent further assumptions. A corollary is that under the same maintained assumption, the counterfactual but a priori plausible observation that $\beta^L + \gamma^L < 0$ would guarantee $\gamma^L < 0$.

10 Are the discrepant coefficients from the IE in Figure 9.2 another instance in which this counsel was ignored? The estimates based on other constraints suggest very little variation in period, and one might well imagine that an age–cohort model would have/should have sufficed from the beginning. However, the improvement in fit observed by Mason and Smith (1985, Table 3) — a reduction in deviance of somewhat over 100 on 8 degrees of freedom — continues to obtain, even with the minor changes to the analysis detailed in note 8. A just-identified model would also be preferred if the Bayesian Information Criterion (BIC) is the model selection criterion ($BIC_{APC} = -73$ versus $BIC_{AC} = +12$).

11 Rodgers (1982, 780–782) was also getting at this point, albeit with an example that elided issues of measurement error with issues pertaining to identification.

12 Thanks to Tomáš Sobotka for his generosity in providing the data and graphics for Figures 9.4 and 9.5.

References

Andvord, Kristian F. [1930] 2002. "What Can We Learn by Following the Development of Tuberculosis from One Generation to Another?" *International Journal of Tuberculosis and Lung Disease* **6**(7):562–568.

Baltes, P.B. 1968. "Longitudinal and Cross-Sectional Sequences in the Study of Age and Generation Effects." *Human Development* **11**(3):145–171.

Chauvel, Louis. 2014. *Le destin des générations: Structure sociale et cohortes en France du XXe siècle aux années 2010 [2e édition].* Paris: Presses Universitaires de France.

Chauvel, Louis, and Martin Schröder. 2014. "Generational Inequalities and Welfare Regimes." *Social Forces* **92**(4):1259–1283.

Clogg, Clifford C., and Scott R. Eliason. 1987. "Some Common Problems in Log-Linear Analysis." *Sociological Methods & Research* **16**(1):8–44.

Cohen, Joel E., Christina Bohk, and Roland Rau. 2018. "Gompertz, Makeham, and Siler Models Explain Taylor's Law in Human Mortality Data." *Demographic Research* **38**(29):773–842.

Dorius, Shawn F., Duane F. Alwin, and Julianna Pacheco. 2016. "Twentieth Century Intercohort Trends in Verbal Ability in the United States." *Sociological Science* 3:383–412.

Duncan, Otis Dudley. 1985. "Generations, Cohorts, and Conformity." In *Cohort Analysis in Social Research: Beyond the Identification Problem*, edited by William M. Mason and Stephen E. Fienberg, 289–321. New York: Springer-Verlag.

Fienberg, Stephen E. 2013. "Cohort Analysis' Unholy Quest: A Discussion." *Demography* 50(6):1981–1984.

Fienberg, Stephen E., and William M. Mason. 1978. "Identification and Estimation of Age-Period-Cohort Models in the Analysis of Discrete Archival Data." In *Sociological Methodology 1979*, edited by Karl F. Schuessler, 1–67. San Francisco: Jossey-Bass.

———. 1985. "Specification and Implementation of Age, Period and Cohort Models." In *Cohort Analysis in Social Research: Beyond the Identification Problem*, edited by William M. Mason and Stephen E. Fienberg, 45–88. New York: Springer-Verlag.

Firebaugh, Glenn, and Kevin Chen. 1995. "Vote Turnout of Nineteenth Amendment Women: The Enduring Effect of Disenfranchisement." *American Journal of Sociology* 100(4):972–996.

Fosse, Ethan, and Christopher Winship. 2018. "Moore–Penrose Estimators of Age–Period–Cohort Effects: Their Interrelationship and Properties." *Sociological Science* 5(14):304–334.

———. 2019. "Bounding Analyses of Age-Period-Cohort Effects." *Demography* 56(5): 1975–2004.

Frost, Wade Hampton. 1939. "The Age Selection of Mortality from Tuberculosis in Successive Decades." *American Journal of Epidemiology* 30(A3):91–96.

Gelman, Andrew. 2008. "Thoughts on New Statistical Procedures for Age-Period-Cohort Analyses." Unpublished paper last downloaded from www.stat.columbia.edu/~gelman/research/unpublished/apc.pdf on 4 April 2019.

Glenn, Norval D. 1976. "Cohort Analysts' Futile Quest: Statistical Attempts to Separate Age, Period, and Cohort Effects." *American Sociological Review* 41(5):900–904.

Granger, Clive W. J. 2007. "Forecasting—Looking Back and Forward: Paper to Celebrate the 50th Anniversary of the Econometrics Institute at the Erasmus University, Rotterdam." *Journal of Econometrics* 138(1):3–13.

Hirschi, Travis, and Michael Gottfredson. 1983. "Age and the Explanation of Crime." *American Journal of Sociology* 89(3):552–84.

Holford, Theodore R. 1983. "The Estimation of Age, Period and Cohort Effects for Vital Rates." *Biometrics* 39(2):311–324.

———. 1991. "Understanding the Effects of Age, Period, and Cohort on Incidence and Mortality Rates." *Annual Review of Public Health* 12:425–457.

Holland, Paul W. 1986. "Statistics and Causal Inference." *Journal of the American Statistical Association* 81(396):945–960.

Hutchinson, Edward P. 1960. "Comment on Ryder, Norman B: The Structure and Tempo of Current Fertility," pp. 131–133. In *Demographic and Economic Change in Developed Countries*, edited by the National Bureau of Economic Research, 117–136. New York: Columbia University Press.

Jacobs, Jerry A. 2005. "*ASR*'s Greatest Hits." *American Sociological Review* 70(1):1–3.

Kupper, Lawrence L., Joseph M. Janis, Azza Karmous, and Bernard G. Greenberg. 1985. "Statistical Age-Period-Cohort Analysis: A Review and Critique." *Journal of Chronic Disease* 38(10):811–830.

Lenart, Adam, and Trifon I. Missov, 2010. "Linking Period and Cohort Life Expectancy in Gompertz Proportional Hazards Models." MPIDR Working Papers WP-2010–024, Max Planck Institute for Demographic Research, Rostock, Germany.

Luo, Liying. 2013. "Assessing Validity and Application Scope of the Intrinsic Estimator Approach to the Age-Period-Cohort Problem." *Demography* **50**(6):1945–1967.

Luo, Liying, and James S. Hodges. 2016. "Block Constraints in Age–Period–Cohort Models with Unequal-width Intervals." *Sociological Methods & Research* **45**(4):700–726.

Mannheim, Karl. 1952. "The Problem of Generations." In *Essays on the Sociology of Knowledge: Collected Works, Volume 5*, edited by Paul Kecskemeti, 276–322. New York: Routledge.

Manski, Charles F. 1995. *Identification Problems in the Social Sciences*. Cambridge, MA: Harvard.

Mason, Karen Oppenheim, William M. Mason, H. H. Winsborough, and W. Kenneth Poole. 1972. "Some Methodological Issues in Cohort Analysis of Archival Data." Working Paper 72–22. Center for Demography and Ecology, University of Wisconsin—Madison.

———. 1973. "Some Methodological Issues in Cohort Analysis of Archival Data." *American Sociological Review* **38**(2):242–258.

Mason, William M., and Herbert L. Smith. 1985. "Age-Period-Cohort Analysis and the Study of Deaths from Pulmonary Tuberculosis." In *Cohort Analysis in Social Research: Beyond the Identification Problem*, edited by William M. Mason and Stephen E. Fienberg, 151–227. New York: Springer-Verlag.

Mason, William M., and Stephen E. Fienberg (eds.) 1985. *Cohort Analysis in Social Research: Beyond the Identification Problem*. New York: Springer-Verlag.

McCullagh, P., and J. A. Nelder. 1989. *Generalized Linear Models*, 2nd ed. London: Chapman and Hall.

Nelder, J. A. 1977. "A Reformulation of Linear Models." *Journal of the Royal Statistical Society. Series A (General)* **140**(1):48–77.

Ní Bhrolcháin, Máire. 1992. "Period Paramount? A Critique of the Cohort Approach to Fertility." *Population and Development Review* **18**(4):599–629.

O'Brien, Robert M. 2011. "Constrained Estimators and Age-Period-Cohort Models." *Sociological Methods & Research* **40**(3):419–452.

———. 2015. *Age-Period-Cohort Models: Approaches and Analyses with Aggregate Data*. Boca Raton, FL: Chapman and Hall/CRC Press.

———. 2016. "Model Misspecification When Eliminating a Factor in Age-period-cohort Multiple Classification Models." In *Sociological Methodology 2016*, edited by Duane F. Alwin, 358–372. Thousand Oaks, CA: Sage Publishing.

———. 2019. "Homicide Arrest Rate Trends in the United States: The Contributions of Periods and Cohorts (1965–2015)." *Journal of Quantitative Criminology* **35**(2):211–236.

Oppenheim, Karen. 1970. "Voting in Recent American Presidential Elections." Ph.D. dissertation. University of Chicago.

Porter, Lauren C., Shawn D. Bushway, Hui-Shien Tsao, and Herbert L. Smith. 2016. "How the U.S. Prison Boom Has Changed the Age Distribution of the Prison Population." *Criminology* **54**(1):30–55.

Riebler, Andrea, Leonhard Held, and Håvard Rue. 2012. "Estimation and Extrapolation of Time Trends in Registry Data—Borrowing Strength from Related Populations." *The Annals of Applied Statistics* **6**(1):304–333.

Rodgers, Willard L. 1982. "Estimable Functions of Age, Period, and Cohort Effects." *American Sociological Review* **47**(6):774–787.

Ryder, Norman B. 1960. "The Structure and Tempo of Current Fertility." In *Demographic and Economic Change in Developed Countries*, edited by the National Bureau of Economic Research, 117–136. New York: Columbia University Press.

———. 1965. "The Cohort as a Concept in the Study of Social Change." *American Sociological Review* **30**(6):843–861.

Shen, Yinzhi, Shawn Bushway, Lucy Sorenson, and Herbert Smith. 2019. "Locking Up My Generation: Cohort Differences in Prison Sentence Spells over the Life Course." Poster presented at the Annual Meeting of the Population Association of America, April 2019, Austin, TX.

Smith, Herbert L. 1987. "The Social Forecasting Industry." *Climatic Change* **11**(1–2):35–60.

———. 2004. "Response: Cohort Analysis Redux." In *Sociological Methodology 2004*, edited by Ross M. Stolzenberg, 111–119. Washington, DC: American Sociological Association.

———. 2008. "Advances in Age-Period-Cohort Analysis." *Sociological Methods & Research* **36**(3):287–296.

———. 2009. "Application de l'analyse des séries chronologiques à la projection d'effectifs de population scolaire par la méthode des composantes." *Cahiers Québécois de Démographie* **38**(1):145–170.

Smith, Herbert L., William M. Mason, and Stephen E. Fienberg. 1982. "More Chimeras of the Age-Period-Cohort Accounting Framework: Comment on Rodgers." *American Sociological Review* **47**(6):787–793.

Sobotka, Tomáš. 2003. "Tempo-quantum and Period-cohort Interplay in Fertility Changes in Europe: Evidence from the Czech Republic, Italy, the Netherlands and Sweden." *Demographic Research* **8**(6):151–214.

Vaisey, Stephen, and Omar Lizardo. 2016. "Cultural Fragmentation or Acquired Dispositions? A New Approach to Accounting for Patterns of Cultural Change." *Socius: Sociological Research for a Dynamic World* **2**:1–15.

Wang, Haidong, and Samuel H. Preston. 2009. "Forecasting United States Mortality Using Cohort Smoking Histories." *Proceedings of the National Academy of Sciences* **106**(2):393–398.

Wickramaratne, Priya J., Myrna M. Weissman, Philip J. Leaf, and Theodore R. Holford. 1989. "Age, Period and Cohort Effects on the Risk of Major Depression: Results from Five United States Communities." *Journal of Clinical Epidemiology* **42**(4):333–343.

Wright, Erik Olin. 1997. *Class Counts: Comparative Studies in Class Analysis*. Cambridge: Cambridge University Press.

Yang, Guobin. 2016. *The Red Guard Generation and Political Activism in China*. New York: Columbia University Press.

Yang, Yang, and Kenneth C. Land. 2013a. *Age-Period-Cohort Analysis: New Models, Methods, and Empirical Applications*. Boca Raton, FL: Chapman and Hall/CRC Press.

———. 2013b. "Misunderstandings, Mischaracterizations, and the Problematic Choice of a Specific Instance in which the IE Should Never Be Applied." *Demography* **50**(6): 1969–1971.

Yang, Yang, Wenjiang J. Fu, and Kenneth C. Land. 2004. "A Methodological Comparison of Age-Period-Cohort Models: The Intrinsic Estimator and Conventional Generalized Linear Models." In *Sociological Methodology 2004*, edited by Ross M. Stolzenberg, 75–110. Washington, DC: American Sociological Association.

10

THE LINE OF SOLUTIONS AND UNDERSTANDING AGE–PERIOD–COHORT MODELS

Robert M. O'Brien

Introduction

We can readily conceptualize the factors consisting of ages, periods and cohorts as having independent effects on a dependent variable. For example, suicides rates could be related to ages: perhaps those who are in their teens and 20s are more likely to kill themselves than those in other age-groups due to the difficulties associated with the transition to adulthood, or perhaps those facing the physical and mental deterioration associated with older ages are more likely than other age group to commit suicide. Periods might differ in their suicide rates due to wars, depressions or great recessions. When a person was born (their birth cohort) may influence their propensity to suicide: they may have grown up during a depression or may be from a baby boom or baby bust cohort. Easterlin's (1987) theory suggests that those born to baby boom cohorts face larger class sizes, have fewer entry level job opportunities, and delay marriage and having children. These factors may make them more susceptible to suicides throughout their lives. Even though all three of these factors (ages, periods and cohorts) are likely related to suicide rates, a major conceptual/statistical problem is that it is not possible to separate the individual effects of ages, periods and cohort, because they are linearly dependent and there are an infinite number of solutions that fit the outcome variable equally well (Mason, Mason, Winsborough, and Poole 1973).

When there is a single linear dependency, as in age–period–cohort multiple classification (APCMC) models, there is a line of solutions (in multidimensional solution space) on which all of the best fitting solutions to the APCMC model lie. The line of solutions contains the infinity of best fitting solutions. Solutions that do not lie on this line do not fit the data as well as those that do. If we use "best fit" as a standard for the best solution, then that criterion supports solutions (or in

TABLE 10.1 Age-period-specific suicide rates for the United States 1980–2015*

Ages	1980	1985	1990	1995	2000	2005	2010	2015
10–14	0.8	1.6	1.5	1.7	1.5	1.3	1.3	2.0
15–19	8.5	10.0	11.1	10.5	8.1	7.5	7.5	9.8
20–24	16.1	15.6	15.1	16.3	12.6	12.4	13.6	15.1
25–29	16.5	15.5	15.0	15.2	12.1	12.2	14.2	15.3
30–34	15.3	14.9	15.4	15.6	12.0	13.3	13.7	16.2
35–39	15.4	14.3	15.6	15.0	13.8	14.0	15.3	16.4
40–44	15.3	14.9	14.9	15.5	15.5	16.2	16.7	17.8
45–49	15.3	15.5	15.0	14.7	15.0	16.9	19.3	19.3
50–54	16.4	15.8	14.7	14.5	14.1	16.1	19.9	21.2
55–59	16.3	17.0	16.1	13.0	12.8	14.2	19.2	20.5
60–64	15.5	16.3	15.9	13.6	11.6	13.3	15.7	17.2
65–69	16.2	16.8	16.6	14.5	11.4	11.7	13.7	15.3
70–74	17.8	20.7	19.6	17.3	14.0	13.4	13.8	15.4

Note: *The cells contain the age-period-specific suicide death rates per 100,000 U.S. residents.

some cases solutions derived from the best fitting solutions) that are on the line of solutions. The line of solutions is a fundamental property of both the APCMC identification problem and of the potential ways to extract information from these models. This chapter uses the line of solutions and the properties associated with it to tie together many of the approaches suggested in other chapters of this book. It can be used to help understand and evaluate old approaches to the APCMC identification problem and to help evaluate and understand new approaches.

To illustrate the properties of the line of solutions with relevant data, I use a dataset based on suicide rates in the United States for those aged 10–14 to 70–74 for the years 1980 to 2015. Table 10.1 presents this data. The age-period-specific suicide rates per 100,000 are drawn from the National Center for Health Statistics (various years). These rates are logged in my analyses. The data for cohorts are on the diagonals of the table. The earliest cohort has one observation: those 70–74 in 1980. The next earliest cohort has two observations: those 65–69 in 1980 and those 70–74 in 1985. The most recent cohort has one observation: those 10–14 in 2015.

The line of solutions

The APCMC model is the most typically analyzed age–period–cohort model and the main focus of this chapter. For a fixed effect regression model it can be written as:

$$Y_{ij} = \mu + \alpha_i + \pi_j + \chi_k + \varepsilon_{ij}.^1 \tag{10.1}$$

Y_{ij} is the dependent variable value for the ijth cell of the age-period table; μ is the intercept; α_i is the age effect for the ith age group; π_j is the period effect for the j th period; χ_k is the cohort effect for the kth cohort (where $k = I - i + j$); and ε_{ij} is the disturbance associated with the ijth cell of the age-period table.[2] Since age, period and cohort are categorically coded, one of the age categories, one of the period categories and one of the cohort categories are dropped from the equation used to estimate these effects.

The problem with such models is that they are not identified (they are rank deficient by one).[3] The problem isn't that we cannot solve such models; the problem is that there are an infinite number of solutions (sets of regression coefficients) that provide solutions that fit the data equally well. These solutions lie on a line in multi-dimensional solution space (O'Brien 2014) and the equation for that line is:

$$b_c^0 = b_{c1}^0 + sv, \qquad (10.2)$$

where b_c^0 is a solution vector that represents any of the least square solutions, b_{c1}^0 represents a particular solution vector (under a just-identifying constraint, e.g., constraint one) and sv is a scalar (real number) times the null vector (v).[4] Equation (10.2) is the vector equation for a line (Kupper, Janis, Karmous, and Greenberg 1985; O'Brien 2011a).

The line of solutions represents what we know statistically about the best fitting solutions to the APCMC model. It does not provide a unique solution, but it does provide information about the best fitting solutions. Although there are an infinite number of solutions that fit the data equally well, only those on the line of solutions are the best fitting.

The line of solutions and constrained solutions

Using a just-identifying constraint has been the most common approach to producing a solution to APCMC models. This approach is typically accompanied by a justification for the use of a particular constraint in terms of its consistency with the data-generating parameters. For example, presenting a justification for why the effects of the two earliest periods should be the same or why the trend of period effects over the time span of the analysis should be zero. If a just-identifying constraint is correct (in terms of being consistent with the parameters that generated the data), then it provides unbiased estimates of the data-generating parameters (given that Equation (10.1) is the correct specification). A just-identifying constraint always produces a solution that is on the line of solutions, and thus a best fitting solution. When we use multiple constraints for a single solution (e.g., that the trend in period effects is zero *and* the trend in cohort effects is zero), the solution will almost always not be on the line of solutions and will not be a best fitting solution.

Table 10.2 presents solutions based on the data in Table 10.1 using three different just-identifying constraints: the two youngest age groups have equal

TABLE 10.2 Three different constrained solutions (using effect coding) along with the null vector (based on the data in Table 1)

	age1 = age2	period1 = period2	Intrinsic estimator	Null vector
Intercept	2.525	2.525	2.525	0
10–14	9.047	-2.616	-2.060	-6
15–19	9.047	-0.672	-0.209	-5
20–24	7.634	-0.141	0.230	-4
25–29	5.741	-0.090	0.188	-3
30–34	3.883	-0.005	0.181	-2
35–39	2.061	0.117	0.210	-1
40–44	0.268	0.268	0.268	0
45–49	-1.555	0.389	0.296	1
50–54	-3.421	0.467	0.281	2
55–59	-5.319	0.512	0.234	3
60–64	-7.264	0.511	0.140	4
65–69	-9.177	0.542	0.078	5
70–74	-10.944	0.719	0.163	
1980	-6.571	0.232	-0.092	3.5
1985	-4.627	0.232	0.001	2.5
1990	-2.757	0.159	0.020	1.5
1995	-0.919	0.053	0.007	0.5
2000	0.810	-0.161	-0.115	-0.5
2005	2.717	-0.199	-0.060	-1.5
2010	4.691	-0.168	0.063	-2.5
2015	6.655	-0.148	0.176	
1905–09	17.869	-0.597	0.284	-9.5
1910–14	16.042	-0.480	0.308	-8.5
1915–19	14.101	-0.477	0.218	-7.5
1920–24	12.180	-0.455	0.148	-6.5
1925–29	10.254	-0.437	0.073	-5.5
1930–34	8.297	-0.450	-0.033	-4.5
1935–39	6.378	-0.425	-0.101	-3.5
1940–44	4.557	-0.303	-0.071	-2.5
1945–49	2.735	-0.180	-0.041	-1.5
1950–54	0.961	-0.011	0.035	-0.5
1955–59	-0.869	0.103	0.056	0.5
1960–64	-2.761	0.154	0.015	1.5
1965–69	-4.739	0.121	-0.111	2.5
1970–74	-6.511	0.293	-0.032	3.5
1975–79	-8.426	0.321	-0.096	4.5
1980–84	-10.266	0.425	-0.085	5.5
1985–89	-12.171	0.463	-0.139	6.5
1990–94	-14.125	0.454	-0.242	7.5
1995–99	-15.973	0.550	-0.238	8.5
2000–04	-17.534	0.932	0.052	

regression coefficients (age1 = age2), the two earliest periods have equal regression coefficients (period1 = period2) and the solution is perpendicular to the null vector: the intrinsic estimator (IE) solution (Yang, Fu, and Land 2004). The final column contains the null vector (note that the elements left out of the estimating equation – the oldest age group, the most recent period and the most recent cohort – are not part of the null vector).[5] Each of these three solutions fits the data equally well. They have the same values for the sum of the squared residuals, R_y^2 is the same $(.985)$ and the information criteria are the same for each of these solutions: AIC = -154.894 and BIC = -54.407. The estimated coefficients, however, differ greatly. The age1 = age2 estimates in Table 10.2 are quite different from the period1 = period2 estimates and from the IE estimates.

We can use the equation for the line of solutions, $b_c^0 = b_{c1}^0 + sv$, to demonstrate that these three solutions, which use just-identifying constraints, are all on the line of solutions. If we treat the age1 = age2 solution as b_{c1}^0, then using $s = 1.944$ (to 3 decimal places) we can obtain the period1 = period2 solution by adding $1.944 \times v$ to each of the corresponding elements in the age1 = age2 solution. To move to the IE solution from the age1 = age2 solution, s equals 1.851. To move from the period1 = period2 solution to the IE solution, s equals -0.093. The reason that the solutions for the period1 = period2 and the IE are relatively similar using this data is that they are relatively close on the line of solutions as indicated by the relatively small difference in the value of s linking these two solutions (see O'Brien 2011a for a discussion of sv as a measure of distance).

In addition to showing how the line of solutions can clarify the problems of identification in APCMC models and their possible solutions, as promised, this chapter examines how the approaches discussed in the other chapters of this book are related to the line of solutions. I briefly outline some of these relationships at the close of the relevant sections of this chapter.

The chapter on the pros and cons of constraining variables (Chapter 2 by Thijs, te Grotenhuis, and Scheepers) argues that we should not reject this oldest approach to identifying APCMC models. They provide some examples of situations in which researchers can decide on a constraint that is likely to be consistent (or nearly consistent) with the data-generating parameters. For example, body length should have a zero linear trend for the age effects from 25 to 39. There is strong theoretical and substantive knowledge that this is the case in the United States (e.g.). One could then use this just-identifying constraint with reasonable confidence to identify the slopes associated with ages, periods and cohorts. Also note that Fosse, Winship and Daoud (Chapter 6) use constrained regression to set bounds such as zero linear trend or a positive linear trend in a particular factor. Smith (Chapter 9) supports constrained regression with different constraints as a solid procedure if guided by theory and substantive research. Each of the solutions on the line of solutions corresponds to a constrained solution, though different explicit constraints can result in the same solution (the same point on the line of solutions). These always have the advantage of being one of the best fitting solutions and the advantage of making the assumptions of the solution explicit, even if difficult to understand (e.g., the IE being perpendicular to the null vector).

The line of solutions and estimable functions

Estimable functions are linear combinations of the best fitting solutions based on any of the different just-identifying constraints. These linear combinations produce the same results no matter which constraint is used (Holford 1983; Clayton and Schifflers 1987). Examples of estimable functions are: the deviations of the age coefficients from the linear trend in the age coefficients; deviations of the period coefficients from the linear trend in the period coefficients; and deviations of the cohort coefficients from the linear trend in the cohort coefficients.[6] The second differences for the age coefficients – for example, $(age2 - age1) - (age3 - age2) = -age1 + 2 \times age2 - age3$ – are estimable functions. There are $I - 2$ second differences for age coefficients, $J - 2$ second differences for periods, and $K - 2$ second differences for cohorts. Second differences indicate changes in the trends of the ages, periods and cohorts. The predicted values of y are an estimable function and thus $R^2_{y \cdot apc}$ is an estimable function. There are many other estimable functions (see O'Brien 2014 for the most common ones).

Estimable functions are unbiased estimates of the linear combinations of the parameters that generated the outcome data (Searle 1971, Chapter 5), under the assumption that the data were generated by the APCMC model (Equation 10.1). This is a very important property: although we cannot obtain unbiased estimates of the unknown data-generating parameters for the full APCMC model, we can obtain unbiased estimates of certain linear combinations of these parameters. If the APCMC model (Equation 10.1) is correct, then the unbiased solution for the data-generating parameters lies somewhere on the line of solutions. Since the estimable functions are the same for all of the solutions on the line of solutions, the estimable functions are unbiased estimates for these linear combinations of the data-generating process.

Estimable functions are intimately related to the line of solutions. Kupper et al. (1985) provide a method for testing whether a linear combination of coefficients is estimable. Note that the line of solutions can be written as:

$$b_c^0 = b_{c1}^0 + sv,$$

(10.3)

and taking a linear combination (l) of both sides of this equation yields

$$l'b_c^0 = l'b_{c1}^0 + l'sv.$$

(10.4)

In Equation (10.4), the linear combination for any particular solution $(l'b_{c1}^0)$ on the line of solutions equals that of the linear combinations of all of the solutions $(l'b_c^0)$ if and only if $l'sv = 0$ (Kupper et al. 1985; O'Brien 2014).[7]

Below I provide examples of how the $l'_{s}v$ criterion is used to show that a specific linear combination of a best fitting solution vector is an estimable function. I order the null vector elements as (intercept; age_1 to age_{I-1}; $period_1$ to $period_{J-1}$; $cohort_1$ to $cohort_{K-1}$) with the oldest age, most recent period and most recent cohort left out of the equation used to estimate these effects. For a 4 by 5 age–period table using effect coding for the independent variables in X, the null vector is $(0; -1.5, -0.5, 0.5; 2, 1, 0, -1; -3.5, -2.5, -1.5, -0.5, 0.5, 1.5, 2.5)'$, where I have used, for clarity, a semicolon to separate the intercept element, the age elements, the period elements and the cohort elements. For dummy variable coding, the elements of the null vector are $(3; -3, -2, -1; 4, 3, 2, 1; -7, -6, -5, -4, -3, -2, -1)'$. In the remainder of this section, I work with the null vector for the effect coded parameterization of the independent variables, though the same results would be obtained, in terms of estimability, using the dummy variable null vector elements.[8]

Using the $l'_{s}v$ criterion and the effect coded null vector $(0; -1.5, -0.5, 0.5; 2, 1, 0, -1; -3.5, -2.5, -1.5, -0.5, 0.5, 1.5, 2.5)'$, I show that the age second difference mentioned above is an estimable function, by showing that the null vector elements associated with the linear combination $(-age1 + 2 \times age2 - age3)$ sum to zero. That is, $\left[-(-1.5) + 2 \times (-.5) - (.5) = 0 \right]$, which establishes that this linear combination of coefficients from a just-identifying constrained solution (a solution that lies on the line of solutions) is an estimable function; the value of this second difference is the same no matter which just-identifying constraint is used, since multiplying these null vector elements by a constant s (which shifts the solution to another point on the line of solutions) will still result in the sum equaling zero. This is the case for the other second differences of ages, periods and cohorts.

As another example, the predicted values of y are estimable functions; they are the same across all of the just-identifying constrained solutions. To establish this using the $l'_{s}v$ approach, note that the null vector elements associated with each of these predicted values are $v_{intercept} + v_{ia} + v_{jp} + v_{kc}$, where v_{ia} is the null vector element for the ith age group, v_{jp} is the null vector element for the jth period, and v_{kc} is the null vector element for the kth $(k = I - i + j)$ cohort. If this linear combination equals zero for all of the predicted values, then the predicted values of y are estimable functions. As an example, take the third oldest age group and second period in our four by five age–period table. The intercept $(v_{intercept} = 0)$, the third oldest age group, has a null vector element value of .5; the second period has a null vector element value of 1.0; and the corresponding cohort is the third cohort $(k = 4 - 3 + 2 = 3)$ which has a null vector element of -1.5. The sum of the null vector elements is $0 \ (= 0.0 + 0.5 + 1.0 - 1.5)$; therefore, the predicted value for this observation is estimable, since multiplying these elements by the scalar s would still result in $l's v = 0$. The reader can verify that the $l's v = 0$ criterion is also met for the other predicted values.

Since the predicted values of y are estimable and the observed values are known, the residuals of these predicted values are estimable; that is, $\left(y_{ij} - \hat{y}_{ij} \right)$ is an estimable function for all of the observed values of y_{ij}. Some other estimable functions are more difficult to derive using the $l'sv$ criterion, but O'Brien (2014) provides an approach that is practical. These estimable functions derive from the line of solutions.

Table 10.3 shows the calculations of the estimable function for second differences. I used the cohort estimates from Table 10.2 based on the age1 = age2 constraint and the period1 = period2 constraint. Note that although the estimates for the cohort effects based on the age1 = age2 and period1 = period2 differ, the second differences calculated from these estimates are the same. The second differences tell us the shift in the rate of change in the cohort coefficients for the parameters that generated the dependent variable values.

Figure 10.1 displays another helpful estimable function, the cohort deviations from the linear trend in the cohort coefficients. Since these are deviations around the linear trend, positive deviations represent greater cohort effects than expected

TABLE 10.3 Second differences of the cohort coefficients as estimable functions (based on the age1 = age2 and period1 = period2 constraint in Table 10.2)

Cohort	Coefficients based on age1 = age2	age1 = age2 first differences	age1 = age2 second differences	Coefficients based on per1 = per 2	per1 = per2 first differences	per1 = per2 second differences
1905–09	17.869			−0.597		
1910–14	16.042	−1.827		−0.480	0.117	
1915–19	14.101	−1.941	−0.114	−0.477	0.003	−0.114
1920–24	12.180	−1.921	0.020	−0.455	0.022	0.020
1925–29	10.254	−1.926	−0.004	−0.437	0.018	−0.004
1930–34	8.297	−1.957	−0.031	−0.450	−0.013	−0.031
1935–39	6.378	−1.919	0.037	−0.425	0.024	0.037
1940–44	4.557	−1.821	0.099	−0.303	0.123	0.099
1945–49	2.735	−1.822	−0.001	−0.180	0.122	−0.001
1950–54	0.961	−1.774	0.047	−0.011	0.169	0.047
1955–59	−0.869	−1.830	−0.056	0.103	0.114	−0.056
1960–64	−2.761	−1.892	−0.062	0.154	0.051	−0.062
1965–69	−4.739	−1.978	−0.085	0.121	−0.034	−0.085
1970–74	−6.511	−1.772	0.206	0.293	0.172	0.206
1975–79	−8.426	−1.915	−0.144	0.321	0.028	−0.144
1980–84	−10.266	−1.840	0.076	0.425	0.104	0.076
1985–89	−12.171	−1.906	−0.066	0.463	0.038	−0.066
1990–94	−14.125	−1.954	−0.048	0.454	−0.010	−0.048
1995–99	−15.973	−1.848	0.106	0.550	0.096	0.106
2000–04	−17.534	−1.561	0.287	0.932	0.383	0.287

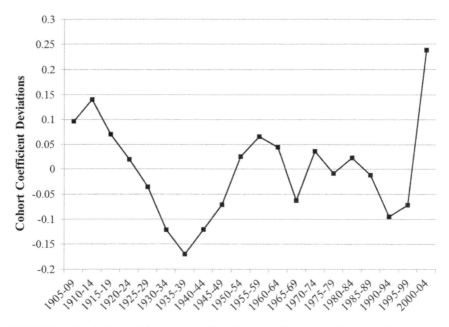

FIGURE 10.1 Deviations of the cohort effects from the linear trend in the cohort effects

given the linear trend, and negative deviations represent lower cohort effects than expected given the linear trend in cohort effects. There are patterns in these deviations; for example, the drop in the cohort effect deviations from the 1910–14 cohort to the 1935–39 cohort and then an increase in the cohort effect deviations from that time to the 1955–59 cohort. This pattern covers 50 years of cohort data. If the linear trend in cohorts were zero, this would indicate a decrease in cohort effects for suicides in the first segment, noted above, and an increase in the second segment. What if there was a positive linear trend in cohort effects over time? This would indicate that the effects of cohorts on average over time are increasing, with cohorts on average becoming more prone to suicides, controlling for period and age effects. The early trend from the 1910–14 cohort to the 1935–39 cohort would then be less negative, perhaps even positive, for those in this downward segment of deviations, and more positive for those in the upward segment of deviations from the 1935–39 cohort to the 1955–59 cohort. Researchers can always determine which cohorts are above or below the secular trend in suicide deaths for cohorts.

In Chapter 4, Minton uses contour plots that do not depend on any statistical manipulation of the data, and it might seem that, in this sense, what he sees on the surface of the contours is unrelated to the line of solutions presented in this chapter. He graphs the observed mortality rates as heights on age–period axes and seems to avoid the identification problem by examining observed data rather than the age, period and cohort effects controlled for one another. Using these contour plots for logged mortality rates for males and females from France (Chapter 4: Figure 4.2), however, Minton can see that the cohort born in 1918 has a lower life expectancy throughout its lifespan. Within the statistical APCMC literature such unusual cohort effects can be detected by the deviation of cohort effects from their linear trend. Minton can view this cohort effect (and I believe it is) with no purely statistical manipulation of the data because the cohorts on either side of the 1918 cohort have a higher life expectancy. The effect of the Spanish flu is also clearly seen in Bell and Jones (Chapter 3: Figure 3.7), where there is a clear spike in male mortality in the UK detectable in the deviations from the linear trend in the cohort effects. This is also the case in Minton's chapter for the detection of period effects for World War I and World War II on mortality rates: the departure of the rates for these periods from those in close proximity on either side of them suggests period effects. These local deviations in period effects are estimable as deviations from linear trends in the statistical APCMC framework, and they can be seen in the Lexis contour graphs.

Importantly, Minton can see more than just these deviations in cohort and period effects from linear trends; for example, he can detect "Lee–Carter drift" in mortality rates and the falling rate of infant mortality. He can see that the period effects for the two world wars differ depending on the ages of people within those periods. These would not be picked up by the traditional APCMC approach and remind us that the traditional APCMC statistical model is one among many tools for analyzing the patterns in the ages, periods and cohorts in the Lexis diagram. We should remember, however, in terms of the APCMC identification problem, that there are an infinite number of age, period and cohort effects that are best fitting models for the observed data used in the Lexis contour plots. The trends in the observed data for ages, periods and cohorts are not the same as the age, period and cohort effects that are statistically controlled for each other.

In Chapter 5, Chauvel, Leist and Smith also use Lexis diagrams. Their diagrams, however, are typically based on residualized data. They use residuals from an age–period model (cohorts are not included in the model) to detect cohort effects and unusual "Black Holes" (greater or less than expected mortality rates given the age–period model). These residuals are estimable (since the age–period model is identified) and, given that they have not included cohorts in the model, are a way to "get at" cohort effects, but the age and period effects in such models are not controlled for cohort effects. They are, however, most interested in deviations of the residuals along the cohort diagonals. They also use the age–period–cohort detrended (APCD) model that Chauvel and coauthors have used very effectively in a number of articles: two examples are Chauvel and Schroeder (2015) and Chauvel, Leist and Smith (2016). These are based approximately on the deviations of cohort effects from their linear trend in the traditional APCMC model, which would (as noted in this chapter) be estimable functions. They, however, use three constraints rather than one constraint on the APCMC model, which results in a solution that is not on the line of solutions (not a best fitting solution): In describing the APCD model Chauvel, Leist, and Ponomarenko (2016, 5) state:

> To provide a correct identification, simple constraints such as $\sum_a \alpha_a = \sum_p \pi_p = \sum_c \gamma_c = 0$ imply centered coefficients. We add three constraints, $slope_a(\alpha_a) = slope_p(\pi_p) = slope_c(\gamma_c) = 0$, where slope is the linear function that gives the linear slope of the coefficients, so that α_a, π_p and γ_c are detrended.

Only one of the slope constraints is necessary to identify the model. If three slopes are constrained simultaneously to zero, to produce a single solution, that solution is not likely to fall on the line of solutions and, thus, likely to degrade the fit of the fixed effect APCMC model.

The analysis of these residuals is important and they provide indications of unusual effects. Unusual effects (cells) in the Lexis diagrams detected as residuals that have been controlled for age and period effects, and age and period and cohort effects, can detect Black Holes correctly. They indicate local discontinuities in age, period and cohort effects. Residuals are not often examined in the traditional APCMC approach (for two recent exceptions, see Luo and Hodges [2020] and O'Brien [2020]), but they can provide valuable information.

The line of solutions and variance decomposition

Variance decomposition uses the fact that the predicted values of the dependent variable are estimable functions. Since the observed values of y_{ij} are known and the predicted values of $\hat{y}_{ij}$ are estimable in the APCMC model, it is possible to estimate the proportion of the variance in y that is accounted for by the full APCMC OLS model that uses a just-identifying constraint. That is, $R^2_{y \cdot apc} = 1 - [\sum(y_{ij} - \hat{y}_{ij})^2 / \sum(y_{ij} - \bar{y}_{..})^2]$, where $\hat{y}_{ij}$ is the predicted value of y for the ijth cell of the age–period table and $\bar{y}_{..}$ is the mean of the observed values of the dependent variable. Since the age–period model, the age–cohort model and the period–cohort model are each identified, we can calculate $R^2_{y \cdot ap}$, $R^2_{y \cdot ac}$ and $R^2_{y \cdot pc}$, which do not depend on the constraint used with the full APCMC model.

Because of these relationships, we can decompose the proportion of total variance accounted for by the APCMC model into parts that are *uniquely accounted for* by age $\left(R^2_{y \cdot apc} - R^2_{y \cdot pc}\right)$, uniquely accounted for by period $\left(R^2_{y \cdot apc} - R^2_{y \cdot ac}\right)$ and uniquely accounted for by cohort $\left(R^2_{y \cdot apc} - R^2_{y \cdot ap}\right)$. Using the F-test for the increment in the variance accounted for (or in the case of GLM the likelihood ratio chi-square test) researchers can assess whether including one of the factors in the model significantly improves the fit of the model.[9]

Care must be taken, however, since in each case the two-factor models take credit for any linear trend in the third factor. This occurs because of the linear dependency between ages, periods and cohorts. For example, we have noted that age and period are linearly related to cohort: cohort = $I - i + j$. Because of this,

TABLE 10.4 Unique proportions of variance accounted for by ages, periods and cohorts based on the data from Table 10.1★

Added factor	F	Degrees of Freedom	P	Increment
Age	199.56	F(11,66)	0.0001	0.4972
Period	8.24	F(6,66)	0.0001	0.0112
Cohort	3.28	F(18,66)	0.0002	0.0133

Note: ★These incremental proportions in the variance accounted for are based on adding a factor after the other two factors are in the model.

when i and j are in the model they account for the linear effects of cohorts. The unique (incremental) variance for the third factor in the above test is based only on the deviation of that factor from the linear trend of that factor. We can conceptually write these increments in variance accounted for as $\left(R^2_{y \cdot apc} - R^2_{y \cdot pc(a_L)} \right)$, $\left(R^2_{y \cdot apc} - R^2_{y \cdot ac(p_L)} \right)$ and $\left(R^2_{y \cdot apc} - R^2_{y \cdot ap(c_L)} \right)$ to emphasize that these incremental tests do not give credit for the linear effect of the factor whose increment to the variance accounted for is being assessed (O'Brien 2016). Because of this, these tests for incremental fit cannot be used to conclude that, for the parameters that underlie these factors, ages and/or periods and/or cohorts are not important, since these tests do not take into consideration the linear trends, if any, in these factors. If the incremental test is statistically significant, however, one can conclude that the factor contributes statistically significantly to the fit of the model.

Table 10.4 shows the results of this variance decomposition for the suicide data. Each of the factors (ages, periods and cohorts) provide a statistically significant improvement to the fit of the model predicting the age–period-specific logged suicide rates ($p < .001$) over a model that contains only the other two factors. The proportion of the variance accounted for in the logged suicide rates when all three factors are in the model is $R^2_{y \cdot apc} = .9850$. This is the R^2 value for any model on the line of solutions, since these models all share the same predicted values of the APCMC suicide rates. For a model that contains just the period and cohort factors (with one variable of each factor left out of the estimating equation) the variance accounted for is $R^2_{y \cdot pc} = .4878$, and the increment in the variance accounted for by age in Table 10.4 is $0.4972 \left(= .9850 - .4878 \right)$. The increments in the variance accounted for are much smaller for periods (.0112) and for cohorts (.0133), but each increment is statistically significant. Each factor adds significantly to the fit of the model even when we are not assessing any of their possible linear trend effects.

The relationship among the linear trends for ages, periods and cohorts

Section 10.4 notes that the deviations of ages, periods and cohorts from their predicted values are estimable functions: they are identified and are the same no matter which of the solutions on the line of solutions is used. What are not identified in such models are the linear trends in ages, periods and cohorts (Holford 1983; Clayton and Schifflers 1987; O'Brien 2011b). There is, however, a systematic relationship between the trends for ages, periods and cohorts in the various constrained APCMC models.[10] The relationship between these trends is summarized in Equation (10.5) based on Rodgers (1982):[11]

$$t_a^* = t_a + k$$

$$t_p^* = t_p - k$$

$$t_c^* = t_c + k. \tag{10.5}$$

Here t_a is the linear trend in the age coefficients under a particular constraint, t_p is the linear trend in the period coefficients under the same constraint, and t_c is the linear trend in cohort under the same constraint. If we use a different constraint the trends will differ. If the trend for age using a new constraint is $\left(t_a^*\right)$ and is k more than the original trend, then the trend for period using the new constraint (t_p^*) will be k less than the original trend for period, and the trend for cohort using the new constraint (t_c^*) will be k more than the original trend. Correspondingly, a decrease of k in the age trend results in an increase of k in the period trend, and a decrease of k in the cohort trend.

Note that a constraint on the trend of the coefficients of one of the factors (age, period or cohort) identifies the model (under that constraint), since there is only one solution on the line of solutions that has a particular trend for one of the factors, just as there is only one solution on the line of solutions that has the age1 coefficient equal to the age2 coefficient (which establishes a trend for the age coefficients). There are times when setting a zero linear trend in the coefficients of one of the factors may be a more reasonable/plausible approximation than many other constraints that are used to identify APCMC models.

Table 10.5 provides the linear trends associated with the three different solutions in Table 10.2 based on the age1 = age2, period 1 = period2, and the intrinsic estimator constraints. Each of these solutions is based on a just-identifying constraint and is on the line of solutions. The linear trends for each of these constrained solutions are different, and it is that difference that makes the solutions different. This statement is literally true, since the deviations around these trends are the same for each of the solutions (those deviations are estimable functions).

Panel (b) of Table 10.5 shows clearly the relationship between the linear trends. For example, the difference in the linear trend for ages between the age1 = age 2 constrained model and the period1 = period2 constrained model is −1.944 (1.7696 − 0.1742). If this difference is −1.944 then the difference between the period coefficients ought to be 1.944 (1.8729 − (−0.0709)), and it is. Panel (b) illustrates these relationships for three different constraints using the results from the suicide data.

Panel (c) of Table 10.5 shows that certain linear combinations of these trends are estimable. The linear trend in ages $\left(t_a\right)$ plus

TABLE 10.5 The linear trends of ages, periods and cohorts for three different constrained solutions (from Table 10.2), differences in linear trends and estimable functions of these linear trends

Trend	(a) Linear trends		
	$Age1 = Age2$	$Period1 = Period2$	Intrinsic estimator
Ages	−1.7696	0.1742	0.0815
Periods	1.8729	−0.0709	0.0218
Cohorts	−1.8707	0.0731	−0.0197
	(b) Differences in linear trends		
	$(a1 = a2) - (p1 = p2)$	$(a1 = a2) - (c1 = c2)$	$(p1 = p2) - (c1 = c2)$
Ages	−1.944	−1.851	0.093
Periods	1.944	1.851	−0.093
Cohorts	−1.944	−1.851	0.093
	(c) Estimable functions of trends		
	$Age1 = Age2$	$Period1 = Period2$	Intrinsic estimator
$t_a + t_p$	0.1033	0.1033	0.1033
$t_p + t_c$	0.0021	0.0021	0.0021
$t_a - t_c$	0.1012	0.1012	0.1012

the linear trend in periods $\left(t_p\right)$ is the same for each of the solutions $\left[(-1.7696 + 1.8729) = \left(0.1742 + (-0.0709)\right) = (0.0815 + 0.0218) = 0.1033\right]$. This makes sense since, according to Equation (10.5), the two solutions differ by k for their age solutions, and $-k$ for their period solutions. It does not matter which of the just-identifying constraints are used; $t_a + t_p = 0.1033$ for this data. Similarly, the period linear trend plus the cohort linear trend are equal across solutions, as is the age linear trend minus the cohort linear trend. Clayton and Schifflers (1987) label $t_p + t_c$ as period–cohort drift.

Figure 10.2 shows an example of the relationship between the different trend estimates for ages, periods and cohorts in the APCMC model in a three-dimensional space (Holford 1991; Fosse and Winship 2019). This figure shows in three dimensions the three components of APCMC models that are not identified (the linear trends of ages, periods and cohorts) and the line of solutions for these linear components of the APCMC model. The full line of solutions shows the solutions for all of the components of the APCMC model. Different points on this line represent different solutions to the APC model, since each solution has a unique trend for age and period and cohort. Figure 10.2 illustrates the situation for which one of the solutions on the line of solutions to the APCMC model has a

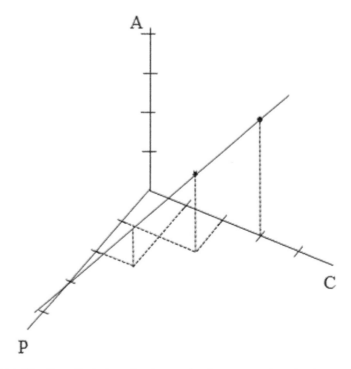

FIGURE 10.2 The line of solutions for the trends of ages, periods and cohorts in the APCMC specification

trend for the ages of $t_a = 2$, a trend for periods of $t_p = 1$ and a trend for cohorts of $t_c = 2$. I have marked this solution with a star in Figure 10.2.

Using Equation (10.5) for the relationship among the slopes for the best fitting solutions, we can find a second point on this line by examining the solution when the age trend is one greater than in the first solution; then, according to Equation (10.5) the period trend will be one less than in the first solution and the cohort trend will be one greater than in the first solution. That is, the trends will be $t_a = 3, t_p = 0$ and $t_c = 3$. This solution is marked with a dot in Figure 10.2 and establishes the line of solutions in terms of trend for ages, periods and cohorts. For additional accuracy in Figure 10.2, I also plotted the solution when the age trend is one and when it is zero, before drawing the line of solutions.

In the first part of Chapter 7, Holford presents data and analysis on ever smoking, duration of smoking, smoking cessation, quantity of cigarettes smoked, and so on. These indicators of smoking prevalence are used to estimate the lung cancer mortality rates for the population based on Knoke's carcinogenesis model. Much can go wrong with such estimates, including the sample used for data collection, a faulty carcinogenesis model and not collecting all of the relevant variables. Holford uses an APC model to calibrate the results of the Knoke carcinogenesis model so that it is consistent with the observed trends in lung cancer mortality rates using the APC model. Holford notes that in the APC model the

Fitted values are also an estimable function of the parameters; hence, the identifiability problem only affects individual temporal parameters and not the calibration factor. Calibration requires fitting the age–period–cohort model to a function of the observed rates, thus obtaining optimal estimates of the temporal parameters.

(Chapter 7, p. 132)

One can see the improvement in fit of the APC calibrated Knoke carcinogenesis model to the observed data in Figure 7.9, when compared to the estimates based on the uncalibrated Knoke model to the observed data in Figure 7.8. This is based on the predicted values from an APC model being an estimable function.

When Holford examines the temporal effects for ages, periods and cohort based on the calibrated Knoke model and the age–period–cohort model (Figures 7.10, 7.11 and 7.12), he sets the period linear trend to zero which makes the trend for cohorts equal to the period trend plus the cohort trend (the period–cohort drift which is an estimable function). This allows him to compare the trends of the calibrated model for the age, period and cohort component and the age–period–cohort model trends and deviations from trends under this constraint. The estimable functions from the APC models used by Holford are properties associated with the line of solutions.

In Chapter 9, Smith notes that the linear elements (trends) in ages, periods and cohorts are not estimable, but the deviations from those trends are estimable. Then the question is how to constrain the trend estimates. He argues that often this should be a constraint on periods so that their linear trend is zero. Not surprisingly, this discussion relates to the line of solutions, the effects of constraints on the linear trends of solutions (Equation 10.5), and the fact that deviations from linear trends are estimable. He focuses on ideas about what constraints might most often be appropriate.

I might add that Smith is absolutely correct that simple constraints such as setting constraints on a pair of effect coefficients, and more complex constraints such as setting the trend in period coefficients to zero or the intrinsic estimator constraint of setting the solution to be perpendicular to the null vector, will differ only in how they constrain the linear trends in the age effects, period effects and cohort effects. Since they all lie on the line of solutions, they will differ in trends to the extent that they lie on different places on that line.[12]

Fosse, Winship and Daoud in Chapter 6, Fosse in Chapter 8 and Smith in Chapter 9 each use linearized APCMC models. These can be derived from the line of solutions: $b_c^0 = b_{c1}^0 + sv$. The null vector (v) has a 0 for the intercept, numbers which increase (decrease) by a set amount for the age elements of the null vector, numbers that decrease (increase) by the same amount for the period elements of the null vector, and numbers that increase (decrease) by the same amount for the cohort elements of the null vector.[13] So when s changes, creating a new solution on the line of solutions, the trend increases (decreases) by s times the distance between the null vector elements for age, decreases (increases) by the distance between the null vector elements for periods, and increases (decreases) by the distance between the null vector elements for cohorts. Since these distances are the same for ages, periods and cohorts, the increase (decrease) in the age trend is matched by the decrease (increase) in the period slope, which is matched by the increase (decrease) in the cohort trend. As noted earlier this matches Rodgers's finding in Equation (10.5).

What does not change are the deviations of the age effects from the linear trend of the age effects, the deviations of the period effects from the linear trend of the period effects, and the deviations of the cohort effects from the linear trend of the cohort effects for the original solution (b_{c1}^{0}) and for the new solution (b_{c}^{0}). The new solution will have different linear trends for the age, period and cohort effects, but their deviations from their linear trends will be the same. When the linear trends change the deviations around the old and new linear trends remain the same. This can be written in several forms; below in my notation, is a form related to the one Smith uses (Equation 9.8) to show the parameter vector of the solutions to the APCMC model:

$$b_{c}^{0\star} = \mu, t_{a} + k, t_{p} - k, t_{c} + k, \alpha_{1}^{d}, \cdots, \alpha_{I}^{d}, \pi_{1}^{d}, \cdots, \pi_{J}^{d}, \chi_{1}^{d}, \cdots, \chi_{K}^{d} \qquad (10.6)$$

where $b_{c}^{0\star}$ represents the full solution vector including the variables left out of the equation used to estimate the model (one for each factor), μ is the intercept, $t_{a} + k, t_{p} - k,$ and $t_{c} + k$ are the trends for ages, periods and cohorts identified up to a shared constant (k), and followed by the deviations from the linear trends.

In terms of predicting the independent variable values, we need to specify the contribution of these trends to the predicted value of the dependent variable. We can drop the constant k, since all of the solutions on the line of solutions are best fitting solutions. Then we must indicate where on the trend lines the ijk th observation falls. We do that using $\left(i - i^{\star}\right), \left(j - j^{\star}\right)$ and $\left(k - k^{\star}\right)$, where $i^{\star} = \dfrac{I+1}{2}$, $j^{\star} = \dfrac{J+1}{2}, k^{\star} = \dfrac{I+J-1}{2}$. Then

$$\hat{Y}_{ijk} = \mu + (t_{a})\left(i - i^{\star}\right) + (t_{p})\left(j - j^{\star}\right) + (t_{c})\left(k - k^{\star}\right) + \alpha_{i}^{d} + \pi_{j}^{d} + \chi_{k}^{d}. \qquad (10.7)$$

This is similar to Equation (6.5) in Fosse, Winship and Daoud (Chapter 6), except that it is the formula for the predicted values of Y_{ijk} rather than the observed values of Y_{ijk} (I do not include a residual term). Using Equations (10.6) and (10.7), it is straightforward to move to the other equations for the linearized APCMC in Chapters 6, 8 and 9.

The line of solutions: mixed models and characteristic models (approximations)

Two popular approaches to APC analysis offer a glimpse of the fundamental nature of the line of solutions and some of its associated properties. Since the line of solutions is based on the linear dependency among the independent variables, it can be helpful even in evaluating solutions that are not based on ordinary least squares or generalized linear models where the line of solutions describes the best fitting APCMC models exactly. It can be helpful in understanding models where the line of solutions does not describe the best fitting solutions exactly. For both the mixed model and the characteristic models (and we will extend this to Bayesian models covered in this book) the line of solutions does not contain the best fitting solution, but some properties derived from the line of solutions hold approximately.

In mixed models, as used in the literature, one or two of the factors typically are treated as fixed effects, and the remaining factor or factors are treated as random (Yang and Land 2006; O'Brien, Hudson, and Stockard 2008). Those using Yang and Land's (2006) approach, hierarchical APC (HAPC), typically code only one of the factors as a fixed effect and code it linearly rather than categorically. They also often code ages, periods and cohorts using different numbers of years for these three factors. Luo and Hodges (2016) note that grouping age, period and cohort categories into groups with different numbers of years produces "block constraints." The use of unequal intervals in this coding produces multiple constraints on the solutions (Luo and Hodges 2016). This use of unequal intervals for classifying ages, periods or cohort would place multiple constraints on traditional APCMC models using the fixed effect analyses and thus identify the model (Osmond and Gardner 1989). It would not, however, produce one of the solutions on the line of solutions, since the unequal interval coding creates multiple constraints.

Mixed models, nevertheless, are identified whether or not a researcher uses unequal intervals in the coding of ages, periods and cohorts (O'Brien, Hudson, and Stockard 2008; Bell and Jones 2014; Luo and Hodges 2016; O'Brien 2017). Mixed or hierarchical models are estimated using a penalty associated with each random factor that is designed to shrink each of the random effects toward their mean. The estimation procedure (typically maximum likelihood or residual maximum likelihood) minimizes the penalty (or penalties) jointly conditional on minimizing the squared deviations of the difference between the observed values of the dependent variable and the predicted values. This predictably results in one of the random factors having a linear trend near zero (O'Brien 2017).

In the case of a mixed model with just one random factor, this makes the linear trend in the random factor's effects near zero. With two random factors the trend in one of those factors is near zero. Importantly, the analysis constrains the trends so that the model fit will be maximized under the fit criterion. The mixed model fixes the linear trends of the factors based on this constraint (a near zero trend in one of the random factors), and this identifies the model.[14]

In terms of identification, the important point is that the penalty or penalties determine the linear trends and thus identify the model. Not surprisingly, if we use different factors as the random effect, the result can be quite different. When a factor changes from being a fixed effect to being a random effect, its estimated trend can shift dramatically. This shifts the trends in the other factors in accordance with the relationships between the trends in the traditional APCMC fixed effect model (Equation 10.5). In the case of mixed models, this systematic shift in the trends approximately follows Equation (10.5).

TABLE 10.6 Linear trends of the age coefficients, period coefficients and cohort coefficients when different factors serve as the only random effect in the APC mixed model

Random factor	Ages	Periods	Cohorts
Age	0.000	0.103	−0.101
Period	0.103	0.000	0.002
Cohort	0.103	0.002	0.000

Table 10.6 shows the results from an APCMC mixed model using just a single random effect. The data are the same as those used for the other data based examples (see Table 10.1). That data has corresponding five-year intervals for ages, periods and cohorts, and the mixed models are identified because the penalty on the single random effect shrinks the coefficients toward their mean and makes the linear trend of the random effect zero. The results in Table 10.6 are from mixed models where one of the factors is treated as random and the other two factors are treated as fixed effects.

In this case, we see that the trend for ages, periods and cohorts are each zero when they are treated as the only random variable in a mixed model. Constraining this trend through shrinkage has implications for the trends in the other factors that follow approximately the pattern suggested by Equation (10.5). When age is the random factor, the trend of the ages from the youngest to the oldest is 0.000; the trend for periods from the earliest to the most recent is 0.103; while, the trend in cohorts from the earliest to most recent is −0.101. In the second row where the trend of periods is 0.000, we would expect (using Equation 10.5) that the trend in ages would increase by 0.103, since the trend in periods has decreased by 0.103 from row 1, and the trend in cohorts should increase by 0.103. This is what happens in the results in Table 10.6. The age trend increases from 0.000 to 0.103 and the cohort trend increases from −0.101 to 0.002. Equation (10.5) holds approximately for the results in the third row. For a more complete set of examples with a different dataset that shows the approximate (though quite accurate) nature of Equation (10.5) with the mixed model, see O'Brien (2017).

Equation (10.5) plays a similar role in characteristic models. Characteristic models typically code two of the factors categorically and use characteristics of the third factor as proxies for the effects of that factor.[15] For example, in the age–period–cohort-characteristic (APCC) model, ages and periods are coded categorically and cohort effects might be represented with the logged rates of non-marital birth [ln(NMB)][16] for members of the cohort and their logged relative cohort size [ln(RCS)][17] (O'Brien, Stockard, and Isaacson 1999). In this case, the slopes of the age and period coefficients are determined by the slopes associated with the cohort characteristics included in the model (O'Brien 2015, 2019).

The second column of Table 10.7 contains the slopes from an APCC model based on our example data and two cohort characteristics: ln(NMB) and ln(RCS).[18] The third column in Table 10.7 contains the slope estimates based on an APCMC model

TABLE 10.7 The relationship of APCC trends to the trends based on the APCMC model that uses the age1 = age2 constraint

	APCC trends	age1 = age2 trends	Difference in the age1 = age2 minus APCC trends
Ages	0.1176	−1.7696	−1.8872
Periods	−0.0174	1.8729	1.8903
Cohorts	0.0211	−1.8707	−1.8918

Note: See Table 10.5 for the age1 = age2 constraint trends.

with the constraint age1 = age2 (see Table 10.5 for these trends). These two columns allow me to illustrate how Equation (10.5) holds approximately for the APCC method. The difference in the slope for ages, as we move from the age1 = age2 solution to the APCC solution for the trend in ages, is −1.8872 (= −1.7696−0.1176). The difference in trends as periods is $1.8903 \left(= 1.8729 - \left(-0.0174\right)\right)$, and the difference in the slopes for cohorts is $-1.8918 \left(= -1.8707 - 0.0211\right)$. These differences are shown in the final column of Table 10.7 and they fit closely what one would expect from Equation (10.5): a decrease in the trend of ages of about 1.89 from one solution to another is associated with an increase of about 1.89 in the solutions for the trend of periods, and a decrease of about 1.89 in the solutions for the trend for cohorts. These trends behave similarly to solutions that lie on the line of solutions.

The constraints implied by mixed models are often hidden from the casual user and are related to the line of solutions through their constraint on the slopes of the solution. Chapter 3, by Bell and Jones, makes these constraints explicit and shows their effects on the solutions produced by these methods. As they note, setting just one of the factors (ages, periods or cohorts) as a random factor identifies the model due to shrinkage and treating that factor as having a zero linear trend. Note that setting a factor to have a zero linear trend also identifies the traditional fixed effect APCMC model. The major point is that the mixed model introduces its own constraints: it is a constrained APC model using a model that is not an ordinary least squares model or a generalized linear model. Imposing a constraint on the trend of one of the factors affects the slopes of the other two factors. Bell and Jones, however, do not stop there; they suggest that researchers pay close attention to the constraints that are being "implicitly made" (to make sure they are theoretically and substantively justified) and they then proceed with a mixed model. For example, they examine the following mixed model:

$$Y_{ij} = \beta_0 + \beta_1 Age_i + \beta_2 Age_i^2 + \beta_3 Cohort_i + \beta_4 Cohort_i^2 + u_p + u_c + e_i$$

Note that it allows for a smooth curve for the age effects, a smooth curve for the cohort effects, and the examination of deviations around the cohort curve $\left(u_c\right)$ and the period zero linear trend $\left(u_p\right)$. They explicitly note the assumption that the trend in periods is flat, which is imposed by this model. They also note the relationship between trends, which in the fixed APCMC model is summarized in Equation (10.5), is at work (though only approximately) in the mixed model context.

In Chapter 8 on Bayesian APC models, Fosse notes that for the Bayesian approach, nonidentification is not inherently a problem due to the fact that a prior distribution is specified. He also notes that: "The Bayesian framework can be viewed as a generalization of the constraint-based approach commonly used by APC analysts coming out of the frequentist tradition." That is, the prior plays a primary role in establishing the trends in the solution given the inherent nonidentification of these trends based on the data. In this sense a frequentist might say: in the frequentist approach, using constrained regression, nonidentification is not inherently a problem due to the fact that a constraint is specified.

This fits the pattern for APC mixed models and APC characteristic models. In the case of mixed models treating one or more factors as random sets the trends of the age, period and cohort factors. In the case of the characteristic model, the characteristics set the linear trends for ages, periods and cohorts. In the case of the APC Bayesian models a moderately strong or even weak prior is responsible for setting the trends. Although I have not addressed Bayesian models formally in this chapter, my working hypothesis would be that the trend(s) that are set will approximately reflect the systematic relationships between trends suggested in Equation (10.5). As Fosse notes, the priors' affect on these trends needs to be consistent with the pattern of the data-generating parameters for these methods to produce estimates of the parameters that are consistent with the data-generating parameters. The priors should be theoretically and/or substantively justified as reflecting the data-generating parameters.

Finally, I should mention that in the Fosse, Winship and Daoud chapter (Chapter 6) their mechanism-based approach is closely related to the characteristic approach, but it is extended to the situation in which there are characteristics for multiple factors. It, like the characteristic approach, is likely to only be approximately related to the line of solution. Future examination of this approach might focus on how closely results from this approach share approximately the relationship between the trends of Equation (10.5) and related properties associated with the line of solutions.

Conclusions

The line of solutions is, in one sense, what we know *statistically* about the solutions to the classic APCMC fixed effect model. That is, the best fitting solutions must lie on this line. This line contains infinitely many solutions; but not just any combinations of coefficients are best fitting solutions. In terms of purely statistical solutions to the fixed effect APCMC problem, one could argue that this is the set of solutions on which to concentrate. For example, there are many linear combinations of the solutions (estimable functions) on this line that are identified and are best linear unbiased estimates of the linear combinations of the parameters that generated the data. But other approaches can have other advantages.

The chapters in this book discuss methods that take advantage of these "on the line" best fitting solutions. These include constrained solutions; the relationships among the trends of age, period and cohort effects; estimable functions; and the analysis of residuals. Importantly, the line of solutions can often be used to evaluate and to gain a deeper understanding not only of methods that produce best fitting results, but also of APC results that do not fall on the line of solutions (e.g., mixed models, characteristic models and Bayesian models) or even approaches that are purely visual. This is because the line of solutions is based in a fundamental way on the null vector, and the null vector describes the linear dependency among the independent variables. In this sense, the line of solutions is fundamental to our understanding of these models and their evaluation, and it reminds us that we need to be particularly modest in our conclusions about many of the results from such models.

Online supplementary material relating to this book can be found at www. routledge.com/9780367174439.

Notes

1 The line of solutions and its associated properties also hold for generalized linear models in general, since the expected value of the dependent variable is a linear function of the same independent variables. The lines may be different between different generalized linear models (logistic, Poisson, negative-binomial, etc.).

2 I is the number of age categories.

3 There is a linear dependency in the independent variables: if the age and period are known, the birth cohort is determined.

4 The derivation for the vector equation for a line, using matrix algebra, appears in O'Brien (2011a); the equivalent equation appears in Kupper et al. (1985) using a geometrical argument. The superscripted 0 indicates that the solution is not unique. The null vector, in this context, is a vector (not containing all zeros) that when pre-multiplied times the matrix of independent variables results in a vector of zeros (indicating and describing the linear dependency among the independent variables).

5 I use effect coding of the categorical variables for all of the data-based analyses in this chapter, and the null vector in Table 10.2 is based on effect coding. I could use different categorical variables for the left out variables and that would change the null vector. It would not affect the solutions for the age1 = age2 constraint or for the period1 = period2 constraint, but would affect the IE solution (Pelzer, te Grotenhuis, Eisinga, and Schmidt-Catran 2014; Luo, Hodges, Winship, and Powers 2016). All of the solutions, however, would be on the line of solutions.

6 To obtain the linear trend for ages, we regress the age coefficients from the youngest to the oldest (for any of the models using a just-identifying constraint) on the integers 1 to I; for periods we regress the period coefficients from the earliest to the most recent on the integers 1 to J; and for cohorts we regress the cohort coefficients from the earliest to the most recent on the integers 1 to K.

7 Note that Equation (10.3) describes all of the possible best fitting solutions to the APCMC model, while Equation (10.4) describes certain linear combinations of those solutions that will be the same no matter which just-identifying constraint is used. O'Brien (2014) uses the $l'sv = 0$ criterion to show that deviations from linear trends, second differences, predicted values of the dependent variable, and other functions are estimable.

8 O'Brien (2015) shows how to derive null vector elements for effect and dummy variable coding based on the dimensions of age–period matrices.

9 Of course, for most GLM models we cannot calculate the variance accounted for.

10 This relationship is based on the line of solutions: $b_c^0 = b_{c1}^0 + sv$ as outlined later in this section.

11 I use my own notation, but the equations appear in Rodgers (1982).

12 Different constraints may result in the same trends and thus be at the same place on the line of solutions. Smith (Chapter 9) notes that when two different substantively motivated constraints result in similar solutions this can provide more confidence in the solution.

13 The null vector is unique up to multiplication by a scalar, whether the age null vector elements increase or decrease does not matter for the derivation.

14 The penalty does not introduce just a single constraint on the model, since it involves several of the coefficients within the factor or factors that are random. See Hodges (2014) for a discussion of degrees of freedom in models with such penalties.

15 Winship and Harding (2008) discuss characteristic models where ages, periods and cohorts can all have proxy variables.

16 Ln(NMB) is the log of the rate per 1000 of the birth cohort that was born to unwed mothers.

17 Ln(RCS) is the percentage of those 15 to 64 who were 15–19 when the birth cohort was 15–19.

18 To find the APCC cohort trend, I multiplied the regression coefficients for ln(NMB) and ln(RCS) from the age–period–cohort-characteristic model times the logged values of ln(NMB) and ln(RCS) for each cohort. I then summed these two products to obtain the total effects for each cohort and regressed these cohort values for the earliest to most recent cohort on the numbers 1 to the total number of cohorts. The trends for ages and periods based on the APCC model were obtained using the same regression procedure (as for Table 10.5). The cohort characteristics are provided in the supplementary material for this chapter.

References

Bell, Andrew, and Kevin Jones. 2014. "Another 'futile quest'? A simulation study of Yang and Land's hierarchical age-period-cohort model." Demographic Research 30: 333–360.

Chauvel, Louis, and Martin Schroeder. 2015. "The impact of cohort membership on disposable incomes in West Germany, France, and the United States." European Sociological Review 31: 298–311.

Chauvel, Louis, Anja K. Leist, and Herbert L. Smith. 2016. "Cohort factors impinging on suicide rates in the United States, 1990–2010." Presented at the Annual Meeting of the Population Association of America, Washington, DC, March 31–April 2.

Clayton, D., and E. Schifflers. 1987. "Models for temporal variation in cancer rates II: Age-period-cohort models." Statistics in Medicine 6: 468–481.

Easterlin, Richard. 1987. Birth and Fortune: The Impact of Numbers on Personal Welfare. Chicago: Chicago University Press.

Fosse, Ethan, and Christopher Winship. 2019. "Bounding analyses of age-period-cohort effects." Demography 56(5): 1975–2004.

Hodges, James S. 2014. Richly Parameterized Linear Models: Additive, Time Series, and Spatial Models Using Random Effects. Boca Raton: CRC Press.

Holford, Theodore R. 1983. "The estimation of age, period, and cohort effects for vital rates." Biometrics 39: 311–324.

Holford, Theodore R. 1991. "Understanding the effects of age, period, and cohort on incident and mortality rates." Annual Review of Public Health 12: 425–457.

Kupper, Lawrence L., Joseph M. Janis, Azza Karmous, and Bernard G. Greenberg. 1985. "Statistical age-period-cohort analysis: A review and critique." Journal of Chronic Disease 38: 811–830.

Luo, Liying, and James S. Hodges. 2016. "Block constraints in age-period-cohort models with unequal width intervals." Sociological Methods & Research 45: 700–726.

Luo, Liying, and James S. Hodges. 2020. "The age-period-cohort-interaction model for describing and investigating inter-cohort deviations and intra-cohort life-course dynamics." Sociological Methods & Research; online first, https://doi.org/10.1177/0049124119882451.

Luo, Liying, James Hodges, Christopher Winship, and Daniel Powers. 2016. "The sensitivity of the intrinsic estimator to coding schemes: Comment on Yang, Schulhofer-Wohl, Fu, and Land." American Journal of Sociology 122: 930–961.

Mason, K.O., W.M. Mason, H.H. Winsborough, and W.K. Poole. 1973. "Some methodological issues in cohort analysis of archival data." American Sociological Review 38: 242–258.

National Center for Health Statistics. (Various years). Vital Statistics of the United States: Mortality. Washington, DC: U.S. Government Printing Office.

O'Brien, Robert M. 2011a. "Constrained estimators and age-period-cohort models." Sociological Methods & Research 40: 419–452.

O'Brien, Robert M. 2011b. "The age-period-cohort conundrum as two fundamental problems." Quality & Quantity 45: 1429–1444.

O'Brien, Robert M. 2014. "Estimable functions of age-period-cohort models: A unified approach." Quality and Quantity 48: 457–474.

O'Brien, Robert M. 2015. Age-Period-Cohort Models: Approaches and Analyses with Aggregate Data. New York: CRC Press.

O'Brien, Robert M. 2016 "Model misspecification when eliminating a factor in age-period-cohort multiple classification models." Sociological Methodology 46: 358–372.

O'Brien, Robert M. 2017. "Mixed models, linear dependency, and identification in age-period-cohort models." Statistics in Medicine 36: 2590–2600.

O'Brien, Robert M. 2019. "Homicide arrest rate trends in the United States: The contribution of periods and cohorts (1965–2015)." Journal of Quantitative Criminology 35: 211–236.

O'Brien, Robert M. 2020. "Estimable intra-age, intra-period, and intra-cohort effects in age-period-cohort multiple classification models." Quality & Quantity 54: 1109–1127.

O'Brien, Robert M., Kenneth Hudson, and Jean Stockard. 2008. "A mixed model estimation of age, period, and cohort effects." Sociological Methods & Research 36: 402–428.

O'Brien, Robert M., Jean Stockard, and Lynne Isaacson. 1999. "The enduring effects of cohort characteristics on age-specific homicide rates: 1960–1995. American Journal of Sociology 104: 1061–1095.

Osmond, C., and M.J. Gardner. 1989. "Age, period, and cohort models: Non-overlapping cohorts don't resolve the identification problem." American Journal of Epidemiology 129: 31–35.

Pelzer, Ben, Manfred te Grotenhuis, Rob Eisinga, and Alexander W. Schmidt-Catran. 2014. "The non-uniqueness property of the intrinsic estimator in APC Models." Demography 52: 315–327.

Rodgers, Willard L. 1982. "Estimable functions of age, period, and cohort effects." American Sociological Review 47: 774–787.

Searle, Shayle R. 1971. Linear Models. New York: Wiley.

Winship, Christopher, and David J. Harding. 2008. "A mechanism-based approach to the identification of age–period–cohort models." Sociological Methods & Research 3: 362–401

Yang, Yang, Wenjiang J. Fu, and Kenneth C. Land. 2004. "A methodological comparison of age-period-cohort models: The intrinsic estimator and conventional generalized linear models. Sociological Methodology 34: 75–110.

Yang, Yang and Kenneth C. Land. 2006. "A mixed models approach to the age-period-cohort analysis of repeated cross-section surveys: Trends in verbal test scores." Sociological Methodology 36: 75–97.

INDEX

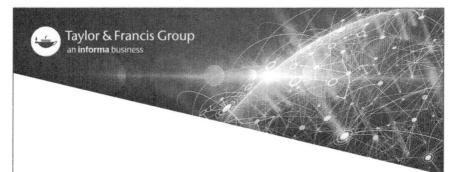